RECENT ADVANCES IN SCIENCE

AUTHORS

H. A. Bethe,
Cornell University, Ithaca, New York

R. M. Bozorth,
Bell Telephone Laboratories, Inc., Murray Hill, New Jersey

F. G. Brickwedde,
National Bureau of Standards, Washington, D. C.

Edward U. Condon,
Washington University, St. Louis, Missouri

Richard Courant,
New York University, New York, New York

Leland J. Haworth,
Brookhaven National Laboratory, Upton, New York

Philip M. Morse,
Massachusetts Institute of Technology, Cambridge, Massachusetts

I. I. Rabi,
Columbia University, New York, New York

Norman F. Ramsey,
Harvard University, Cambridge, Massachusetts

William Shockley,
Shockley Semiconductor Laboratory of Beckman Instruments, Inc., Fullerton, California

C. H. Townes,
Columbia University, New York, New York

V. F. Weisskopf,
Massachusetts Institute of Technology, Cambridge, Massachusetts

RECENT ADVANCES
IN SCIENCE
Physics and Applied Mathematics

Edited by

Morris H. Shamos
Chairman, Department of Physics, New York University

George M. Murphy
Professor of Chemistry, New York University

SCIENCE EDITIONS, INC. • NEW YORK, 1961

FOREWORD

At the start of World War I, rumor has it, the old War Department declined with regret the proffer of aid from the American Chemical Society on the grounds that the Department already had a chemist thinking about their problems. No significant scientific advance in armament had taken place by the opening rounds of World War II. However, in the relatively short span since 1940 a scientific and technological revolution has swept this planet with a pace hitherto unknown.

New discoveries have unleashed forces, opened vistas, and laid bare accomplishments of the magnitude that makes addicts of science fiction enthusiasts. New industries literally have sprung forth from the fruits of scientific research, creating unforeseen demands for trained, skilled, and educated personnel. From a nuclear pile under the stands at Stagg Field, Chicago, has grown a multibillion-dollar industry just in its swaddling clothes. From the fertile imagination of mathematicians has emerged the fountainhead of the scientific revolution excited by the high-speed digital computing machine. The electronics industry of 1940 has little resemblance to the lusty giant of today. And many of the tools with which the biologists and medical scientists attack the problems of cancer and other dread diseases were not yet born at the outbreak of World War II.

Not only did these vast new frontiers of science open, but new ones are threatening to push on to the stage at any time. The storehouse of scientific information increases with positive acceleration. Each new basic scientific discovery is multiplied in significance because of its meaning and power for other scientific activity and because of its impact upon our economy and society through application and new industry.

A problem facing scientists for more than a generation has now reached major proportions and threatens to stem the tide of the necessary flow of knowledge: How is it possible to keep abreast of developments in one's own field, as well as being aware, if only through mental osmosis, of developments in peripheral realms? The problem is further complicated. Each expert speaks a language probably meaningful to the few who are likewise expert in that field. But could not the engineer, chemist, or solid state physicist profit significantly from a knowledge of the work done by the mathematician or the nuclear physicist? Is there a common methodology that would bear fruit in all of the physical sciences?

In terms of this thinking, it is eminently clear that an educational and training need exists. To meet this need, the Division of General Education of New York University, with the co-operation of scientific leaders from industry, Government laboratories, and the University, developed a series of co-ordinated lectures by the outstanding men in scientific fields of current interest to industry, research laboratories, and the universities.

The First Symposium on Recent Advances in Science was held at Washington Square during the spring of 1954. It attracted 225 men and women from metropolitan industries and faculties. This book, an outgrowth of that Symposium on applied mathematics and physics, is, we believe, a contribution to the fundamental understanding of the important work explicated by the several lecturers. It is obvious that both the Symposium and this book have required a large degree of active co-operation and participation from many different sources. The enthusiastic response to the need from the Planning Committee was both inspiring and gratifying. It is only fitting that recognition be given to them for their efforts.

To the members of the committee from industry and the research laboratories, Lloyd V. Berkner, Richard Emberson, Elmer W. Engstrom, James Fisk, Mervin J. Kelly, A. B. Kinzel, Eger Murphree, C. G. Suits, I, on behalf of New York University, wish to acknowledge my debt for their ideas, support, and general helpfulness. Without their devotion to the twin causes of education and science, this Symposium would not have been possible. These scientific leaders were always available for advice and took time from their extraordinarily busy lives to consult with university representatives throughout the planning year.

Our university representatives likewise did yeoman work to make the Symposium an important event for the scientific community.

Dean Paul A. McGhee of the Division of General Education, Chan-
cellor Henry T. Heald, and Dean Thorndike Saville of the College
of Engineering encouraged and co-operated with the committee to
garner the best scientific talent to come to the podium. Professor
Serge Korff acted as chairman of the meetings; Professors George
Murphy and Morris Shamos did much of the preliminary work before the opening of the Symposium and have performed a superb
task against overwhelming odds in getting the Symposium into this
permanent form. In addition to these, our grateful acknowledgment
for their support goes to the other university members of the
Planning Committee: Professors Yardley Beers, Myron A. Coler,
Richard Courant, James Mulligan, John Vance, Carel van der
Merwe.

SIDNEY G. ROTH

New York University
May 1956

PREFACE

Scientific historians of the future may attach special significance to the fact that the first half of the twentieth century saw the establishment of a number of highly technical industries. Many of the basic discoveries of the first few decades have already been put to commercial practice, and the fundamental ideas now being developed will form the nuclei for new industries of the future. The very rapid growth of the physical sciences quite naturally has led to specialization, with the result that practicing scientists and engineers too often are but dimly aware of the latest developments outside their immediate fields.

This book is a product of the First Symposium on Recent Advances in Science, held at New York University during the spring of 1954. The purpose of the Symposium, which was confined to physics and applied mathematics, was to convey the basic ideas in some of the newest and most active fields of study. The level of presentation is probably best described as intermediate, inasmuch as the lectures presupposed some scientific training, although not necessarily in the particular subject areas. Nevertheless, it was apparent that much benefit was derived from the lectures even by those actively engaged in these fields.

Prominent among the topics will be found several phases of atomic and nuclear physics. This is probably to be expected in view of the enormous advances in these fields and the impact they have made upon modern engineering. The rapid rise of interest during the recent years in the physical properties of solids is reflected in those chapters that treat some of the aspects of solid state physics. Similarly, the techniques of operations research, developed primarily for military application, have only recently been turned to industrial problems, for which they appear to offer great promise. The opening chapter deals with what is probably the most important tool of the engineer, applied mathematics, while the concluding chapter reviews the recent advances in the light of their implications for future trends in industrial development. Although the related topics of information theory and computing machines were presented at the Symposium, it unfortunately has not been possible to include this material in the present volume.

We are grateful to the contributing authors for generously giving their time to the preparation of their manuscripts, and we wish to thank the *American Scientist* for permission to reprint Dr. Shockley's article.

For various reasons it has not been easy to prepare this printed volume, as is evident from the publication date. However, we still believe the title to be exact in that the contents reflect the most recent advances in these fields. The chapters were prepared by some of the most distinguished scientists in this country, and their subjects are those in which they are acknowledged experts. Some repetition and lack of continuity are perhaps inevitable in a volume of this sort, yet we feel that the primary purpose of the book has been realized. We trust it may prove as rewarding to the reader as the original lectures were to the listeners.

G. M. MURPHY

May 1956   M. H. SHAMOS

CONTENTS

Methods of Applied Mathematics

RICHARD COURANT

Introduction

"Applied" mathematics as distinct from "pure" mathematics is a relatively recent phenomenon of scientific specialization. The distinction does not refer to fields of knowledge but rather to human attitudes and motivations. Pure mathematics is directed towards logical crystallization, abstraction, generalization; applied mathematics means close interconnection of mathematical methods with physical reality, and it may mean subordination of logical completeness to the need for results obtained by a mixed approach which may, if necessary, utilize analytical methods as well as physical intuition, numerical computation, and empirical reasoning.

Until the middle of the nineteenth century it was usual for great mathematicians to represent both the pure and applied trends in mathematics. The most striking example was Gauss. As a matter of course, this great creator of modern algebra, number theory, function theory, differential geometry, and non-Euclidean geometry took an active part in the development of geodesy, astronomy, and electrostatics. He built the first electrical telegraph (with Weber) and was fully conscious of the importance of this invention. He laid the foundation of the pension fund for the widows and orphans of his faculty colleagues. Although he valued highest his construction of the regular 17-gon and proclaimed number theory the queen of sciences, he spent most of his professional life enthusiastically on what we would call today applied mathematics. The mathematician Clerk Maxwell, interpreting in the form of partial differential equations the intuitive notions of Faraday and the quantitative formulation of Biot-Savart, created the basis for modern electromagnetic theory and practice. Henri Poincaré, another of the great mathematicians of the past century, made decisive contributions to the understanding of the propagation of radio waves across the surface of the earth. Perhaps one may consider Bernhard Riemann as the last of the mathematical universalists who made a deep mark in pure as well as applied mathematics. His paper on dynamics of compressible gases opened up an entirely novel field. The professional mathematicians remembered only the elegant, purely mathematical appendix to this paper, and it was left to engineers and physicists to develop the field of gas dynamics and aerodynamics, which some of them did with amazing mathematical insight and ingenuity. Likewise in other directions great mathematical contributions have been made by physicists, in particular in connection with quantum theory.

In this country the trend among professional mathematicians toward isolation from other sciences was interrupted when, during World War II, many pure mathematicians volunteered to give needed mathematical help. Sometimes service of high scientific and technological caliber was rendered by mathematicians who before had belonged to the purist camp. Since the war, government agencies, foremost among them the Office of Naval Research, have successfully tried to maintain a better balance between the applied and pure aspects of scientific activities in this country, and it seems certain that these efforts will have a lasting effect.

There are two principles involved in all problems and methods of applied mathematics, the principle of idealization and the principle of approximation. Idealization is fundamental even for the formulation of the basic concepts and laws of nature. For example, the density of a gas or fluid at a point P is determined by an idealized limiting process; we take the total mass of gas in a small sphere of radius ϵ about P, divide this mass by the volume $(4\pi/3)\,\epsilon^3$, and then let ϵ tend to zero. This limiting process is actually an unrealistic idealization, since in a very small volume gas molecules are sparsely and irregularly distributed. Still, without this and innumerable other idealized concepts, physics and mechanics would be utterly impossible. Newton's laws and celestial mechanics deal with ideal mass points, elasticity, and acoustics with ideal continua, although these continuous media consist actually of a finite but large number of discrete individual particles.

Methods

The general scheme of methods of applied mathematics can be represented by the following diagram:

$$I \rightarrow I_n$$
$$R \nearrow \qquad \downarrow \cdot$$
$$S \leftarrow S_n$$

R symbolizes a problem posed by reality, I the mathematical idealization, S its solution, I_n an approximate problem tending to I for $n \rightarrow \infty$, S_n its solution. The task of the mathematician is to formulate a proper I, to find a proper approximation I_n, and to identify approximately the desired S with S_n.

For many individual problems the step $R \rightarrow I$ is the most decisive; it often requires ingenuity, experience, and intuitive understanding of the realities of physics, engineering, and other fields. Of course, this step leaves great leeway for the applied mathematician. The next step, $I \rightarrow I_n$, is decisive for mathematical success or failure; this step also leaves open many possibilities for constructive imagination. The comparison of S_n with the theoretical solution S is often a difficult theoretical problem which, however, must be tackled to make sure that the whole process is meaningful.

Examples

We now turn to the discussion of a number of concrete examples which will illustrate the general methodical scheme just described.

Domes

The transition $R \rightarrow I$ from reality to an acceptable idealized mathematical model may be first illustrated by a quite special question that arose in the winter of 1942–1943 in connection with underwater warfare. Underwater sound ranging, as is well known, depends on sending out a sound beam in water from a properly designed projector. If the projecting plate is submerged in water and attached to a fast-moving ship, the water streaming around the plate causes serious disturbances. To eliminate these disturbances the projector is enclosed in a so-called "dome," as shown in Fig. 1, which is a convex shell of metal or other material filled with water. Such domes, as first constructed by the British, interfere only slightly with the formation of a concentrated sound beam. However, during that winter a great number of small submarine chasers were built and equipped with sound gear similar to but smaller than the gear used before. While the manufacture of domes to fit this smaller gear was under way, it was discovered that these smaller domes led to an intolerable diffusion of the sound beam. A quick remedy was imperative, and mathematical analysis of the problem was needed to sup-

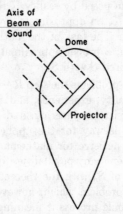

Fig. 1. Dome

port and to speed up experimental work. At first the mathematical problem seemed formidable because it involved the integration of the equation

$$\nabla^2 P + k^2 P = 0, \quad \nabla^2 = \frac{\partial^2}{\partial x^2} + \frac{\partial^2}{\partial y^2} + \frac{\partial^2}{\partial z^2}, \tag{1}$$

in which the factor $k = \omega/c$ has different values within the shell of the dome and outside, ω denoting the frequency and c the sound velocity. However, a suitably idealized mathematical model was found by the following process. The actual dome of small but finite thickness is replaced by an ideal infinitely thin surface. The influence of the dome is then replaced simply by conditions for jump discontinuities of the disturbance q of the beam across this surface. These conditions are:

$$[q] = \frac{\rho_1}{\rho_0 - 1} \frac{\partial p}{\partial n},$$

$$\left[\frac{\partial q}{\partial n}\right] = \frac{\rho_0}{\rho_1}(k_0^2 - k_1^2)\, p - \left(1 - \frac{\rho_0}{\rho_1}\right)\left(\frac{\partial^2 p}{\partial n^2} + 2H \frac{\partial p}{\partial n}\right), \tag{2}$$

in which the symbol $[f]$ means the jump of the quantity f across the surface, q is the disturbance of the acoustic pressure p caused by the dome, and the normal derivatives $\partial/\partial n$ are to be evaluated on the surface S. The quantity H is the mean curvature of S, i.e., the average of the curvatures of any two normal plane sections at right angles to each other. In addition to conditions (2) to be satisfied by q on S, q should be a solution of the differential equation

$$\nabla^2 q + k_0^2 q = 0, \tag{3}$$

which is regular everywhere except on S and which has the same behavior as P at ∞. This problem possesses the unique solution

$$q = -\frac{1}{4\pi} \iint\limits_{S} \left[\frac{\partial q}{\partial n}\right] \frac{e^{ik_0 r'}}{r'} \, dS + \frac{1}{4\pi} \iint\limits_{S} [q] \frac{\partial}{\partial n}\left(\frac{e^{ik_0 r'}}{r'}\right) dS, \tag{4}$$

in which the integration is to be extended over the dome surface S. The quantities in square brackets are, of course, those given by conditions (2), and r' is the distance from a fixed point (x, y, z) at which $q(x, y, z)$ is to be determined to the point of integration on S. This formula yields the disturbance as the effect due to a layer of point sources and a layer of dipoles distributed on S with intensities which are known as soon as the original pressure p is known, since the quantities in brackets are fixed in value by conditions (2). The relative directional disturbance $\left|\dfrac{p_1}{p_0}\right| \cdot \mathrm{Re}\, h\left(\dfrac{q_1}{p_1} - \dfrac{q_0}{p_0}\right)$ would, finally, be obtained from (4).

The solution (4) is valid for a shell of constant thickness, but it could be extended without essential error to cases in which the dome shell is made up of a not too large number of pieces, each of which is of constant thickness. All that would be necessary would be to insert a numerical factor d in the integrands on the right-hand side of expression (4) which would be piecewise constant on S. This formula makes it quite easy to analyze the contribution to the distortion of various factors, such as the curvature of the dome and the density and sound velocity within it. Therefore, this little example of proper idealization, even without detailed numerical computation, proved helpful to the designing engineer.

Shocks

The second, much broader, example of mathematical idealization refers to the dynamics of compressible fluids, a field with many applications of ever-increasing importance. Here the complex reality of a gas or fluid consisting of an enormously large number of discrete particles requires a great deal of mathematical idealization. One has to introduce such averages as density, pressure, temperature, entropy, and flow velocity; one makes further idealizing assumptions by neglecting viscosity and heat conduction. Even so, one arrives at systems of differential equations which are nonlinear and which thus present essentially new mathematical situations leading to phenomena of the greatest practical importance.

Bernhard Riemann, Rankine, Hugoniot, and Rayleigh discovered in the middle of the nineteenth century that the nonlinearity of compressible flow problems necessitated deviations from the traditional belief of Newton and Laplace that solutions to physical problems are determined by differential equations and initial conditions. Indeed, discontinuities may occur in a compressible flow even though the initial data are wholly continuous, so that no continuation of given initial data into a regular solution may be possible. "Shocks," i.e., discontinuities in density, pressure, and entropy which travel through the fluid at high speed, occur in many cases. The problem of determining flows with shock discontinuities which are not known a priori is extremely difficult, though of utmost importance for modern aerodynamics and explosion theory.

The partial differential equations governing compressible flow in the simplest cases are:

1. One-dimensional flow (of a polytropic gas)

$$\rho_t + (\rho u)_x = 0 \qquad\qquad \text{(conservation of mass)},$$

$$(\rho u)_t + (\rho u^2)_x + p_x = 0 \qquad\qquad \text{(conservation of momentum)},$$

$$\left[\rho\left(\frac{u^2}{2} + e\right)\right]_t + \left[\rho u\left(\frac{u^2}{2} + i\right)\right]_x = 0 \quad \text{(conservation of energy)},$$

with $p = A\rho^\gamma$ (equation of state), $i = \gamma/(\gamma - 1)$, and $(\gamma - 1)e = p/\rho = c^2/(\gamma - 1)$, where c = sound speed, ρ = density, p = pressure, u = particle speed, e = internal energy, and i = enthalpy.

2. Steady irrotational two-dimensional flow

$$\mu^2(u^2 + v^2) + (1 - \mu^2)c^2 = c_*^2 = \text{const.},$$

$$(c^2 - u^2)u_x - uv(u_y + v_x) + (c^2 - v^2)v_y = 0,$$

$$u_y = v_x,$$

with $\mu^2 = (\gamma - 1)/(\gamma + 1)$, where u and v are the components of the fluid velocity; or

$$(c^2 - u^2)\Phi_{xx} - 2uv\Phi_{xy} + (c^2 - v^2)\Phi_{yy} = 0,$$

with $u = \Phi_x$, $v = \Phi_y$, where Φ is the velocity potential. Flow is supersonic if $u^2 + v^2 > c^2$ everywhere, subsonic if $u^2 + v^2 < c^2$ everywhere, transonic if both inequalities may hold (at different points).

These differential equations can be valid only in regions of continuity. At shock transitions certain "shock conditions" restricting the nature of permissible discontinuities must be satisfied. The principle followed by Riemann, Hugoniot, and others in deriving these conditions, which have the form of finite equations, is that they should express at the shock the same "conservation laws" (in particular, conservation of mass, of momentum, and of energy) as the differential equations of flow in regions of continuity.

It would at first seem that mathematical shock discontinuities do not represent physical reality, since, strictly speaking, fluid flows are continuous. However, the above equations represent an idealized flow without viscosity or heat conduction. Thus it is natural to try to set up the full set of equations governing the flow, taking these effects into account, solve these equations, and then let the viscosity and heat conductivity approach zero. One may expect that for small values of viscosity and heat conductivity the solution, though continuous, will vary extremely rapidly in a narrow strip of the x,t-plane, and that as these parameters approach zero this strip will contract to a curve, while the solution will approach different values on the two sides of this curve. Indeed, in the simple cases in which this has been done the curve so obtained corresponds in position to the shock predicted by the "idealized" set of equations, and the limiting values of the solution on the two sides of the shock satisfy the shock conditions mentioned in the preceding paragraph.

Shocks, or "shock waves" as observed in many phenomena, have striking properties not present in acoustical, electromagnetic, or optical wave propagation. Their speed is "supersonic." The angle at which they are reflected from a rigid wall is different from their angle of incidence, as may be seen in Fig. 2. They may lead to very high pressures.

Problems involving shocks pose many questions of theoretical interest. These questions deal with the existence and uniqueness of the solution of the initial value problem for a partial differential equation if this solution is permitted to have discontinuities but is required to satisfy shock conditions at these discontinuities. Only very rudimentary results have as yet been obtained in this area, since even the simplest problems involving shocks seem to defy the power of pure analysis.

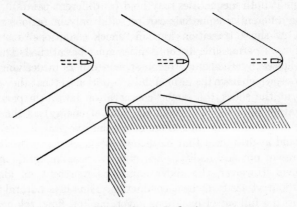

Fig. 2. Shock Reflection

Indeed, the flight of high-speed airplanes and missiles, as well as phenomena occurring in jets and nozzles, in combustion chambers of engines, and in all sorts of explosions, leads to fluid flow problems of such variety and difficulty that in only a few typical but highly simplified cases are analytic results available. It is therefore of the utmost significance that the development of high-speed electronic computing machines has recently made it possible to apply to many of these problems numerical methods which bring their solution within the range of present-day mathematical capabilities.

Numerical Methods

We shall now describe the general procedures involved in the application of numerical methods to the solution of differential equation problems.

Historically, the first such methods arose from consideration of boundary value problems and eigenvalue problems for elliptic partial differential equations which correspond to conditions of equilibrium.

These problems are related to the following "variational" principle: States of equilibrium have minimum potential energy. Indeed the equivalence between boundary value problems of partial differential equations and problems of the calculus of variations has been a central point in analysis since the time of Gauss. At first, theoretical interest in existence proofs was dominant; only much later were practical applications envisaged by two physicists, Lord Rayleigh and Walther Ritz, who independently conceived the idea of utilizing this equivalence for numerical calculation of the solutions by substituting for the variational problems simpler approximating extremum problems in which only a finite number of parameters need be determined. In the works of Rayleigh, especially in his classical *Theory of Sound*, this procedure was first used. However, Ritz gave a masterly account of the theory and at the same time applied his method to the calculation of the nodal lines of vibrating plates, a problem of classical physics that previously had not been satisfactorily treated.

Thus methods emerged which could not fail to attract engineers and physicists; after all, the minimum principles of mechanics are more suggestive than the differential equations. Great successes in applications were soon followed by further progress in the understanding of the theoretical background, and such progress in turn has resulted in advantages for the applications.

It turned out that the specific procedure used by Ritz and Rayleigh was practical only in particular cases and that the use of finite difference methods was preferable. Methods of the latter type have since become universally accepted as the most direct and promising tools of numerical analysis.

Finite Differences

In these methods, the continuum of values which can be assumed by the independent variables x, y, $\cdots$, t is replaced by a finite set of "net points" whose coordinates are integral multiples of certain fixed "mesh widths," one for each variable. Usually equal mesh widths are chosen for the space dimensions, with possibly a different one in time. Differential equations become equations involving a finite number of difference quotients; integrals are replaced by finite sums. Thus the differential equation problem is reduced to a problem with only a finite number of unknowns.

A typical equilibrium problem is to solve the two-dimensional Laplace equation

$$\nabla^2 u = u_{xx} + u_{yy} = 0$$

for a domain G in the x, y-plane, with the values of u on the boundary of G arbitrarily prescribed. The corresponding finite difference equation

$$u(x + h, y) + u(x - h, y) + u(x, y + h)$$
$$+ u(x, y - h) = 4u(x, y)$$

for a square net of mesh width h simply states that the value $u(P)$ of the unknown function u at a net point P is the arithmetic mean of the function values $u(P_i)$ at its four neighboring net points P_1, P_2, P_3, P_4. The classical boundary value problem is then to find in a finite net domain a net function having this mean value property which also has prescribed values on the boundary, i.e., at those points of the net domain that have at least one neighbor outside the domain. This problem immediately leads to a system of N linear equations for the values of u at the N interior net points; it lends itself easily to processes of numerical calculation.

Random Walk

The above "harmonic" difference equation can immediately be interpreted by the "stochastic" process of random walk in a street net of which the net points are the intersections. A particle beginning at a net point is assumed to move in the next instant to one of the four neighboring net points, with equal probability for each direction. If this random walk is arrested, and the particle absorbed, at the boundary of a finite net point region, then a particle starting from a point P will ultimately be stopped at the boundary. What is the probability of its being absorbed exactly at a fixed boundary point R? This probability, regarded as a function of P, is immediately seen to be a solution of the harmonic difference equation. Moreover, it has the boundary values 1 at R and 0 at every other boundary point; therefore it solves a specific boundary value problem. By superposition of such functions corresponding to different points R of the boundary one can then solve every boundary value problem for our difference equation.

Such an interpretation of partial differential equations by random walk phenomena can be widely generalized. Moreover, it can be utilized for numerical computation if one constructs mechanical models or computing schemes which simulate the random walk. Such methods, using high-speed computers, have been developed and applied under the name of "Monte Carlo" methods.

Initial Value Problems

For nonlinear problems in diffusion theory, fluid dynamics, and gas dynamics finite difference methods have proved of decisive importance, often as the only means of overcoming, by numerical computation based on profound theoretical analysis, obstacles heretofore prohibitive.

The general approach is again to employ a net of mesh width h in space and τ in time, and to replace the differential equations I by appropriate difference equations I_n for this net. Then in an initial value problem the values of the unknown functions for $t = 0$ are given; the difference equations permit a direct step-by-step calculation of these functions for $t = \tau$, then successively for $t = 2\tau$, $t = 3\tau$, and so on. Thus high-speed computing machines can in many cases produce an approximate solution within a reasonable time. It has been discovered, however, that to make this finite difference solution an acceptable approximation to the solution S of the differential equation, the time step τ must not exceed a certain upper limit, the size of which depends on the space mesh h and possibly also on $x, y, \cdots$ and t. If such a precaution in regard to τ is taken, and if both mesh widths are made small, a good numerical solution is insured as long as no shock discontinuities occur.

Shocks

To master phenomena of shocks by numerical procedures, two methods which have been successfully tested in problems of great practical importance are available. The first method, due to von Neumann and Richtmyer (*Journal of Applied Physics*, **21** [1950], 232–37), starts from the fact that shocks are idealized limiting phenomena for infinitely small viscosity of the fluid medium. If one introduces a realistic viscosity term in our differential equations the solutions become continuous and shocks appear merely as zones of rapid change. For numerical purposes, however, the Stokes' equations for a fluid with viscosity (and heat conductivity) are not entirely practical. Von Neumann and Richtmyer, to counter such difficulties introduce an "artificial" viscosity term q by replacing the quantity p in the equations of an ideal fluid by the quantity $p + q$. For one-dimensional flow q is defined by

$$q = \begin{cases} (kh)^2 \rho^{-1}(\rho_t + u\rho_x)^2 & \text{if } \rho_t + u\rho_x > 0, \\ 0 & \text{if } \rho_t + u\rho_x \leq 0, \end{cases}$$

where k is a dimensionless constant near unity and h is the mesh width. A great deal of experience has shown that this "viscosity method" is practical and reliable; yet its theoretical basis is still incomplete and remains a challenge to the theoretical mathematician.

More recently another promising method, not necessitating a modification of the equations for ideal fluids, has been proposed by P. Lax. It is based on expressing these equations in the mathematical form of "conservation laws," as we did above for the one-dimensional flow. Then the suitable replacement of the derivatives as they occur in this formulation by difference quotients leads to a simple step-by-step procedure which can be expected to yield, approximately, the flow including shocks. For, since the shock conditions are nothing but the same conservation laws for rapid (discontinuous) changes, one may expect that shocks simply appear as changes of the dependent quantities which are locally very large relative to τ or h. A theoretical justification is necessary but has been only partially achieved so far. Yet, experimental calculations in typical cases have been most encouraging, so that from this method and its generalizations to more space variables useful results may be expected.

Finally, a few remarks should be made about some current examples of attacks on difficult problems by high-speed numerical computations in conjunction with highly theoretical mathematical analysis.

Synchrotron

One mathematical application concerns the multibillion-volt proton accelerators, as planned on the basis of the recently discovered "strong-focusing" principle. This principle is closely related to the stability of solutions of ordinary linear differential equations of second order with periodic coefficients. The results of the classical theory and its easy extensions are most encouraging, indeed sufficiently so that definite plans have been drawn up in this country and in Europe for building several such machines at very considerable cost. There seems, however, to be some cause for caution, since the actual orbits, owing to the unavoidable imperfections of magnets and other causes, do not strictly obey the ideal linear periodic equation but do so only approximately. Because in the machine the protons will have to make up to about 500,000 revolutions on a circle with a circumference of the order of 1500 feet, the problem of stability obviously requires thorough study. Yet, solving the modified nonlinear differential equations is not possible analytically; one does not even know exactly the deviation of these equations from the linear ideal. As a mathematical remedy, apart from all sorts of experimental studies, recourse has been taken to a combined attack by analysis and computing. A fairly comprehensive program of computing such orbits under various assumptions concerning the deviation from the ideal case is under way, and it appears likely that this program will give encouragement and some guidance to the designers.

Weather Prediction

Another potentially very useful field of application of numerical procedures is weather analysis and forecasting on the basis of "dynamic meteorology," i.e., formulation of the laws of atmospheric phenomena as a rather complicated system of partial differential equations. When Professor Bjerknes of Leipzig and Oslo first proposed this line of attack on meteorological problems about forty years ago he felt that to predict tomorrow's weather on the basis of today's complete data would require a large group of mathematically qualified computers to spend about six to twelve months of intense work at numerical calculation with desk computing machines. Even today one is far from being in a position to actually predict weather by such comprehensive calculations, notwithstanding the spectacular development of computing machines. Success on this score may or may not be far off.

Flood Control

However, definite success in a related, though much simpler, problem of great practical importance, namely, the problem of prediction and control of river floods, seems all but assured. A rough but adequate theory reduces the course of flow in a given river to a system of two nonlinear (actually quasi-linear) partial differential equations for the average height and the average speed of the river as functions of location and time; the coefficients are empirical functions determined by topography and by quantities observable daily. Then the theory of such partial differential equations, which are similar in nature to those governing some of the fluid flow problems discus ed above, allows us to deduce mathematically from the situation observable today along the whole river what will happen at later dates at certain points. Here the amount of computation needed for useful forecasting is well within the range of modern computing equipment, and all that is necessary, in addition to a sufficiently precise and complete service of observation and data processing, is to set up the computational procedure once and for all. Test computations now under way should soon reveal how near one is to practical flood prediction.

Concluding Remarks

We have seen that "exact" physical laws are only idealizations of reality. Any given physical situation, however, is capable of being idealized mathematically in many different ways. Thus it is important to be able to tell which of these idealizations are reasonable. There are three criteria that ought to be satisfied by any well-formulated mathematical problem which purports to represent reality: first, the problem should possess a solution; second, the solution should be unique; and, third, the solution should be stable, i.e., a small change in any of the data of the problem should produce only a correspondingly small change in the solution. The criteria of existence and uniqueness together express a belief in causality or determinism without which experiments could not be repeated with the expectation of consistent results. The criterion of stability is necessary for two reasons: the data, especially if obtained by experiment, always contain small margins of error, which cannot be allowed to cause too great an uncertainty in the solution; moreover, the stability criterion insures that the solution S_n of an approximating problem I_n will be for large n a good approximation to the "true" solution S.

It should be observed, however, that these criteria reflect only a general orientation of thought and are not always literally binding. Indeed, various developments in physics point up the need for restrictions on their validity with important consequences for natural philosophy as well as for practical applications.

The Future of Operations Research

Philip M. Morse

No doubt most people have a rather vague idea regarding the nature of operations research: some are confused as to its scope and its relation to other, better known activities concerned with industrial and military management. This is not surprising; anyone with a reasonable amount of skepticism *should* be confused when first getting acquainted with operations research.

In fact, anyone with a reasonable amount of skepticism should be confused when first getting acquainted with *any* scientific activity. What is a nice, tidy definition of physics, or of chemistry, for example? What is the difference between a chemist and a physicist? Several different kinds of scientists can appear to be interested in the same thing. Consider a cup of coffee, for example. A physicist could be interested in the ripples on the surface of the coffee. He might wish to find the relationship between these ripples and the vibrations of an atomic nucleus just before it disintegrates, for example. The chemist certainly could be interested in the relationship between the smell of the coffee and its temperature as an indication of the relationship between the molecular structure of the aromatic esters in coffee and their vapor pressure curves. And the biologist could also be interested in this cup of coffee; after all, the coffee bean is a part of the reproductive processes of the coffee tree, and there are good biological reasons why many reproductive processes are accompanied by perfumes and strong flavors.

Of course, the management type person can also be interested in this cup of coffee. He can come along and . . . drink it.

What is just as confusing, a single science seems to be interested in a wide variety of seemingly unrelated things. Physics includes acoustics, the theory of metals, and also the theory of the atomic nucleus, for example, and mathematics covers an even wider range of rather unconnected topics.

At any rate, logically minded persons can ask why label a part of science physics and another part chemistry? Why not call the man

15

studying the cup of coffee just a "man who prefers to think about
the coffee in front of him rather than drink it"? Why try to enclose
a part of the study of the world around us by one label and differ-
entiate it from other parts? Such labels always cause confusion at
first, but they do turn out to be quite handy. It seems useful to have
a few people around who prefer to think about the cup of coffee rather
than drink it, so useful that it is worth while catching them young
and training them to think about coffee. The labels help us catch
them and train them. They divide science into areas large enough so
that the resulting trainees are not too-narrow specialists but yet not
so large that the student becomes a superficial dilettante.

The labels serve also to unify the thinking of each area of science
and so to help its progress. The area of physics, for instance, includes
the basic knowledge behind radio and radar transmission, that behind
the technology of metallurgy, and that behind the nuclear reactor.
These are quite different areas of application; problems in the work-
hardening of alloys do not seem to have much in common with problems of beaming a signal half way around the world or with problems
of keeping neutrons from flooding a control room. But electromagnetic wave theory and the theory of metals and the so-called age
theory of neutron diffusion have many concepts and techniques of
analysis in common. Advances in one often suggest advances in the
others, and every expert in one of these fields is a better expert if he
knows more than a smattering of the others. In a very real sense this
is an age of integration of scientific knowledge as well as one of
specialization.

It is not surprising therefore that there is a present urge toward
integration of the scientific study of the operations of industry,
government, and the military. Narrowly specialized techniques of
efficiency engineering, of quality control, and of production planning
are being cross-fertilized by the application of more powerful methods
of analysis. Methods developed in physics, psychology, and economics are illuminating many problems which hitherto had seemed
unconnected and are pointing the way toward more powerful techniques of solution. The introduction of the term "operations research"
has served to emphasize this tendency toward integration and has
called the attention of other scientists to this new field for research
effort. Even if the integration should go further and operations research should later be absorbed in some larger synthesis, it is clear
that the term operations research is now doing a useful job by sym-

bolizing the essential unity in the study of the operations of men and machines.

As with any newly developing area in science, we cannot expect very impressive practical applications at the very outset. The first tasks of operations research are to pull together the component specialties and techniques, to devise more general mathematical and experimental methods of analysis, and to build up well-tested theories relating each operation with other aspects, operational, physical, and psychological. There have already been a number of applications of operations research, some of which have been quite successful. Yet these results are only implications of more widespread and more basic successes which will come later, after our understanding has deepened and our analytical tools have been sharpened.

It is doubtful whether the delay from initial study to final application can be as long as it is in the physical sciences, however. There can never be the same physical separation between fundamental research and applied research in operations research as there is in physical science. Operations research studies operations, including men and equipment, and most operating groups cannot be carried off to a separate laboratory for study; they must be studied on the spot, in the factory or wherever they are in action. In order to observe or carry out experiments, the operations research worker must work closely with the administrator in charge of the operation and so get acquainted with his practical needs and worries. Therefore, even if the immediate goal of the operations research worker is an increase in fundamental understanding or an improvement of the mathematical model describing some operation, his close contact with the executive will make him aware of immediate needs and so will produce practical applications from the start. Operations research, like any other branch of scientific research, does not always pay off quickly; one should not expect full returns from a new operations research team in a few months, or even in a few years. The team's full value will come when it really understands the operations it has under study, and true scientific understanding is not arrived at quickly.

But let us get back to this integration of methodology and the basic concept of operations research. Waiting-line or queueing theory is a good example of the unifying influence of the use of the mathematical model. Most of the concepts of waiting-line theory arose in the study of the telephone exchange, more than twenty years ago, but for a long time they were used only to work out the requirements for new telephone switchboards. Only recently, since the introduction of the concept of operations research has induced the study of operations in general instead of each operation separately, has it become apparent that waiting-line theory applies to automobile traffic, to airplane landings at a large airport, to customers in a chain store, and to many production lines as well as to telephone switchboards. In fact it is becoming apparent that waiting-line or queueing theory will contribute to the understanding of any operation wherein units arrive at an irregular rate at some point, whence they are "serviced" or passed on to some other point at a different rate.

Unless the mean service rate is greater than the mean arrival rate, a waiting line or queue of units waiting to be serviced will be formed and will increase in length continually. But even if the mean service rate is larger than the mean arrival rate, the waiting line is not abolished unless both arrivals and service operations are regularized, not random. A central problem of waiting-line theory is to calculate the relationship between the mean length of waiting line and the degree of randomness of arrival and disposal. On it can be based estimates of the optimum capacity of the servicing facilities when the cost of letting the unit wait in line is balanced against the cost of increasing the service rate. These calculations are not very difficult if both arrivals and servicing take place in a purely random manner, as in the case of people coming into a store from the street.

Having made the calculations, we can proceed to apply them to a specific operational problem by first determining whether arrival and service are, in fact, random. For example, the arrivals and dockings of ships in a harbor seem to be close enough to random to apply the simple theory, unless ships are routed in convoys; aircraft arriving at an airport come at random unless special efforts are made to adjust their speeds during the half hour preceding their arrival.

Next, one has to compare the cost of having n units waiting in line against the cost of increasing the service rate. If the ratio of arrival to service rates is small, there is no great amount of time lost, but if the facility becomes popular and arrival rate begins to approach service rate, the waiting line increases rapidly in length, and money must either be spent to increase service or an effort must be made to reduce or to schedule arrivals. Administrators not familiar with waiting-line theory can make wrong decisions, with serious consequences, in such cases. Not so long ago, a shipping firm noticed that one port was somewhat more efficient than two others and decided to route all its ships to the one port. This had the effect of increasing the mean arrival rate up to 0.9 the service rate for that port and of increasing the mean waiting time threefold. Management misinterpreted the resulting considerable delay, attributing it to a sudden decrease in efficiency of the chosen port. When the theory was worked out, it was apparent that the increased delay was entirely due to the increase in arrival rate, not to a deterioration of service, and that the diversion of a few ships to the less efficient ports would reduce the waiting line considerably. In other words, a small use of the less efficient ports would produce the best results overall. Subsequent experience bore out the predictions.

In the case of aircraft stacking over airports in bad weather when landings take time, it was hoped that careful scheduling of aircraft arrivals would materially reduce the line. Computing the effect on the waiting line of changes of randomness in arrivals and landings is a difficult mathematical problem. Preliminary analysis indicates that if arrivals are completely regular, each an equal time after the next previous, but if servicing is still purely random, then the mean queue length is about half that predicted for the case of both arrival and service random. However, the actual case of aircraft stacking is a still more difficult analysis, for both arrivals and landings are "partially random" in the cases where scheduling of flights and landings is attempted. No matter how hard they try to keep to schedule, some randomness creeps in.

To solve this problem, a procedure known as the Monte Carlo technique was employed. By the use of a table of random numbers and of empirically determined probability distributions for scheduled and nonscheduled arrivals and for landings, a whole series of virtual arrivals and landings could be worked out on a high-speed computing machine, which would have the same statistical properties as actual plane arrivals and landings. Instead of using planes and landing strips to get the figures, the electronic computer could be used to reproduce the essential elements of the problem and thousands of cases could be run off in a short time. The results do not have the elegance of generality of an analytic solution but they have the advantage of being numerical answers corresponding to the case of interest. They give, in an afternoon, data equivalent to several years of counting and timing at an actual airport.

Analysis of these Monte Carlo calculations indicates a small reduction of queue length with improvement in scheduling arrivals. Finally, it is then possible to find out whether any practicable procedure for tight scheduling of plane arrivals would or would not cost more than would be gained by the calculated reduction of delay time.

Perhaps by now one can see the parallelism between the study of waiting lines and the study of some physical phenomenon. In both cases one abstracts from the complexities of the specific case the typical aspects which are to be correlated with some mathematical model. From the model, the hypothesis which one fits to the data, one can learn the interdependence of these aspects and can begin to understand the phenomenon. At first the model is very crude, including only the few most outstanding aspects, but as understanding grows, the model can be complicated to the extent needed to work out cases of practical interest. In neither physics nor operations research is the research a purely statistical hunt for correlations by taking data and calculating cross correlations or using the chi-squared rule. Observation and hypothetical model making go hand in hand. As pointed out in many recent books on the scientific method, there is a very close relationship between the progression from tentative hypothesis to final theory and the growth of what we call scientific understanding.

In the case of waiting-line theory a great deal of elaboration is possible to fit specific examples. In many cases there are several parallel service facilities, each of which can draw from the waiting line, for example, the several toll lanes across toll highways or the several docks in a port. In a production line or a traffic network there may be a sequence of bottlenecks, the waiting lines being in series, with the randomness of output of one affecting the arrival rate of the next. Some of these cases can be worked out analytically; others must be computed by Monte Carlo techniques. In most cases which have been worked out, the results have helped the executive in charge to understand the possibilities and limitations of the operation he controls and have helped him make appropriate administrative decisions concerning it.

Many other mathematical models appropriate for the analysis of various aspects of operations are being developed and applied. The techniques of linear programming can be applied to optimize the scheduling of production and the warehousing of various items. In many applications of production scheduling large-scale electronic computers will have to be used to work out specific cases in a reasonable time. Operations research workers will have to become familiar with the capabilities and the techniques of programming these high-speed computers, for many of their calculations will be too complex to do by hand.

Incidentally, the utility of the concept of operations research was demonstrated recently during a discussion with some oil company engineers. These engineers had been using the methods of linear programming in solving the following problem. The oil company can produce various proportions of fuel oil, gasoline, and aviation fuel from its cracking plants, depending on the kind of crude oil they use, and can produce various proportions of these end products from a given crude, depending on the cracking process used. But crudes differ in price and cracking processes differ in cost. Suppose the company has orders for definite quantities of end products to be delivered in the next three months. What amounts of which crude shall it buy, and which processes shall it use in its cracking plants, to produce the required amounts of products at the least cost, subject to limitations of supply of crudes and of output of their plants?

This is a straightforward linear programming problem, and the engineers had been doing a good job of solving it. The persons who worked out those solutions did not call what they were doing operations research; many of them had not heard of operations research. But neither were these engineers aware that many other problems in the company's operations were also amenable to the analysis. Their training and point of view had been too specialized to see the wider possibilities. The value of the concept of operations research to this oil company lay in making their research men aware that the techniques of theoretical analysis they had been using could be applied to a much wider range of operational problems than they had hitherto conceived, and in showing the company executives that they could use their own research departments to help solve production and sales and distribution problems where they had not hitherto been used.

Game theory is another mathematical model which is of considerable importance in the analysis of military operations and which may be of use in industrial planning where competition is an important aspect. Communication theory is another analytic tool which will be useful.

Let us consider just one more example of the unification of viewpoint which mathematical models can bring. It started during World

War II in connection with problems of naval operations as a theory of search. Since the war its application in a number of industrial cases suggests our calling it the theory of the *optimum distribution of effort*. Its naval aspect concerns the operation of search for an enemy vessel, submarine, or aircraft. The enemy is somewhere in a given area of the sea. How do we deploy our aircraft to find him? The connection between the mathematical model and the actual operation is the *rate of search*. A single plane can see the enemy vessel (by radar or sonar, or visually as the case may be) R miles away, on the average. The plane can "sweep" out a band of width $2R$ as it moves along; the picture is analogous to a vacuum cleaner, of width $2R$, sweeping over the ocean at a rate equal to the speed of the plane and picking up whatever comes beneath it. An area equal to the speed of the plane times twice the mean range of detection will thus be swept in an hour. The sweep rates of planes vary from a few hundred square miles per hour to several thousand square miles per hour, depending on the plane, the radar equipment, and the vessel being searched for.

If the enemy is equally likely to be anywhere within a certain area, then the problem is a straightforward, geometrical one. The search effort is evenly laid out over as much of the areas as one has planes available to cover. The problem is a little complicated by the fact that since detection is not certain at extreme ranges, the probability of detection falls off near the edge of the swept band, and there should be a certain amount of overlap between bands to improve the chance of detection near the edges.

But if the chance that the enemy is present varies from area to area, the problem becomes quite difficult, and nonmathematical intuition may lead to quite erroneous use of available effort. For example, if the enemy is twice as likely to be in one area as in another and if only a small amount of search effort is possible, all this effort should be spent in searching the more likely area; if more effort is available, some time can be spent on the less likely area, and so on. A definite formula can be worked out in each specific case. Search plans for various contingencies were worked out by the operations research team attached to the Navy during the war; they materially aided the naval efforts in many cases.

It seems a far cry from planes and ships and submarines to industry and business activities. But the utility of the mathematical models is their wide range of applicability. One possible business application of search theory comes in the problem of assignment of sales effort. Suppose a business has a limited number of salesmen who are to cover a wide variety of dealers. Some of these dealers are large stores, which will usually produce large orders when visited; some are small stores with correspondingly smaller sales return. If there are enough salesmen, every dealer can be visited every month and the optimum number of sales can be made, although the sales cost will be high. With fewer salesmen available, search theory indicates that the large stores should be visited more often than the small stores; with very few salesmen it may be that only the large stores should be visited. If the probable return per visit for each store is known, the optimum distribution of sales effort can then be calculated.

An interesting and typical variation on this problem arises when we consider the action of the individual salesmen, when we try to make their behavior conform to the best overall distribution for the company. For each individual salesman, with his limited effort, it may be best *for him* to visit only the large stores; if his visits are uncontrolled and if he is paid a flat commission, it may turn out that the large stores are visited too often, the small stores too seldom, for best returns *for the company as a whole*. It then becomes necessary to work out a system of incentive commissions designed to induce the salesmen to spread their efforts more evenly between large and small customers. If the general theory has been worked out, this additional complication can be added without too much difficulty.

This problem of balancing the tendencies of different parts of a large organization is one which is often encountered in industrial operations research. The sales force is out to increase the sales of all items, though some items may return less profit than others; production resists the change-over to making another product, though sales on the other product are increasing; and the financial department frowns on building up large inventories, though small inventories always put the production division at the mercy of sales fluctuations. It is often not too difficult to suboptimize each of these divisions separately, so that each is running smoothly and effectively as far as its own part of the business is concerned. But to be sure that all these parts mesh together to make the company as a whole operate most efficiently requires much more subtle analysis and very careful quantitative balancing.

In the interest of reducing factory overtime and of keeping down inventory, for example, it may be necessary to modify the salesman's incentive commissions, so that he will be induced to push one line over another. It may be necessary for the production division to allow more overtime in one department than in another, to make some part of its operation run at less than optimum in order that the overall operation be optimum, and one must take care not to have a conflicting bonus policy which will penalize the production department for reducing *its* efficiency so that the effectiveness of *the whole* is improved. Solutions of company-wide problems of this type require all of the techniques of operations research and then some. These are not problems for a newly formed Operations Research team to try at first, but they are problems to head toward. If the team can be of even the smallest help to the top executive in solving such company-wide problems, they will have paid their way manyfold.

In tackling such general problems, the operations research team is entering the field hitherto monopolized by management consultants. This should not be a subject of concern to either management consultants or operations research workers. There should be very little overlapping between the two, for the point of view and background of the operations research worker differ considerably from those of the usual management consultant. The management of the operations of a large company is usually a complicated enough problem so that there is room for the help of both types of expert.

There are many other research tools available to operations research besides the mathematical model. The model, in fact, should be only one step in the sequence of observation-model-experiment-theory which most scientific investigation uses. Nuclear physics grew from observations of radioactivity and of cosmic rays, from the subsequent hypotheses which were built to account for the observations, from the controlled experiments on high-voltage machines which the hypotheses suggested, and from the unfolding of the theory based on the earlier hypotheses and checked successively by experiment.

Automobile traffic might be an example showing how this step-by-step progress can be made. A very large amount of data has been obtained, for example, on traffic through intersections, with and without stop lights. Much of this has been analyzed statistically, and some of the results have suggested a few things to be done to improve traffic flow. But raw observational data are only the beginning of the process. We must get a mental picture of the flow, in a quantitative form, to begin really to understand the problem.

For instance, it has been observed that, when a line of waiting cars starts after the traffic light turns green, the entire line of cars does not start as a unit; first one starts, then the next, and so on. A *wave of starting* travels down the line. Some observations indicate that the velocity of this starting wave is nearly the same for any line of cars; it seems to move at a rate of about 30 miles an hour down the line. If a car were traveling in the opposite direction and adjusted its speed so that it passed the first car just as it started, the next car just as it started and so on, it would be traveling at about 30 miles an hour.

This is an observation about the dynamics of traffic flow, about the overall relation between present car design and human reactions, which is worth further investigation. Mathematical models have been set up to take into account this dynamical inertia of traffic, their constants have been adjusted to fit the observed speed of propagation of the starting wave, and the other consequences of the model are being worked out. For example, the model indicates that it is possible to have too short a period for the green light, since it takes a while for the line to start. Such predictions need to be checked against other observations, of course, in order to check the model in more detail.

But it is also necessary to devise controlled experiments to give us a real understanding of the model. Teams of cars and drivers could be put through the stop-start cycle at a specially devised intersection equipped with measurement equipment, in order to see whether training would change the reaction time and whether the mathematical model no longer applies under extreme conditions. Some of these experiments may suggest that certain modifications of car design will change the dynamics or that some of the delay times are directly limited by human capabilities. Following up these leads will suggest mechanical experiments on cars and psychophysiological experiments on people before we can say we really understand the problem.

Only at the end of such a step-by-step investigation, combining mathematical models and the results of various experiments, can we say that we understand the dynamics of stop-start at a traffic intersection. From this understanding, of course, can come true control of the phenomenon; we can then not only devise an optimum red-green cycle to fit present circumstances but also work out what to do if the circumstances change, if, for example, a greater proportion of trucks is present, or what modification should be made for conditions at night or for icy conditions.

So we must be prepared to devise operational experiments in each of the operations we study, to check our mathematical models, and to gain deeper insight into the reasons for the equations. Some of these experiments can be performed on computing machines, of course, the way the landing schedule of aircraft has been analyzed. Machines devised to duplicate the essential behavior of complex equipment or operations are called analogue computing machines. Some of these machines have been devised to duplicate the behavior of waiting lines. Many other analogue computers can and should be built, to duplicate other operational situations: those arising in production-sales scheduling, in various production lines, in railroad and bus scheduling, and in the flow of orders and reports in a large company, to name a few. By their use we can rapidly gain insight which would take much longer to obtain by observation of the operation itself. Continuous checking between the actual operation and the results obtained from the analogue computer is necessary, of course, to make sure the computer is really duplicating the essential elements of the actual operation.

This is not intended to imply that operations research is going to make the executive obsolete, that the general manager or the general or the admiral is going to be replaced by a bespectacled operator of an oversized electronic computer. Far from it; one need only be reminded that "research" is a part of the title and that research is concerned with understanding, not deciding. Having had some experience in management as well as in research, the writer can say that the process of management is inimical to the process of research. This does not mean that the two must be opposed in aims, but it does mean that when a person is bossing an outfit he cannot be doing research, and vice versa. Consequently, it should be evident that the operations research team can never replace the executive and at the same time continue to do operations research. On the other hand, an executive and an operations research team can make a most potent combination, the team foreseeing the problems and providing the factual background for decision, the executive adding his experience and intuition to reach the necessary decision. Such close partnership between executive officers and their operations research teams is now the usual pattern in our military forces. It is being tried with success in a number of large industrial concerns; perhaps it will become the usual pattern here also.

Atomic Structure

I. I. RABI

Introduction

Some 2500 years ago Democritus of Greece had the remarkable idea that one could explain all visible phenomena by assuming the existence of small things which he called atoms; these were intended to be discrete units of matter, which by their motion and general configuration would give the appearance of what we see. Twenty-five years ago it seemed that this scheme of things was virtually fulfilled, for we had the Democritus atom: the electrons and protons were the units of which the universe was constructed. However, science goes forward and we are now very far from having fulfilled the program of Democritus, for the simple picture of electrons and protons has become complicated by the addition of neutrons, positrons, neutrinos, and a variety of mesons which is almost equal to the number of original chemical elements as they were known before all this began. Thus the atom which we shall consider is not the atom envisioned by Democritus but rather a complex structure which in itself is made up of other units, or particles.

The modern atomic story really started to unfold about 1911 with the experiments of Rutherford, who bombarded matter with alpha particles, which are the nuclei or massive cores of helium atoms. He found, to his surprise, that very large deflections of the alpha particles occurred; this could mean only that the particles experienced some strong center of force. Furthermore, the deflection was that caused by a repulsive force. Thus, since the electron, or unit of negative electricity, was already known, Rutherford's experiment established the planetary atom, namely, a central nucleus with positive charge of amount Ze, about which move in some manner the electrons, or negative charge. Now, when we picture an atom in this manner, we are faced with a major problem: what accounts for the extraordinary stability of the atoms? We know from geological considerations that matter has been around for a very long

27

time, of the order of several billion years. Yet the atom described
above would not be stable, according to the physical laws known
at the time. Simple electrodynamics would tell us that electrons
moving about a nucleus undergo an acceleration because of the
changing velocity vector; hence they should radiate energy. As
they lose energy their orbits would decrease and the acceleration
would increase, thereby increasing the rate of energy loss. The net
result of such classical considerations is that the electrons must
fall into the nucleus, and the simple criterion of stability is not
satisfied by this picture of the atom.

This problem was solved by Niels Bohr, who cut the Gordian
knot with a pronouncement so startling that it may be likened to
that made by Joshua when he commanded the sun to stand still.
Bohr followed some ideas suggested by Max Planck in 1900, who
came upon two significant concepts while considering the properties
of temperature radiation. One was that a harmonic oscillator,
which is simply a mass oscillating under the action of a central
force, could have only certain discrete energy levels given by

$$W_n = nh\nu, \tag{1}$$

where W_n is the energy, ν is the frequency of oscillation, h is a
universal constant which was named for Planck and which can be
evaluated by considerations of temperature radiation, and n takes
on integral values. Planck also suggested that radiation is emitted
only in whole quanta, that is, in discrete units of energy, $h\nu$.

Albert Einstein took these two ideas suggested by Planck and
extended them to fields other than temperature radiation. One of
the perplexing problems at that time was the photoelectric effect,
which is the emission of electrons from a surface when light falls
upon it. Now, experimentally, one finds that the maximum energy
of the emitted electrons is independent of the intensity of the light;
even with illumination so weak that a straightforward calculation
of the amount of energy falling upon a single atom, as determined
from the area occupied by the atom, is much less than the energy
with which the electron is emitted, it is found that electrons are
emitted immediately. Einstein suggested that light may have some
properties of a particle, in that the energy is concentrated in definite
units of amount $h\nu$. When it falls upon an atom, this energy may or
may not be given up, but if it is, then the entire energy $h\nu$ is given

to the atom. Thus the kinetic energy E_k of the ejected electron is given by

$$E_k = h\nu - \phi, \tag{2}$$

where ϕ is the work function of the material, that is, the amount of energy required to remove an electron from the surface.

Still another problem attacked by Einstein was that concerning the specific heat of crystals. According to ordinary statistics, the specific heat of a crystal should be large and fairly constant, even at low temperatures. Yet at very low temperatures it is found that the specific heat disappears. When Einstein applied the Planck relationship to the vibrations of the atoms in the crystal, he obtained a specific heat curve which agreed fairly well, although not completely, with experiment. At the same time Einstein showed that if light is emitted in quanta of energy $h\nu$, then each quantum has a momentum $h\nu/c$ (where c is the velocity of light) and a mass to conform with the electrodynamics of $h\nu/c^2$.

The Bohr Atom

These were the developments up to 1911, when Rutherford's experiments suggested the planetary atom, following which Bohr resolved the chief difficulty of the classical atom in 1913. He accomplished this by means of two statements or postulates, which were unsupported by theoretical physics but which were supported by the experimental facts. These statements were analogous to Planck's concept of definite energy levels for a harmonic oscillator, which he used to explain temperature radiation. Bohr postulated that the atom itself has a series of energy levels, which he called stationary states of definite energy; the stationary states correspond to those electron orbits for which the angular momentum is a whole multiple of $h/2\pi$, and no energy is radiated while the electron is in one of these "allowed" orbits. The atom can pass from one of these states to another of lower energy with the emission of radiation; if the energies of the two states are W_a and W_b, respectively, the frequency ν of the emitted radiation is then found from the relation:

$$h\nu = W_a - W_b. \tag{3}$$

Conversely, the atom may be raised to a higher energy state by the absorption of this amount of energy. This was an extraordinary suggestion, for classically the frequency of the radiation from an oscillatory system is just the frequency of oscillation; thus, an antenna emits radiation of a frequency corresponding to the electrical oscillations which take place in the associated circuit. By the same token one might expect that the radiation from an atom would be associated in some way with the frequency of rotation of the electron. This is not the case, however; the frequency is determined from Equation 3 above, where ν does not correspond, in general, to any of the frequencies of motion. Still another break with classical theory was the concept of stationary states, and the suggestion that an atom can exist in such a state for a finite time. It is clear that if we have a set of discrete stationary states, there must be a lowest state, and when the atom finds itself in this state it can simply remain there indefinitely. After making this break with classical ideas, Bohr nevertheless used classical dynamical theory to calculate the orbits and energy levels of the atom.

The Bohr postulates seemed perfectly arbitrary and did not form the basis for a cohesive system of ideas. Yet they led to conclusions that agreed remarkably well with the observed facts. The radiation which is emitted by atoms can be measured with great precision; it is not unusual to determine frequencies to within one part in 10^7, so that it was possible to test the Bohr theory in minute detail. Consider a series of energy levels $W_1, W_2, W_3 \ldots$ Then the frequency of the radiation emitted in a transition from W_1 to W_2 would be, according to Eq. 3 above,

$$\nu_{12} = \frac{W_1 - W_2}{h}.$$

Similarly

$$\nu_{23} = \frac{W_2 - W_3}{h}.$$

Also

$$\nu_{13} = \frac{W_1 - W_3}{h} = \nu_{12} + \nu_{23}. \tag{4}$$

Thus, we see that the sum of the two frequencies is just that due to a transition from W_1 to W_3. This had actually been observed earlier by Ritz, who found that the sums and differences of observed frequencies are also frequencies very exactly. This is known as the combination principle and is generally expressed in terms of wave numbers, which are more convenient experimentally. The wave number of a spectral line is simply the reciprocal of the wave length; hence, it is proportional to the frequency, since

$$\text{wave number} = \frac{1}{\lambda} = \frac{\nu}{c},$$

where λ is the wave length and c, of course, is the velocity of light. It had been found that it was much simpler to analyze complex spectra by specifying certain quantities called terms; numbers which were not observed themselves, but which yielded the frequency, or wave number, of a line when one took the difference between two terms. In 1885 Balmer observed that the wave numbers of the lines in the hydrogen spectrum could be expressed very accurately by the formula

$$\text{wave number} = R\left(\frac{1}{4} - \frac{1}{n^2}\right) \text{cm}^{-1}, \tag{5}$$

where R is a constant (determined experimentally to be 109,737) called the Rydberg number after the spectroscopist who found regularities in the spectra of certain atoms other than hydrogen, and n is an integer which has the values 3, 4, 5, $\cdots$. Note that the wave number of a spectral line in the Balmer series is the difference between two numbers, or terms, given by R/n^2, where $n = 2$ for one of the terms and $n = 3, 4, 5, \cdots$ for the other term.

The importance of the Ritz combination principle can be seen in the fact that a large number of spectral lines can be expressed by means of a much smaller number of terms, or rather by the differences in these terms. For example, with n terms one can have $n(n - 1)/2$ differences, which may be substantially greater than n. While not all the possible differences are actually observed as spectral lines, it should be evident that the combination principle simplifies considerably the tabulation of spectroscopic observations.

Despite the vast amount of empirical data which had been accumulated by spectroscopists from roughly the middle of the nineteenth century, there was no reasonable suggestion of an explanation until Bohr turned his attention to the problem. It was known that the radiation somehow was emitted by the atoms, but there was no way of relating the observed frequencies to any property of the atom. However, on the basis of Bohr's suggestion, one knew at once the energy levels of the atom from the observed spectrum, and the term values which had been found experimentally could be identified with the energy levels; his theory gave meaning to the empirical conclusions of Balmer, Ritz, and Rydberg.

Bohr did not stop at this means for identifying the energy levels of the atom but went on to develop a system for predicting these levels. He did this, as has been pointed out, by calling upon classical electrodynamics. We know that the law of force between the nucleus and an orbital electron is Coulomb's law. Consider a nucleus of charge $+Ze$ and an electron of charge $-e$ moving in a circular orbit about the nucleus. We take the circular orbit as the simplest case, since we know that the electron, under the action of an inverse square attractive force, must move in elliptic orbits. The angular momentum of the electron when in an orbit of radius r is mvr, where m is the electron mass, and according to Bohr this must be set equal to $nh/2\pi$, where n is an integer. Writing the expression for the total energy of the system and introducing the selection rule given by Bohr, we find for the energy levels the values

$$W_n = \frac{2\pi^2\mu e^4}{h^2} Z^2 \cdot \frac{1}{n^2}, \qquad (6)$$

where μ is the reduced mass of the system. The atomic constants are well known, and it is convenient to write the formula as

$$W_n = Z^2 hc R \cdot \frac{1}{n^2}, \qquad (7)$$

where $R = 2\pi^2\mu e^4/ch^3$ is found to agree very closely with the experimental value of the Rydberg constant. Note that the value of R given above will vary slightly for different hydrogen-like atoms, such as the hydrogen isotopes deuterium and tritium, singly ionized helium, doubly ionized lithium, and so on. The reason for this is the fact that the reduced mass μ, while very nearly equal to the electron mass for all these atoms, does depend upon the mass of the nucleus. Thus, the lines for deuterium and helium should be slightly displaced from the hydrogen spectrum, and the discovery of helium in the spectrum of the sun and of deuterium in the laboratory, could be explained in just this manner.

To obtain the wave number of the spectral lines from Equation 7 we need only recall the second Bohr postulate, Equation 3, and substitute. Then the frequency is given by

$$\nu = Z^2 Rc \left(\frac{1}{n_f^2} - \frac{1}{n_i^2} \right),$$

and the wave number $\bar{\nu} = \nu/c$ becomes

$$\text{wave number} = \bar{\nu} = Z^2 R \left(\frac{1}{n_f^2} - \frac{1}{n_i^2} \right), \tag{8}$$

where n_f and n_i refer to final and initial states, respectively. If n_f is set equal to 2, it is seen that the expression gives the lines of the Balmer series when $n_i = 3, 4, 5, \cdots$. Setting n_f equal to 1 gives still another observed series, the Lyman series, and so on.

The success of the Bohr theory was immediately apparent, for despite the seemingly arbitrary nature of the postulates, it agreed extremely well with the experimental facts. It provided a recipe for calculating the energy levels, although the mathematical scheme was not understood. This accomplishment provides a good illustration of how far one can proceed in science without basic knowledge, provided one has a mathematical scheme to follow. The scheme was not always successful, but suppose we examine briefly just how far it could go.

The Bohr theory dealt only with circular orbits but was extended by Sommerfeld to include the more general case of elliptic orbits. Sommerfeld generalized the Bohr quantum postulate to read

$$\oint p_i dq_i = n_i h, \tag{9}$$

where q_i is a coordinate which undergoes a periodic variation, p_i is the momentum associated with this coordinate, and n_i is an integer. For circular orbits this becomes the familiar Bohr condition: $mvr = nh/2\pi$. When applied to elliptic orbits, there are now two coordinates, radial and angular, for which the quantizing condition must be established. Thus there will be two equations of the form of Equation 9 to be satisfied. If the problem is set up, not in plane polar coordinates, but in spherical polar coordinates in three-dimensional space, there will be three quantum conditions corresponding to the three variables. These relationships fix the size and shape of the elliptic orbits.

Space Quantization

The energy depends simply upon the length of the semimajor axis, and the plane of the orbit can have only certain discrete orientations in space. This is known as space quantization, and one of the consequences of the theory was that if an orbit had a total angular momentum specified by the quantum number j, then the plane of the orbit could take on $2j + 1$ possible orientations in space. Of course, it is difficult to imagine discrete space orientations without some direction which can serve as a guide. If an external magnetic field is applied, for example, then space quantization can be carried out with respect to the direction of this field.

In 1922, Stern and Gerlach did their well-known experiment in which they passed silver atoms through an inhomogeneous magnetic field. In such a field an atom is deflected by an amount proportional to that component of the magnetic moment of the atom which lies in the direction of the field. Now, since the silver atoms emerge from a hot oven, it would seem that they should have every possible orientation, which would mean angular deflections ranging from zero, when the magnetic moment stands perpendicular, to a maximum, when it is parallel or antiparallel to the field. This would be the expected result on classical grounds. However, since $j = 1$ for silver, space quantization would indicate that the atoms could have only three possible orientations: parallel, antiparallel, or perpendicular to the field. Indeed, the experimental result showed the atoms were oriented either parallel or antiparallel to the field; those perpendicular were actually absent. This was a very strange relation, because if one assumes that the atoms enter the field with all possible orientations, then in order to take on the directions determined by space quantization the atoms must gain or lose an appropriate amount of energy. This they could do only by radiation, but if one calculates the rate of radiation from a dipole it is clear that this is not possible, for it would take an enormous amount of time to radiate the requisite energy. In other words the atom must somehow enter the field with the proper orientations.

This was still another example of the power of the Bohr theory, as modified by Sommerfeld, in explaining the experimental facts. Yet the difficulties were nevertheless present because there was no systematic theory. The quantizing conditions were simply artificial restrictions which had no justification except that they worked. A major difficulty arose when one began to consider the next more complex atom than hydrogen, namely, helium, with a nuclear charge of two and with two electrons. A great deal of attention was given to the helium problem, but the methods which had proved successful in the case of hydrogen, and in numerous other problems, did not work at all for helium. The reason for this is fairly evident. We know from the Bohr theory that the frequencies of radiation are not the frequencies of motion. Yet if one were to attempt a calculation for the helium atom, the influence of one electron on the other would correspond more or less to the frequencies of motion. But we know that the electrons cannot be affected in this manner; instead, the influence of one on the other should depend upon the radiation, that is, the difference in energy levels. Hence, there was a fundamental contradiction between the two ideas, if within the atom the electrons were affected by the frequencies of motion. There was no way of treating the problem at that time except to make various simplifying assumptions which did not lead to answers corresponding to experimental facts. It was almost as though the theory had reached its end—an end that proved successful in certain applications, but one without rationality.

De Broglie's Hypothesis

At this point a number of ideas came along which should have occurred earlier. Let us consider chiefly the idea suggested by de Broglie. We have seen that the momentum of a light quantum is $h\nu/c$, but since $\lambda = c/\nu$ we can write

$$p = \frac{h\nu}{c} = \frac{h}{\lambda}.\tag{10}$$

De Broglie raised the question: "If light exhibits certain particle properties, may a particle have wave properties? Is it possible to associate with a particle the wave length $\lambda = h/p$?" This was another bold suggestion and one that sheds light on the quantizing relationship (Equation 9). For if we substitute for p the value h/λ, we have

$$\oint \frac{h}{\lambda} \, dq = nh$$

or

$$\oint dq = n\lambda. \tag{11}$$

If, for simplicity, we take the case of a circular orbit, Equation 11 yields $2\pi r = n\lambda$, where r is the radius of the orbit. Here one finds a physical interpretation of the quantum condition, for this simply states that those orbits are allowed for which the circumference is an integral number of wave lengths. In this sense it resembles the familiar classical problem of standing waves. Imagine a wave accompanying the electron as it moves around its orbit. This would be something in the nature of a standing wave, and the condition for stability is that there be a whole number of wave lengths in the orbit, so that the wave interferes constructively with itself.

If particles exhibit a wave character, then, as was pointed out by Einstein, diffraction effects should be observed, just as in the case of light. Shortly afterward in 1925, Davisson and Germer demonstrated that electrons could be diffracted and that patterns were obtained that were similar to the diffraction patterns observed with light; furthermore, the wave length was just that given by $\lambda = h/p$. To show that this was not simply a property of electrons, T. H. Johnson later carried out similar experiments with hydrogen atoms and showed that the same relationship applied. In other words, it is apparently a property of all matter that one can associate a wave length with the momentum. This was carried still further by Stern, who demonstrated wave properties for helium atoms and, most important, for hydrogen molecules. Having demonstrated this property for a complex entity such as a molecule, one finds it easier to believe that the same should be true of a baseball or of a table. Thus we find complete symmetry between light and matter in regard to this dual role.

The Uncertainty Principle

Having arrived at this point, it is well to reconsider the fundamental problem in dynamics in the light of these developments. This problem is simply the following: Given the position and velocity of a particle at time $t = 0$, to find its subsequent position as a function of time. Now it turns out that a serious obstacle stands in the way of a solution to this problem, not because Newton formulated his laws of motion incorrectly, but because the particles he spoke about do not exist in nature when one is concerned with particles of atomic dimensions. When we talk about the position of a particle we might just as well talk about the position of a wave. The location of a wave naturally depends upon the kind of wave under consideration. If it is a plane wave in an infinite medium, it is obviously everywhere in the region through which it has propagated, up to the wave front. On the other hand, if we were to construct a wave packet by superimposing a number of neighboring frequencies, and imagine that the particle is located within the packet, then the more we attempt to localize the wave packet, the greater will be the frequency band required. Thus, if the particle is to be represented by a wave, the only means of localization one can consider is a superposition of waves of different wave lengths. This means a superposition of different momenta, so that any attempt to locate the position of a particle within certain limits, let us say Δx, results in an uncertainty in momentum, Δp_x. It was just such considerations that led Heisenberg to his formulation of the well-known uncertainty relationship, which states that the product $\Delta p_x \cdot \Delta x$ is of the order of magnitude of h, where p_x is, of course, the x component of momentum. It should be borne in mind that the uncertainty relationship is simply a direct consequence of the fact that particles and waves exhibit this dual character.

Wave Mechanics

Once a wave length has been assigned to a particle it becomes reasonable to derive a wave equation that will describe the motion. De Broglie derived such an equation but did not take into account the necessary dispersive medium; if a particle moves in a field of force it is effectively moving in a dispersive medium, since its momentum changes and hence so does its wave length. This is similar to the case of light moving through a medium of changing refractive index; the wave length of the light changes. A correct formulation of the wave equation was developed by Schrödinger, who showed that one could guess at the form of the equation in a fairly simple way. Without going into the details of the derivation, let us write the equation in the usual form:

$$\left(\frac{\partial^2}{\partial x^2} + \frac{\partial^2}{\partial y^2} + \frac{\partial^2}{\partial z^2}\right)\psi + \frac{8\pi^2 m}{h^2}[E - V(x, y, z)]\psi = 0, \quad (12)$$

where E is the total energy, V the potential energy, and ψ the wave function, which function is a function of the coordinates of the system and of the time. If H is the Hamiltonian expression for the energy, considered here as a differential operator, Schrödinger showed that the time-dependent wave equation was given by

$$H\psi = -\frac{h}{2\pi i}\frac{\partial\psi}{\partial t}. \quad (13)$$

A partial differential equation, such as Equation 13 above, has, as we know numerous solutions. These can be limited only by imposing certain requirements on the solutions. The conditions are quite reasonable: since ψ must represent a physical quantity, we should require that the function be continuous and possess derivatives. Still another condition is that it be quadratically integrable, which means that it can be normalized, and hence set equal to unity by multiplying by a suitable constant. No attempt will be made to go into the subject of wave mechanics in any detail. Instead, some of the more important concepts have been described in order to lead up to the consequences of the wave equation.

If we substitute for V the proper potential energy for an electron in the field of a nucleus, we have $V = Ze^2/r$. We would then find that there are only certain values of the energy E for which the Schrödinger equation has a solution, at the same time satisfying the conditions imposed upon it. These eigenvalues, as they are called, correspond exactly to the energy values which Bohr first found for the hydrogen atom. And so here at last was a consistent theory for the hydrogen atom. Equally important was the fact that one could treat many-particle problems simply by adding the momenta of the various particles. Thus, for two particles one has six variables in the equation instead of three, and the correct values for the helium atom are obtained.

Zeeman Effect

Let us now consider the effect upon the spectral lines of imposing a magnetic field upon the radiating atoms. Towards the end of the nineteenth century Zeeman tried such experiments and found that the lines split into a number of lines as a result of the magnetic field. This is known as the Zeeman effect; of the two types, normal and anomalous, the latter is more frequently observed. It will be convenient, however, to consider the normal effect first.

An electron traveling about a nucleus constitutes a current, and since the current encloses an area it is equivalent to a magnetic shell and hence has a magnetic moment, μ. Again, the magnetic moment is quantized, since it depends upon the angular momentum of the atom. In an external magnetic field H the atom will have a magnetic energy given by the product of the field intensity and the component of the magnetic moment in the direction of the field. This additional energy will also be quantized, and we should then expect that each of the energy levels given by Bohr's theory will be split into a number of levels. Consequently, since the spectral lines result from transitions between levels, these may be split into several components. The actual number of components would depend upon the angular momentum of the atom and upon the selection rules that govern the transitions.

When the magnetic moment of the atom depends solely upon the area of the orbit or, more correctly, upon the orbital angular momentum of the electron, we have the normal Zeeman effect, as described above. However, this simple picture did not agree with the facts for hydrogen, and the explanation of what is known as the anomalous Zeeman effect remained a major problem until 1926, when it was finally resolved by the suggestion of Goudsmit and Uhlenbeck. Their idea was that the electron, in addition to its usual properties, had an intrinsic spin, very much like the spin of a top. Thus, the total angular momentum is now given by the sum of the orbital angular momentum and the spin angular momentum; it was the introduction of the electron spin that led to complete agreement between experiment and the theory of the anomalous Zeeman effect.

Periodic Table

We are now in a position to consider the structure of the periodic table as it was described by Pauli prior to the development of quantum mechanics. Suppose we have an atom with a number of orbital electrons, and let us assume that these electrons do not influence one another in their motion. Such an assumption should not affect our fundamental principles. Now what is required to specify the motion of the electrons? As we have seen, there must first be a quantum number which specifies the energy of the orbit, or the semimajor axis of the ellipse. This is the usual principal quantum number n, which takes on the values 1, 2, 3, $\cdots$. Another quantum number l is used to designate the number of units of orbital angular momentum which the electron has, and l can take the values 0, 1, 2, $\cdots$ $(n - 1)$, or a total of n values. It will be recalled that space quantization limits the possible orientations of l with respect to a magnetic field; thus, if m_l is the component of l in the direction of the field, m_l can take on the values $-l$, $\cdots$ 0, $\cdots$ l, for a total of $(2l + 1)$ values. Finally, the spin of the electron is specified by the component m_s along the direction of the field, and this can have only the values $\pm\frac{1}{2}$, corresponding to parallel and antiparallel orientations of the spin vector. These four numbers, n, l, m_l, m_s, specify the state of a given electron in the atom, and Pauli's exclusion principle states simply that no two electrons in an atom can have the same set of four quantum numbers. This is the same as stating that no two electrons in the atom can be in the same state.

If we ask how many electrons can have the same principal quantum number n on the basis of Pauli's principle, we find that the total is $2n^2$, for as we have seen, there are $(2l + 1)$ possible values of m_l. Therefore, we sum this over the values of l from 0 to $(n - 1)$, and since there are two possible m_s states for each of these values, we multiply by 2. Hence, the number of electrons is given by:

$$2 \sum_{l=0}^{n-1} (2l + 1) = 4 \sum_{l=0}^{n-1} l + 2 \sum_{l=0}^{n-1} 1$$

$$= 4 \cdot \frac{n}{2}(n - 1) + 2n$$

$$= 2n^2.$$

We can now see how this is applied to the periodic table. For hydrogen, of course, the problem is very simple, since there is but one electron; hence $n = 0$, $l = m_l = 0$, and $m_s = \pm\frac{1}{2}$. Note that there are the two possible values for the spin orientation; these correspond to the two possible states of hydrogen. Going to a more complex atom, let us consider a nucleus of charge Z and see how the electrons are to be fit into the atom. The lowest energy level, or orbit closest to the nucleus, has principal quantum number $n = 1$. The orbital quantum number l must be zero since the largest value it can assume is $(n - 1)$. Thus m_l is also zero, but $m_s = \pm\frac{1}{2}$, which means that two electrons can occupy the innermost, or K-shell; the two electrons have their spins antiparallel. These are the only electrons possible for $n = 1$, and the next electron must have $n = 2$. Note that the atom which has two electrons in the lowest energy level is neutral helium. In order to construct a lithium atom we must place the next electron in a higher energy level; hence this electron is not bound as strongly to the atom. If we continue this process for $n = 2$ we have $l = 0$ or 1; two electrons can be in the $l = 0$ state (these are usually termed s electrons). There are three states for $l = 1$, corresponding to the three possible values of m_l, and each of these states can have two spin orientations for a total of six electrons in the $l = 1$ state (known as p electrons). This makes a total of eight electrons in the second, or L-shell, and brings us to atomic number 10, which is another inert gas, neon. To continue this process further, the next electron must go into the M-shell, for which $n = 3$. Here there can be a total of 18 possible states: two s-states, six p-states for $l = 1$, and ten states for $l = 2$, these being known as d-states. A subshell is completed with the rare gas argon, $Z = 18$, which uses up the s- and p-states.

Here we find a rather interesting departure from the procedure we have followed thus far. Potassium, $Z = 19$, has its nineteenth electron in the N-shell ($n = 4$), instead of in a d-state of the M-shell. Similarly, calcium, $Z = 20$, has two electrons in the N-shell ($n = 4$, $l = 0$). It would have been expected that these two electrons would fit into the still incomplete M-shell ($n = 3$, $l = 2$). However, spectroscopic evidence runs contrary to this, although succeeding electrons do fill the M-shell. The guiding principle is that those states are filled first which correspond to the lowest energy, and this depends on the distribution of charges.

In terms of wave mechanics, the Pauli principle corresponds to the statement that the wave function ψ must be antisymmetric upon the exchange of any two particles. That is, if ψ is the wave function of a multiparticle problem, such as electrons in an atom having position coordinates r_1, r_2, r_3, $\cdots$ r_n and spin coordinates s_1, s_2, s_3, $\cdots$ s_n, which may be positive or negative, then if the position and spin coordinates of any two particles are interchanged, the new wave function must have the same magnitude but be of opposite sign. This is the statement of the Pauli principle and is the fundamental property leading to the Fermi statistics.

Positronium

One of the most interesting developments of recent years was the discovery of what may be considered a new element; not one of the transuranic elements but one which has a mass roughly one-thousandth the mass of the proton. This new element is positronium. It is perhaps difficult to view it in exactly the same light as our stable elements, since it exists for a time which is only of the order of 10^{-10} second. However, this time is not particularly short on the atomic scale, for the frequency of revolution of the electron in a hydrogen atom is about 10^{15} per second. Thus, 10^{-10} second would correspond to some 10^5 revolutions, and this is sufficient time for the positronium to settle down and exhibit definite properties which can be measured. Actually, as we shall see, it has another state of longer life, about 10^{-7} second. We can look upon the positronium "atom" as an analogue of the hydrogen atom. In the latter we have a proton and an electron, while in the former we have a positron and an electron. Hence, the reduced mass of positronium is just one-half the electron mass, while in hydrogen, it will be recalled, it is but slightly less than the electron mass. By reference to Equation 6 it is seen that the energy levels are separated by about one-half the corresponding separation for hydrogen, because of the reduced mass factor. The lowest state of hydrogen has angular momentum $l = 0$. However, it does have spin because the electron has spin. If we recall that protons also have spin, of magnitude $\frac{1}{2}$ in units of $h/2\pi$, then the lower states of hydrogen are those in which the proton and electron spins are parallel, for a total spin of l, or antiparallel for a total spin of zero. These are just the two states of hydrogen mentioned earlier.

It should be evident that there will be a difference in energy between these two states. This energy difference was measured directly by resonance methods, resulting in the well-known 21-cm line (approximately 1,420 megacycles), which has become an essential means for identifying hydrogen in radioastronomy. It should be noted that the accuracy of the measurement was roughly one part in 10^7. Now in positronium one should expect to find a similar situation, for the positron and electron can have parallel or anti-parallel spins, resulting in different energy levels. The mutual energy of two magnets varies inversely as the cube of the distance between them. In positronium the distance between particles is about twice as great as in hydrogen, because of the mass difference. Thus, if the positron had the same magnetic moment as the proton, the separation between the two levels would be expected to be ⅛ the separation of the hydrogen states. But the positron has a moment some 650 times greater than the proton moment, so that the separation should be roughly 8/650 or 1/80 as great as that for hydrogen. Thus, the corresponding frequency is some 80 times greater, or about 1.16×10^5 megacycles. It should be noted that the result of this simple estimate does not agree with experiment; instead the frequency separation between levels is found to be about twice as great. The factor 2 results from the fact that the electromagnetic interaction is more complicated than the classical Coulomb law of force. The complete theory must take account of the possibility that an electron-positron pair can be created out of radiation alone and, conversely, as will be described below, of the fact that an electron and positron can annihilate one another, producing an amount of radiation equal to the combined rest masses.

Such considerations point out another difference between the hydrogen and positronium atoms. As one can see, in the former the magnetic moment of the atom is determined primarily by the electron, since the proton moment is so small in comparison, and hence cannot be zero. On the other hand, in a positive electron the magnetic moment lies in the same direction as the angular momentum, while in a negative electron the two are in opposite directions. Thus, in the spin-0 state, where the momenta are opposite, the positronium has a large magnetic moment; in the spin-1 state, however, the magnetic moment is zero. The two states differ appreciably when regarded from the point of view of experiment. It will be recalled that the positronium atom is unstable; the positron and electron ultimately combine to produce radiation. When the positronium is in state-0, two light quanta are produced, each of energy mc^2, the rest mass energy of an electron. This is the well-known annihilation radiation and, being of discrete energy (0.51 Mev), is easily observed. Since originally the momentum was zero, or very close to zero, the two light quanta must be emitted in opposite directions. This is the short-lived state, having a mean life about 10^{-10} second. It is evident that such a decay scheme cannot serve for the spin-1 state, which has a total angular momentum of one. Instead, in order to conserve momentum, this state must decay with the emission of three quanta, all lying in the same plane. These quanta are not necessarily equal, but their energies must total $2 mc^2$. Thus, one would not expect to find a discrete radiation resulting from such three-quantum annihilation, but a continuum which is readily distinguishable from the more familiar sharp-line annihilation radiation. This is the state of longer lifetime, approximately 10^{-7} second, since it is more "difficult" to produce three quanta than two.

Starting with a sample of positronium, the two states would be populated according to the number of possible orientations. Thus, the ratio of spin-1 to spin-0 states would be $3:1$. After a time of the order of 10^{-10} second, virtually all the spin-0 states would be annihilated and only the spin-1 states would remain.

Let us consider briefly the type of the experiment by which M. Deutsch demonstrated the existence of positronium and measured the separation between the two states. Imagine a source which emits positrons into a gas such as Freon at a pressure of a few atmospheres. The positrons lose energy by collisions with the gas molecules until they are slowed down to thermal energies. They then capture negative electrons to form positronium. Now Freon is a gas which has zero magnetic moment; argon, for example, could be used just as well. If one observed the spectrum of the emitted photons, he would then find a sharp peak corresponding to the annihilation radiation, and a continuum, somewhat in the nature of a background, caused by the three-quantum annihilation. If a gas such as nitric oxide, which has a magnetic moment, is added to the Freon, collisions between the positronium and the NO molecules can alter the spins and transform spin-1 atoms to the lower spin-0 state; this results from the interaction with the magnetic moment of the NO molecule. Since the spin-1 state has a comparatively long life, transforming these to the spin-0 state generally results in two-quantum decay from this state before the atom can revert to the spin-1 state. Not very much nitric oxide is required to demonstrate this effect; the addition of several per cent of NO to the Freon results in a marked change in the observed spectrum. By this means one has a measure of the type of positronium with which he is dealing. Now imagine a magnetic field applied to the Freon in the absence of nitric oxide. This has much the same effect as the addition of NO, for in the presence of the field, spin-1 positronium exhibits some of the properties of spin-0 positronium; in other words, an atom in the spin-1 state will be found to spend part of its time in the spin-0 state, because of the induced magnetic moment. Owing to the much shorter life of the spin-0 state, the decay takes place preferentially from this state. For a more detailed analysis of the actual process one must appeal to the quantum mechanical treatment, which is beyond the scope of this discussion.

The essential features to keep in mind are the transitions induced by the field and the sensitive means of determining the relative populations of the states by observation of the gamma spectrum. If the applied field is sufficiently weak so that the spin-1 state is depopulated only partially, the application of a radio-frequency field of the proper frequency can then induce additional transitions. This is a sharp resonance, and the frequency can be determined with great precision, thus giving the energy difference between the two states. The experimental value for the separation between levels is 2.0335×10^5 megacycles, almost twice that determined by the simple analogy considered earlier. It is important to note that modern quantum theory can predict this result, the theoretical value being 2.0337×10^5 megacycles.

Conclusion

The comment was made at the outset of this discussion that in a sense the more we learn, the less we know. It was very fashionable at the turn of the century to talk of an ether; Maxwell was attracted to the idea and Kelvin apparently was convinced of the existence of the luminiferous ether. However, this went out of fashion with the introduction of Einstein's special theory of relativity, because there was no real need for an ether. Yet we now find that space has some strange properties. The annihilation of electron pairs and the materialization of matter would seem to endow space with rather substantial properties. This, in fact, is one of the consequences of quantum electrodynamics; we refer to the polarization of the vac-

uum, which means the polarization of the ether. Thus, we have
returned to the concept of an ether; not the ether envisioned by
Maxwell or by Kelvin, which had complete rigidity and yet was
completely permeable, but a very remarkable kind, of which we are
just beginning to learn the properties. It was pointed out that modern theory agrees with experiment with regard to the separation of
the positronium levels. However, this should not be taken to mean
that we really understand these phenomena, for the theory does not
converge but is made to agree with experiment through systematic
mathematical manipulation.

We started by describing how Bohr in 1913 put rationality aside
and enunciated his postulates because they agreed with experiment, and we find that some four decades later the same thing is
being done, perhaps in a more sophisticated fashion.

Microwave Spectroscopy

C. H. TOWNES

The general potentialities of spectroscopy are well known, and the results obtainable in the infrared, visible, ultraviolet, and X-ray regions are familiar. Microwave spectroscopy, however, is rather a late comer, and its methods are less familiar than the classical techniques in regions of shorter wave length. It may be defined as the study of interactions between electromagnetic radiation and matter but at wave lengths from about one millimeter up to about one meter. This region has only recently been accessible to study, and, in fact, some parts of it, particularly in the millimeter range, still cause difficulty.

Primarily as a result of intense work on radar and other electronic techniques during World War II, the field of microwave spectroscopy has become prominent. In the future, it seems likely that this region of the spectrum will contribute to both technology and science in a manner comparable to that of X-ray, infrared, or any of the other major spectroscopic regions. Microwave methods are especially fascinating because this is a field where electrical engineering overlaps with the fine details of matter as described by quantum mechanics. It is, of course, a familiar fact that optical spectroscopy is dominated by quantum mechanical laws and these, in turn, seem quite remote from the general macroscopic engineering behavior of matter. Yet, as will be seen, it is actually possible to measure the rate of rotation of molecules or to watch and measure their quantum mechanical behavior with electronic devices.

Microwave spectroscopy of gases is the simplest type, for a gas is understood theoretically in considerable detail. Although molecular collisions may occur frequently, a gas consists essentially of collections of isolated molecules. Moreover, the experimental procedures are also basically very simple, as shown in Figure 1. The apparatus is quite similar to that used in studying absorption spectra in any region and consists of three main parts: a source of radiation, an absorption cell for the gas, and a detector of the transmitted radiation.

The absorption cell, which is called a wave guide, is simply a hollow metal pipe, but its dimensions are of some importance. Since the microwaves are electromagnetic radiations with wave lengths of a few inches or a few centimeters, it can be shown that the wave length of radiation used for gaseous absorption must be

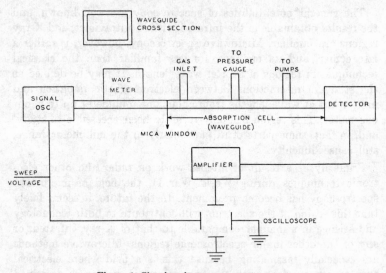

Figure 1. Simple microwave spectrometer

at least as short as the diameter of the absorption cell before transmission through the cell can occur.

The source of radiation is usually an electronic signal oscillator known as a klystron. By applying the appropriate voltage to it, radiation with wave lengths near one centimeter can be produced. These waves then travel through the wave guide which contains the gas under study. As shown in Figure 1, the wave guide is closed at each end with a mica window through which the microwaves can penetrate. After passing through the gas and emerging from the second mica window the waves reach the detector, which is very much like the old-style radio crystal detectors. Its voltage output is proportional to the power received by it from the microwave beam, and this voltage output, after amplification, deflects the beam in the vertical direction on the front of the oscilloscope, thus completing the detection system.

Let us suppose that the frequency of the oscillator is varied and that there is a certain frequency at which the gas responds. It will absorb a small amount of radiation and in that case the voltage from the amplifier will decrease. But as shown in Figure 1, the frequency of the oscillator is varied by the same changing voltage

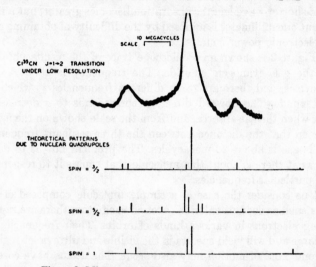

Figure 2. Microwave spectrum of cyanogen chloride

applied to the horizontal plate of the oscilloscope. The result on the face of the oscilloscope is thus a direct plot of a quantity proportional to frequency in one direction and a quantity proportional to power in the other direction. A typical result is shown in Figure 2.

The observed absorption of microwaves by a gas can be moderately large or can be very small. Generally, it is not very large, and refined electronic techniques must be used to detect it. Characteristically, the absorption might be one part in 100,000 or less in a path length of one meter. This is small but detectable. It is important, of course, to detect still smaller effects because there may be relatively few molecules of the desired type in the wave guide. In fact, spectrometers are now available, similar in principle to that of Figure 1 but with more complicated electronic components, that will detect amounts of absorption corresponding to a power decrease by a factor of two for a wave which has traveled a distance equivalent to the circumference of the earth. Molecular absorption of this type increases very rapidly with increasing frequency. For this reason microwave spectroscopy of gases is limited to wave lengths shorter than about one meter, since for longer wave lengths the absorption becomes too small for detection. In the direction of shorter wave lengths absorption becomes greater, but a limit of about one millimeter is imposed by the difficulty of obtaining suitable electronic power sources.

In Figure 2 is shown an oscilloscope trace of the results obtained with the gas cyanogen chloride. The frequency is about 24,000 megacycles, and there are three different frequencies at which the gas responds. The upward direction corresponds to a decrease in power when the gas absorbs, and from the scale shown on the figure, it is seen that the distance between the three resonant frequencies for this gas is about 20 megacycles. The problem now is to determine what there is about this molecule that causes it to respond at these particular frequencies.

Let us consider the case of a simple molecule composed of two atoms such as sodium chloride. Around each atom there are rapidly moving electrons in various kinds of orbits. Their frequencies are thus large and will yield spectra in the visible and ultraviolet regions. A second kind of motion may also occur. The atoms have cores of very heavy nuclei which, because of their weight, move more slowly than the electrons. Their vibrational motion results in frequencies which lie in the infrared region and have been studied in considerable detail by infrared techniques. A third type of motion is that of end-over-end rotation of the entire molecule. Classically, one would expect that the molecule could rotate thus at any arbitrary speed, but quantum mechanics predicts that angular momentum is quantized and that hence the molecule may have only certain frequencies of rotation. Suppose that I is the moment of inertia of the molecule and that ω is its rotational angular velocity. Then its angular momentum is $p = I\omega$. Now the laws of quantum mechanics show that

$$p = \frac{hJ}{2\pi}, \tag{1}$$

where h is Planck's constant and J is an integer. Angular velocity is related to frequency by the equation

$$\omega = 2\pi\nu, \qquad (2)$$

so that we obtain

$$\nu = hJ/4\,\pi^2 I; \quad J = 0, 1, 2, \cdots. \qquad (3)$$

We thus expect a series of equally spaced frequencies corresponding to the permitted values of the rotational quantum number J, and they would extend onward from the position determined by $J = 1$. However, for large J their intensity decreases rapidly, since thermal energy at ordinary temperatures does not give the molecules enough rotational energy to rotate as rapidly as required by high values of J.

The preceding results are expected for any simple molecule such as a diatomic one or for a molecule containing more than two atoms, provided that the atoms are all arranged in a straight line. If the molecule is more complex, it will have more than one moment of inertia, and it can then rotate around more than one axis. The general nature of the results is, however, not greatly changed. There will now be a number of different frequency combinations allowed and the spectrum will be more complex, but it may be predicted quite completely.

To summarize the different spectroscopic regions, let us refer to Figure 3. The optical and ultraviolet spectra, at wave lengths of

	Microwave Spectra	Infra Red	Optical & Ultraviolet
Wavelengths	10^2 cm. – 10^{-1} cm.	10^{-1} cm. – 10^{-4} cm.	10^{-4} cm. – 10^{-6} cm.
Sources of Typical Spectra	Molecular Rotation	Molecular Vibration	Electron Motions

Figure 3. Part of electromagnetic spectrum

10^{-4} to 10^{-6} cm, correspond to the motions of electrons within atoms or molecules. The infrared region extends to about one millimeter, although the techniques at that longer wave length are exceedingly difficult. The infrared region, as we have seen, is characterized by molecular vibrations. Finally, there is the microwave region, typical of molecular rotation and arbitrarily placed at one millimeter to

100 cm in wave length. Actually, of course, these various regions cannot be so clearly separated as indicated, for there are some molecular vibrations which occur in the microwave region and there are some molecular rotations which fall in the infrared region.

One great advantage of microwave spectroscopy, not at first recognized, is the fact that molecular absorption, although weak, may be exceedingly sharp. Moreover, the intensity does not decrease as the gas pressure is decreased. Consider a molecule in a wave guide filled with gas. It will collide frequently with other molecules in the wave guide and the rotational motion of the given molecule will be badly disturbed. At atmospheric pressure, there would be little if any observed resonance in the gas and the free rotational motion of the molecule would be hardly recognizable. If the pressure is decreased, however, the molecules present in the wave guide become more and more isolated so that a given molecule may now rotate freely in an ideal way. As shown in Figure 4, the intensity of absorption is hardly changed, although

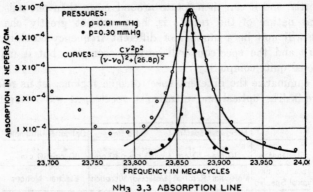

PRESSURES:
o p=0.91 mm.Hg
• p=0.30 mm.Hg

CURVES: $\dfrac{C\nu^2 p^2}{(\nu-\nu_0)^2+(26.8p)^2}$

NH_3 3,3 ABSORPTION LINE

Figure 4. Pressure dependence of absorption by ammonia gas

actually there are fewer molecules present. This absorption line, which is observed with ammonia, has a rather wide resonance peak at a gas pressure of about one millimeter. As the pressure is reduced to about 1/3 mm, the resonance becomes three times as sharp; that is, the width of the line decreases by a factor of three but the height of the line remains unchanged. This is a very strange but useful phenomenon for as the pressure is continually reduced the line becomes increasingly narrow, and, in fact, it may become so sharp that its width could not be drawn on the scale of Figure 4. Normally, the pressures used are of the order of a millionth of an atmosphere, and under these conditions the molecules are essentially free and their response is thus quite sharp.

Let us return to Equation 3 and look at some of the things which this simple formula shows are to be learned from microwave spectra. Obviously, we could determine the moment of inertia of the molecule. This quantity is related to the square of the distance between the atoms in the molecule and, for a diatomic molecule,

$$I = \mu r^2, \tag{4}$$

where μ is the reduced mass of the two atoms and r is the internuclear distance. Thus, from a measurement of the frequency, the moment of inertia and the internuclear distance may be calculated provided J, the rotational quantum number, and h, Planck's constant, are known. The frequencies themselves may be measured to a precision of about one part in 20 to 50 million, or more ordinarily to at least one part in a million. Unfortunately, Planck's constant is known only to one part in 20,000, so in terms of absolute quantities the distances and masses can be given only to this precision. The result for relative masses and distances is, of course, many times more precise.

Suppose now that the molecule is no longer linear and that hence there will be two or three different moments of inertia and more than one distance involved. The additional information now required to determine all of the distances is furnished by the isotope effect. Assume that one atom in the molecule is chlorine. This element has two naturally occurring isotopes of mass numbers 35 and 37. Each of them will produce a different moment of inertia in the molecule and therefore a different spectroscopic line. The observed result will then be a splitting of the rotational lines into two rotational transitions. The effect of each isotopic species may be analyzed, and from their different moments of inertia two independent distances in the molecule may be determined. Even for very complex molecules, one need only have enough isotopic species to determine completely the positions of all atoms.

There are still many smaller effects in microwave spectroscopy
which give interesting results. If one looks more and more carefully
at a given line, it is found that the structure is more complex than
it was first thought to be. One reason lies in the fact that the molecule is vibrating as it rotates. The moment of inertia thus changes
slightly owing to vibration, and since the vibrational motion is
quantized, there will be a series of lines corresponding to the different vibrations which the molecule undergoes.

Another reason for the splitting of microwave absorption lines
is because of what is known as hyperfine. structure. This is most
readily explained with the diatomic molecule, using sodium chloride again as the example. This time let us focus our attention on
the nucleus, in particular chlorine. It cannot properly be considered
a little round point, but it actually has a shape. Moreover, in addition to the fact that the molecule is rotating, the nucleus is also
spinning, and thus it has spin angular momentum. Quantum mechanics must again be consulted, and it says that the nuclear angu-

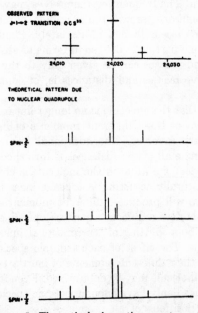

Figure 5. Theoretical absorption spectrum for
different values of nuclear angular momentum

lar momentum can have only certain specific orientations with respect to the overall rotation of the molecule. In the particular case of the chlorine nucleus there are just four such orientations and no other. Since the chlorine nucleus is not spherical, each of these orientations will affect the energy of the molecule slightly because of interaction between the rotation of the molecule and the spinning of the nucleus. The resulting absorption band will then split into a pattern of "side bands." The particular pattern that results will depend on the specific value of the nuclear spin and on the deviation of the nucleus from a truly spherical shape. Theoretical patterns expected for various values of the nuclear angular momentum are shown in Figure 5. We have seen in Equation 1 that angular momentum for a molecule, in units of $h/2\pi$, may have the values $J = 1, 2, 3, \cdots$. For the nucleus, a slight modification is necessary, since the quantum number may now have, in addition to integral values, also half-integral values, such as $1/2$, $3/2$, $5/2$. In Figure 6 some of these hyperfine structure effects are shown for the molecule cyanogen chloride (ClCN) in which the three atoms

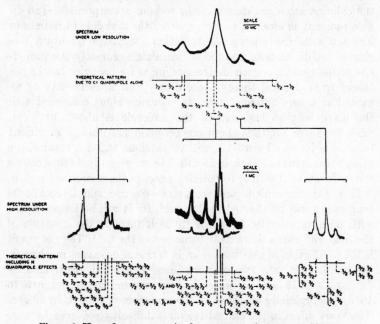

Figure 6. Hyperfine structure in the spectrum of cyanogen chloride

chlorine, nitrogen, and carbon are arranged in a straight line. From this spectrum, it is found that the chlorine nucleus is actually flattened into a disc shape. Further splittings of the line arise from the fact that the nitrogen nucleus is not spherical either. Complete analysis of such resulting patterns gives extensive information on molecular and nuclear structure. It is noted that the individual lines are about 100 kc wide out of a total frequency of 24,000 megacycles, so that the effects are quite fine. In terms of energy, the resolution is about 100,000 times greater than that obtained in the infrared or optical regions, so that microwave techniques may be considered in some respects to provide a detailed microscopic view of molecular frequencies, a view with a resolution many times better than that available in the classical varieties of spectroscopy.

Still further information may be obtained from molecules when they are put in electric or magnetic fields. An electric field affects the molecule of sodium chloride through the tiny electric dipole associated with the molecule. The sodium atom loses some electrons to the chlorine atom so that the excess charge tends to make the chlorine atom negative and the sodium atom positive. The dipole moment so created, in fact, enables the molecule to radiate or interact with the microwave radiation. Although quantum mechanics would have to be used to calculate accurately the properties of the system, a good understanding of its behavior can be obtained from classical theory. Accordingly, the molecule may be regarded as a tiny antenna which is extremely short compared with the wave length. The size of the molecule is about 10^{-8} cm, while the wave length is about one centimeter. Although inefficient because of its small size, it is still an antenna, and if it rotates, the charge is accelerated back and forth. The varying dipole thus causes the molecule to absorb or to radiate energy in the microwave region.

Now if the molecule is put into a static electric field, its rotational frequencies will be affected by the field, for it will no longer rotate with uniform velocity. It speeds up as it turns in the direction of the field and slows down as it turns out of the field. The net result is the production of side bands, or, in terms of quantum mechanics, the line is split into two or more lines. This effect, discovered by J. Stark in 1913, and for which he was awarded the Nobel prize in 1919, was orginially observed in the spectrum of atomic hydrogen. The Stark effect in the optical region is difficult to observe because of low resolution there, but by microwave techniques it is easy to obtain. Fields of a few volts per centimeter up to about 1000 volts per centimeter give an appreciable splitting of the lines. Expected variations of the spectra with voltage and with molecular frequencies may be easily calculated from quantum mechanics. The results give a precise measurement of the molecular dipole moment since the size of the Stark effect clearly depends on the magnitude of the dipole.

Suppose that a given molecule also has a magnetic moment. Similar effects should then be expected in the presence of a magnetic field. This too has been known for atoms, the discovery having been made by P. Zeeman in 1897, who received the Nobel prize for it in 1902. The Zeeman effect is readily achieved in molecules by microwave methods, and it is thus possible to obtain information about magnetic effects in molecules.

Let us now look at some of the other kinds of things which can be done with microwave spectroscopy. We have seen that microwave spectroscopy is a study of the interaction between electromagnetic radiation and matter, but we have been concerned until now with matter in the gaseous state. If we put a diatomic molecule in liquid, the molecules are all closely packed and they certainly cannot rotate freely. In fact, they cannot make even one complete turn before interference occurs from surrounding molecules. There is then no free rotation, nor is there a sharp frequency of absorption. However, there is a characteristic frequency, which is related to the relaxation time. Suppose a molecule in a liquid is given a twist. The relaxation time tells us how long it will take for the molecule to get rid of the extra energy of rotation. In slightly different terms, if the molecule has been displaced, the relaxation time tells us how rapidly it will move over to some other position. Thus the relaxation time is a measure of how rapidly the molecule can move around past its neighbors.

Since a molecule has an electric dipole, we expect it to rotate when put into an electric field, and this it does. A plot of absorption against frequency will show a peak at a frequency ν, where

$$\nu = 2\pi/\tau$$

and τ is the relaxation time. The result may be interpreted in an electrical engineering way as follows. When a static field is applied the molecules will slowly rotate and adjust themselves to the field. If the field is reversed, the molecules change their direction so that they follow the static field around and become polarized in the new direction. If the field is varied more rapidly, the molecules can follow the field partly but now not completely. The situation is similar to hysteresis lag and a power loss is involved. At very high frequencies, the molecules can no longer follow the rapidly varying field, so there is no longer any effect and no power loss. It is in the range where the molecules can almost, but not quite, follow the

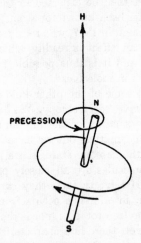

Figure 7. Gyroscopic precession of electron in a magnetic field

field that the largest losses are observed, and from these peaks one can measure the rapidity with which the molecules slide past their neighbors. The results tell us something about the viscosity of the liquid and also about the molecular size. The effects are gross and diffuse, quite unlike those in gas spectroscopy, for the frequency absorption occurs over a wide range. Nevertheless, considerable information is obtainable, especially for those interested in the behavior of the liquid state.

Still another kind of microwave response is observed in some liquids and in many solids. Normally in a crystal the atoms or molecules are arranged in definite positions and nearly frozen there, so that free rotation is no longer possible except under extreme conditions or when the crystal is near its melting point. There are some solids, however, which contain free electrons, and these can respond to microwave radiation. We remember that a free electron has an angular moment of 1/2 in the usual units of $h/2\pi$ caused by electron spin. The electron spin is relatively unaffected by many of the atomic or molecular surroundings in which the electron finds itself. The electron also has a magnetic moment parallel to the spin moment. If now a magnetic field is applied to the electron, the magnetic moment will attempt to align itself with the direction of the applied field. The result is that of a gyroscopic action, for the electron itself is spinning and so the electron will precess around the magnetic field, as shown schematically in Figure 7. The frequency of precession around the field is fixed and constant, depending only on the field and the properties of the electron. The electrons in a solid can thus be considered as approximately isolated quantum systems, unless other large magnetic fields are present. Both paramagnetic and ferromagnetic substances show precessional resonances of this type. Figure 8 shows absorption due to electron precessional resonance which for a microwave frequency of about 25,000 Mc/sec occurs at a field strength of 9000 oersteds.

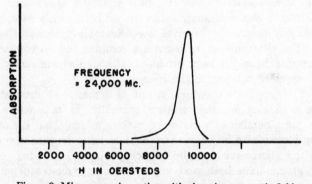

Figure 8. Microwave absorption with changing magnetic field

One other obvious kind of application which is in fact not yet very widely used is chemical analysis. Let us suppose that a hundred different gases are put into a wave guide. Precise measurement of the position of only one line would probably make it possible to identify the gas responsible for the line, for microwave resolution is so great that it is unlikely that any of the other 99 gases present would produce a line at the same place. Chemical analysis of this type can be used only for gases. However, a vapor pressure of only 10^{-6} atm is needed, so that most liquids and many solids would have sufficient vapor pressure for microwave spectroscopy. The other requirement is that the gas have a dipole moment. Hydrogen, nitrogen, and a number of hydrocarbons, for example, have no permanent dipole moment and therefore could not be identified. Except for these limits, however, the microwave method should be a potent tool for chemical analysis and in the future it will probably be used often.

In addition to the high resolution and specificity of the method, one may use very small samples, in favorable cases as little as 10^{-12} gram. In less favorable cases, as much as a microgram of material might be needed, but the quantities are still so small that the method allows microchemical analysis. Still another advantage is the fact that electronic techniques are used. Although these may be complicated in order to obtain the required sensitivity, they are readily adapted to fast observation and to automatic control. It would be possible, for example, to record the amount of material present in a sample in as short a time as 1/60th of a second.

Microwave chemical analysis has not yet been widely used, probably largely because it involves a considerable amount of equipment. The electronic components are complex and no commercial instruments have yet been produced, although several companies have expressed interest in the process.

Another application, which is not of commercial interest but which is fascinating to scientists generally, is radioastronomy. There are a number of varieties of radioastronomy, but the one to be considered here involves those characteristic frequencies which lie in the microwave or radio-frequency range. A number of different groups have been studying a particular radio-frequency line of atomic hydrogen. This line is associated with the precessional motion of the nucleus, produced by the electron's magnetic field. The frequency of precession lies in the microwave region, and its wave length is about 20 cm. Although the nuclear response is very sharp in frequency, the microwave signals produced by hydrogen in interstellar space are exceedingly weak. However, as one looks through our own galaxy an emission line can be observed from the large amount of matter there, the emitted radiation corresponding exactly to this precessional motion of the hydrogen nucleus.

Our galaxy, the Milky Way, is a large group of stars and clouds with the space in between containing very rarefied gas, which is largely composed of hydrogen atoms. Our sun is located more or less toward the edge of this galaxy, the largest dimension of which is about 100,000 light years. It is more or less flat in shape, but the details of its structure have not been well known. For example, it was not certain that our galaxy is a spiral nebula until the recent microwave experiments of Dutch astronomers. If the Milky Way is a spiral nebula, it has some kind of core and a few arms, extending from the core and rotating. As we look at one arm, it may be moving away from us at a fairly high velocity owing to the galactic rotation, while another arm, in a different direction, may be moving with a lower velocity. The hydrogen emission lines from these various arms of the nebula will each exhibit a Doppler shift, but because of the different velocities, the shift will not be the same in each case. By making measurements of the Doppler shift in various directions, it was thus possible for the Dutch astronomers to show that the rotational velocities of the arms increase with distance from the earth. They conclude that the Milky Way is definitely a part of a spiral nebula and that possibly the nebula is winding up on itself since its core appears to be rotating faster than the outer parts.

Consider now the means of controlling microwave radiation. For ordinary electronic circuits operating at acoustic or radio frequencies, one uses condensers, inductances, electronic tubes, etc. In the microwave region, resonant cavities replace capacities and inductances, and special tubes such as klystrons and magnetrons must replace the ordinary triode because of the shorter wave length. At still shorter wave lengths, i.e., for wave lengths less than a few millimeters, even these circuit elements, such as resonance cavities, become hard to make, for they must have dimensions which are comparable with the wave lengths at which they are to be used and usually require very close tolerances. We may then hope to use molecules or electrons as substitute components. These, of course, are precisely made by nature and quite reproducible.

Suppose, for example, a filter is required. Since a given molecule has an absorption band at some fixed wave length, it could be used as a filter. Moreover, the frequency of response can be varied by means of the Stark and Zeeman effects. Such devices will probably be not very important until the millimeter range or a still shorter one becomes useful, for then the ordinary techniques become quite difficult.

However, there are some atomic effects which are large and which may be very useful even for normal microwaves of one centimeter or longer. An example is the gyrator shown in Figure 9. It is made

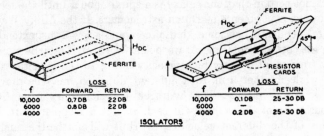

Figure 9. Ferromagnetic gyrator

from a ferromagnetic material subjected to a magnetic field. Suppose a microwave is sent into the wave guide, with its electric vector perpendicular to the flat side of the guide. When it reaches the circular section the guide expands and the microwave electric field is a plane-polarized vector in a circular wave guide. As it goes through the region where there is ferromagnetic resonance, the wave splits up into two circularly polarized waves, with the electric vector rotating in opposite directions in the two cases. Since the electrons are precessing around in the magnetic field, the two different states of polarization are affected in different ways, so that one slows down with respect to the other. This allows a rotation of the plane of polarization so that the electric vector is perpendicular to a vane of absorbing material and perpendicular to the broad dimension of the wave guide. In other words, the wave has been rotated 45° in passing through the guide. However, if we send a wave back again in the opposite direction, it is rotated by 45° in the opposite direction so that when it emerges from the guide its electric vector is now parallel to the flat surface rather than perpendicular as it was originally. Since such a wave is subjected to enormously large loss in the resistive material, it cannot get out of the wave guide.

These properties are very strange, for the well-known reciprocity theorem of ordinary electrical engineering predicts that transmission in one direction should be the same as that in the opposite direction. If there is a loss in one direction, there should be the same loss in the opposite direction. However, in this case, there is a transmission of almost 100 per cent in one direction and essentially no transmission in the opposite direction. In some actual results at a frequency of 10,000 megacycles there is a loss of 0.1 db in the forward direction and a loss of 25 to 35 db in the backward direction. This device provides a completely new type of circuit element which isolates the source from the output. The effects of the load on the source may hence be made negligible.

Another type of transmission device, using ferromagnetic material, is shown in Figure 10. In this case, the wave is crowded over

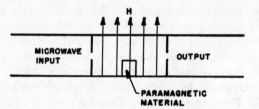

Figure 10. Paramagnetic transmitter

to one side of the wave guide. When it goes in one direction it is crowded to the left-hand side and is not much affected by loss in the material there. If it goes in the opposite direction, it is crowded to the other side and is largely lost in the resistive material. In the forward direction the loss is only about one decibel, but in the opposite direction it may be more than 20 db.

Another example of the use of resonance is the atomic clock, although some may prefer the name molecular clock, since molecular properties are utilized. The rotational frequency of a molecule is completely determined by the atoms composing the molecule as long as it is completely isolated. Its frequency is thus reproducible, and it provides a natural absolute standard of frequency. Normally, the rotation of the earth has been used for that standard. Unfortunately, the earth's rotation is not too constant but, in fact, varies by about one part in 100 million. Astronomers have detected such variations in recent years by showing that the rate of rotation of the earth about its axis is not consistent with the rate of motion of the moon around the earth. The latter is presumably also constant, but astronomical observations indicate that the two motions are not entirely consistent. Since one of the two rotations is wrong, and presumably the motion of the moon is more accurate, one concludes the the rotation of the earth around its axis is not constant. The variations have been as large as a part in 50 million, but more generally they are of the order of one part in 100 million. Part of this variation is seasonal, for during half of a year the winds blow more or less in one direction and their force against the mountains speeds up the earth's rotation. In other seasons, they blow in the opposite direction and slow down the earth. Other, and at times larger, variations are not so well understood, but are presumably associated with shifts of matter within the earth.

For most purposes, one part in 10^8 is a sufficiently precise determination of time, but there are scientific and engineering applications for which a better frequency standard is needed. By using molecules or atoms for the purpose, we have, at least in principle, a standard which is unaffected by temperature and which will be relatively unchanged by other effects. A suitable molecule for use is ammonia. The problem is to synchronize motions with some kind of clock so that it can be used for telling time. Fortunately, ammonia and other molecular spectra lie in the microwave region where electronic techniques can be used. So far such synchronization has been precise to only one part in 10^8, but it appears that concentrated effort should increase this to one part in 10^{12}. Presumably this will ultimately provide our standard of frequency and time. The particular methods for producing synchronization will not be discussed because they are varied and none has yet been completely successful.

Another device, which we may call a molecular amplifier, is not at the moment practical, but it has interesting potentialities. Its general principles are shown in Figure 11. We start with a source of ammonia gas at a certain pressure inside a tube. There is a small hole in the tube so that the ammonia streams out, and as it passes through a focuser it is subjected to an electric field. We have seen that an electric field can interact with the dipole moment of a molecule. This interaction allows the molecules to be refocused into a little hole in the cavity. It is now necessary to use quantum mechanical language. The molecule may exist in two states, one the ground state and the other an excited state. The former is affected by the electric field in a slightly different way than the latter so that one or the other may be defocused. Only the excited molecules are permitted to enter the cavity. These are now in a nonequilibrium state thermodynamically, since all are in the upper quantum level and none in the lower level. This is impossible in an ordinary statistical thermodynamic distribution. The focuser may be regarded as a "Maxwell demon," for it picks out the excited molecues and

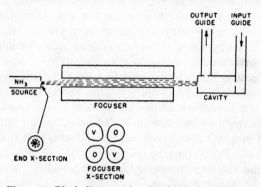

Figure 11. Block diagram of molecular beam oscillator

throws away the rest of them. These excited molecules are in a condition to radiate, but they cannot absorb microwave energy. The radiation can be stimulated by supplying the correct frequency to the cavity. Then the wave which is supplied goes out the output guide along with the energy radiated by the molecules. Thus there may be more energy emerging from the cavity than was introduced. The unstable molecules are triggered by the input radiation. After several years of design and building, this device has lately been put into operation. It is not small—but it works and gives power amplification.

It is well known that a regenerative amplifier will oscillate if it has sufficient gain. The device described here is regenerative, and if enough molecules are supplied it will oscillate of its own accord. When the molecules start to radiate, the energy builds up, the field also builds up, and the system should be self-stimulating. It thus becomes an oscillator producing microwave power at a frequency determined by the frequency of the molecules. Moreover, the frequency could be varied by using electric or magnetic fields. The power output, which is only about 10^{-9} watt, is quite small. However, the device has some very interesting properties. One interesting property of the molecular amplifier is that there is no excess noise. In the usual type of electronic oscillator, the stream of electrons in the tube produces noise which is much larger than the fundamental limit of thermal noise, $kT\Delta\nu$. Here T is the absolute temperature, k is Boltzmann's constant and $\Delta\nu$ the band width over which noise is measured. In the microwave region, the usual amplifiers have noise which is about 100 times the quantity kT because of the high-energy electron stream. Here, however, there are no high-energy electrons and there is no source of noise except the random thermal fluctuations occurring in the cavity or in the wave guide. The noise figure may be very close to unity, that is, only fundamental thermal noise is left. Furthermore, the whole system could be cooled down to very low temperatures and the noise figure could be less than unity if based on room temperature.

Another property of the molecular amplifier is that it has a very narrow band. The frequency over which it responds is about 8 kc, and since the total frequency is 24 megacycles, the system has a Q-value of about 3 million.

The device may also be operated as a frequency standard if used as an oscillator, and one no longer need worry about synchronizing an oscillation with the molecules, since the molecules themselves produce an oscillation. The purity of frequency should be at least comparable with other varieties of atomic clocks. It will be somewhat affected by variations in the cavity, but these can probably be made to vary the oscillation frequency less than one part in 10^{10}, and perhaps as little as one part in 10^{12}. It may thus be possible to attain the goal suggested above for an atomic clock and obtain a frequency standard with an accuracy near one part in 10^{12}.

Nuclear Structure and Transmutations

H. A. BETHE

General Description

An atom, as we know, is a very small thing. Its radius is about 10^{-8} cm. Yet it is enormous compared to the atomic nucleus, which has a radius of 10^{-13} to 10^{-12} cm. Thus, if we imagine a microscope which would magnify the atom so that it is about the size of a room (about 10^3 cm), then the nucleus would still appear only as a dot (10^{-2} to 10^{-1} cm).

A nucleus may be identified by two quantities, its charge and its mass. The charge of any nucleus is an exact multiple of the charge of a proton e. The charge of a nucleus is usually denoted by Ze, where the integer Z is called the atomic number or the "charge number" of the nucleus. In a neutral atom, the nucleus of charge Ze will be surrounded by Z electrons, and the number of electrons in turn determines the chemical properties of the atom, its spectrum, etc. Thus it is essentially this one quantity, the nuclear charge, which determines those properties of an atom which are most easily observable.

The mass of an atom is conventionally measured on a scale in which the mass of the neutral oxygen 16 atom is set exactly equal to 16. Then the mass of every atom turns out to be very nearly equal to an integer; that integer which is closest to the mass is called the mass number of the nucleus and is denoted by A. The mass number has essentially no influence on the chemical properties of an atom, i.e., atoms of the same Z and different A (isotopes) behave chemically alike. The electrons in the atom contribute a negligible fraction (about 1/4000) of its total mass.

Nuclei are known with many different mass numbers and many different nuclear charges. The charges of the nuclei now known extend from zero to 101, since the element 101 has recently been discovered. The mass number goes from one to about 250. For every mass number between one and 250, with one exception, there is at least one known nuclear species. That one exception is number 5. There is some correlation between Z and A: the higher the nuclear charge, the higher the mass number. But for any given Z, usually several different mass numbers are possible; these are called isotopes. For instance, for $Z = 8$, which is the element oxygen, we know nuclei with mass numbers ranging from 14 to 19. Some of them are stable and appear in nature; some are unstable and break up spontaneously. For xenon, which has charge 50, there are exactly 20 isotopes known, differing in their mass numbers, and there are some other elements for which nearly as many isotopes exist. Conversely, for a given mass number A, often several different values of Z are possible. These are called isobars (from the Greek *barys*, meaning heavy).

Constituents of the Nucleus

A particularly important pair of isobars are those of mass number 1, the neutron and the proton. The proton has a charge of one unit; the neutron has no charge. It is very tempting, and it is in fact well established in nuclear physics, to believe that all nuclei are built up of neutrons and protons, each contributing one unit to the mass number. The number of protons in the nucleus gives the total charge of the nucleus. The number of neutrons is then given by the difference between the mass number and charge number. Thus Z is the number of protons and $A - Z$ is the number of neutrons in the nucleus.

The neutron was discovered only in 1932. Before it was discovered, only two elementary particles were known, the proton and the electron. In those days, therefore, the nucleus was supposed to consist of protons and electrons. Nowadays, however, we are quite convinced that electrons cannot be in the nucleus. There are a number of reasons for this, of which only two will be considered here. One of these has to do with the processes occurring when a nucleus is bombarded by some particle. To understand this, let us first consider the behavior of an *atom* when it is bombarded with particles. An atom of course consists of a nucleus and electrons, of which only the electrons can be moved easily. If the atom is hit by another electron, very often some electrons are ejected from the atom. This electron emission from atoms is quite important for many technical applications. But at present we are simply interested in the fact that when energy is supplied to an atom, what comes out most easily are electrons, i.e., the particles which were in the atom to start with. Now when we bombard a nucleus with some nuclear particle, let us say with a proton or a neutron, then what comes out of the nucleus will in general be again nuclear particles, namely, protons or neutrons or combinations of these. There are exceptions: sometimes there is not enough energy available to eject a particle, and sometimes, even though a nuclear particle *could* be emitted by the energy available, something else will come out instead. This will be considered in greater detail when we discuss nuclear transmutations. But generally the preference is for the emission of neutrons or protons or small nuclei made up of these particles. Never in any such collision is an electron emitted. This is a good reason to believe that the electron is not actually contained in the nucleus but that the particles which *are* in the nucleus are those which are observed to come out, i.e., neutrons and protons.

There is another more indirect line of argument which has to do with quantum mechanics. One of the simplest statements of quantum mechanics is the uncertainty principle, namely, that the position and the momentum of a particle cannot be determined simultaneously with infinite accuracy. The product of the uncertainty in the measurement of these two quantities is of the order of Planck's constant h divided by 2π,

$$\Delta x \Delta p \approx h/2\pi. \tag{1}$$

In order to use this equation, we need some knowledge about the maximum uncertainty permissible for the momentum. For this we can make use of a very crude argument: the highest velocity that a particle can have is the velocity of light, and therefore Δp cannot easily be greater than the mass of the particle times the velocity of light:

$$\Delta p < mc. \tag{2}$$

From this it follows that

$$\Delta x > \frac{h}{(2\pi mc)}. \tag{3}$$

This means that it is essentially impossible (there are some clever exceptions to this) to localize a particle to better than $h/2\pi mc$.

Now for an electron, this quantity is 4×10^{-11} cm. The size of the largest nucleus is 10^{-12} cm, and therefore it is not possible to fix the position of an electron accurately enough to be sure that it is in the nucleus. This is a more theoretical argument than the one given above, but both of them show that electrons are not in the nucleus. There are three or four further arguments which will not be discussed here.

In the nucleus we have then neutrons and protons. Both of these have mass number 1, but they differ in the charge. When the neutron was first discovered, it was suggested that it might be a composite particle consisting of a proton and an electron and that only the proton was a fundamental particle. This again is untenable for the same reasons which forbid the presence of electrons in the nucleus. We now have very good reasons to believe that protons and neutrons should be treated as equally fundamental particles. Some of these reasons will become clearer when we consider nuclear structure. The two fundamental nuclear particles, proton and neutron, can transform into each other. When this happens we have beta radioactivity, i.e., the emission of electrons or positrons from a nucleus, a subject to be discussed later on.

Binding Energy and Stability

We shall now discuss how nuclei are built up of neutrons and protons. In particular, we are interested in the energy with which neutron and proton are held together in any given nucleus, i.e., in the binding energy of the nucleus. As was mentioned earlier, these binding energies are very large. They are conveniently measured in millions of electron volts. A million electron volts (Mev) is the energy which an electron would acquire if it were allowed to "fall" through a potential difference of one million volts. Such potential differences can actually be established, and either by using large potential differences or by other means, protons, electrons, and other charged particles can be accelerated to energies of many millions of electron volts and can then be used for nuclear experiments. Concerning the unit of energy, it should be noted that one million electron volts is 1.6×10^{-6} erg, which appears to be not very much energy. However, one nucleus is also not much matter. If one considers instead *all* the nuclei contained in a gram of matter, then if each has one million electron volts, all of them together would have an energy content of about 10^{18} ergs, or 25 million kwhr, and this of course is a great deal of energy.

The binding energy of nuclei is determined experimentally in various ways. One of the simplest is by means of Einstein's relation between mass and energy, i.e., by measuring the mass of a nucleus. This is done by placing an ion of an atom in an electric and a magnetic field. Then its mass can be determined by the amount of deflection. Another way of determining the mass of nuclei is to measure the energy released in a nuclear transformation; this method will be discussed further on.

Table 1 shows the masses of some nuclei at the very beginning of the periodic table. One should notice the extreme accuracy with which these masses have been measured; all of them are given to six decimals. In some cases, even the sixth decimal is fairly accurate; for instance, in the case of hydrogen, the mass is 1.008142 with three units in the last decimal uncertain. The mass of hydrogen is measured by means of the mass spectrograph.

Table 1. Masses of atoms*

	A mass number	M, atomic mass from nuclear data (amu)
n	1	1.008 982 (±3)
H	1	1.008 142 (±3)
H	2	2.014 735 (±6)
H	3	3.016 997 (±11)
He	3	3.016 977 (±11)
He	4	4.003 873 (±15)
He	6	6.020 474 (±27)
C	11	11.014 916 (±24)
C	12	12.003 804 (±17)
C	13	13.007 473 (±14)
C	14	14.007 682 (±11)
N	13	13.009 858 (±14)
N	14	14.007 515 (±11)
N	15	15.004 863 (±12)

* Source: Lauritsen, Tollestrup, *et al.*, *Phys. Rev.*, **83** (1951), 512

Table 2. Binding energies of He^4 and N^{13}

2n	=	2.017 964	C^{12}	=	12.003 804
2H	=	2.016 284	H	=	1.008 142
		4.034 248			13.011 946
He^4	=	4.003 873	N^{13}	=	13.009 858
Binding	=	.030 375mu			.002 088
	=	28.284 Mev		=	1.944 Mev

Table 2 gives examples of computations of the binding energy of some nuclei. On the left side of the table this has been done for the nucleus He^4 (helium^4), also known as the alpha particle, which is one of the most stable nuclei known. The masses of two neutrons and of two protons are added, giving a total of about 4.034 mass units; then the mass of the helium nucleus, as measured by the mass spectrograph, is subtracted; it is 4.004 units. The difference of 0.030 mass unit is the binding energy. This can then be converted into millions of electron volts: one mass unit is 931 Mev. We then find that the He^4 nucleus is bound together with a binding energy of 28 Mev, almost 10 million times as tightly as the water molecule.

On the other side of Table 2, we find another example, the nucleus nitrogen 13, which is compared not to its basic constituents, neutrons and protons, but to carbon 12 and hydrogen. This is related to an important point about the stability of nuclei. Every nucleus, especially the lighter ones, up to atomic weight about 100, must be stable against all possible splittings into subunits. Consider, for instance, the nucleus $^7N^{13}$ (we put the nuclear charge as a left superscript on the chemical symbol in order to make sure that we keep it the same in all the splittings we consider). We can then imagine that we split $^7N^{13}$ into $^6C^{12} + {}^1H^1$, or $^6C^{11} + {}^1H^2$, or into $^5B^{10} + {}^2He^3$, or $^4Be^7 + {}^3Li^6$, or a number of other pairs of nuclei. Of all these pairs, that which has the smallest total mass is carbon 12 plus a proton, and therefore of all the possible breakups of the N^{13} nucleus, this particular one is the easiest to accomplish. It is therefore listed in Table 2. As the table shows, the sum of the masses of C^{12} and a proton is about 13.012, and this is about two-thousandths of a mass unit more than the mass of the N^{13} nucleus. Thus the N^{13} nucleus is stable, with a binding energy of about

2 million volts, against breaking up into carbon 12 and a proton. It is stable by a much larger amount against breaking up into any other possible pair of smaller nuclei.

Table 3. Instability of three nuclei against α and β disintegration

A.	$2He^4$ =	8.007 746	C.	Th^{234} =	234.115 7
	Be^8 =	8.007 850		He^4 =	4.003 9
	Excess	.000 104			238.119 6
	=	.097 Mev		U^{238} =	238.124 1
B.	N^{13} =	13.009 858		Excess	.004 5
	C^{13} =	13.007 473		=	4.2 Mev
		.002 385			
	=	2.221 Mev			

In Table 3 are shown some unstable nuclei. Example A is the nucleus beryllium 8, a light nucleus which violates the stability rule very slightly. It is just a little more massive than two alpha particles, which together contain just the same number of protons and neutrons as beryllium 8. The difference in mass is only 0.1 Mev, yet it is sufficient to cause the beryllium 8 nucleus to disintegrate into two alpha particles if left to itself. The time for which the Be^8 nucleus can hold together in spite of its instability (its "half life") is about 10^{-16} second, too short to be measured by any techniques known to us, and yet long enough to permit us to consider Be^8 as a well-defined nucleus.

Example C on the right-hand side of Table 3 shows a similar situation but for one of the heavy nuclei. It shows how the uranium 238 nucleus is unstable against disintegration into an alpha particle and the residue, which in this case is thorium 234. The two nuclei, thorium 234 and an alpha particle, together have just the same mass number and the same number of positive charges as the uranium nucleus. The uranium nucleus is heavier than the sum of the other two nuclei by an amount equivalent to 4.2 Mev, and it is therefore able to split in this manner, i.e., to emit an alpha particle and leave the thorium nucleus behind. In this case, however, it generally requires a very long time before this split occurs: the average lifetime of the U^{238} nucleus, its half life, is 5 billion years. This enormous difference between the half lives of U^{238} and Be^8, which exists in spite of the much greater energy release in the disintegration of uranium, is due to the high nuclear charge of uranium and will be discussed later on in the section on "Potential Barrier."

Example B in Table 3 shows a completely different type of instability of a nucleus. The masses of the two nuclei nitrogen 13 and carbon 13 are compared in this example, and N^{13} is found to be about 2.2 Mev heavier than C^{13}. Now clearly, N^{13} cannot transform into C^{13} by emitting nuclear particles since both nuclei contain the same number of nuclear particles. Nevertheless, a transformation of nitrogen of mass number 13 into carbon of mass number 13 is possible. To bring such a transformation about, we must get rid of one positive charge, since nitrogen has seven charges and carbon has six. This emission of one unit of charge must be done without changing the mass number. Now as far as nuclei are concerned, an electron is such a light particle that its mass hardly counts at all, so what the nucleus can do is to emit an electron with a positive charge, and this process will not change its mass number. We might assume as a first guess that whatever energy is available, in this case 2.2 Mev, would be given to the electron as kinetic energy. Actually, the process is not quite as simple as this: not all the energy goes to the electron, but some of it goes to a particle called the neutrino, which we shall consider in more detail later on. At any rate, a transformation of this type can take place; i.e., N^{13} can simply emit a positive electron without changing its mass number. Such a transformation, or the inverse transformation in which a negative electron is emitted and the nucleus *gains* one unit of charge, is called a beta decay.

Even if a nucleus can undergo beta decay, it is convenient to consider it as a *stable* nucleus, meaning that it is stable against any disintegration with the emission of *nuclear* particles. If for instance N^{13} were unstable against such emission then it would behave like beryllium 8 and would disintegrate in an "infinitesimal" fraction of a second. Being able to emit only electrons, the nucleus has a half life of about 10 minutes, which is a very long time for a nucleus. It is therefore essentially stable, enough so that its properties can be observed in the laboratory in all details, which could not possibly be done with the beryllium 8 nucleus.

We see at this point that there are two entirely different kinds of transformations. Those which involve the emission of nuclear particles, neutrons, protons, or alpha particles are always very fast in light nuclei, while those which involve the emission of electrons go exceedingly slowly on a nuclear scale. Therefore, what was stated in the beginning, namely, that electrons "never" come out of nuclei, should be modified into "hardly ever." They do come out when their emission leads to a decrease of the energy of the nucleus, but they come out exceedingly slowly. If a nucleus is left alone and if it cannot emit anything else but electrons, then it will finally emit an electron and transform into another nucleus. But it will prefer to get rid of its energy in any other conceivable way first before resorting to electron emission.

Nuclear Forces

We have seen that the binding energies of nuclei are very large. It can easily be calculated that such large energies cannot result from any of the forces which were known in physics before the study of atomic nuclei. The gravitational force, for instance, is just hopelessly small, too small by a factor of about 10^{40}. The electric force is also much too small, in this case only by a factor of about 100, and in addition to this it is quite unsuitable because a nucleus contains only positive charges and neutral particles. Positive charges will repel each other so that their electric interaction will never lead to a bound nucleus. Neutral particles will not be subject to any electric force and therefore will also not be bound by electric forces. Thus we must seek another force; we call it the nuclear force.

The nuclear force is obviously very strong, and we know quite a lot about its properties. We describe it by certain parameters which determine its strength and its range, i.e., the distance over which it acts. Figure 1 shows an artist's conception of the dependence of the nuclear potential on distance. An exponential potential is shown by the solid line. The attractive potential reaches a maximum value of 120 Mev at zero distance between the two nucleons; then at a distance of 1×10^{-13} cm, the potential has decreased to about 30 Mev, and so on. The broken curve is the so-called Yukawa potential, which probably comes closest to the actual dependence of the nuclear potential on distance. This is a much deeper potential well than the exponential at small distances, it becomes less deep than the solid curve at *intermediate* distances, and finally at large distances it again becomes less deep than the exponential. The last curve shown in Figure 1 is the so-called square well. It is particularly pleasant for the theoretical physicist because it is very easy to solve the Schrödinger equation when the potential is constant over certain ranges of r, but the square well certainly has nothing to do with the actual potential acting between nuclear particles.

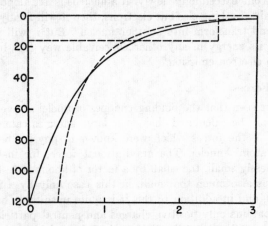

Figure 1. The interaction potential between two nucleons, on various assumptions

Figure 2 shows the stable lighter nuclei, with stability defined as including stability against emission of electrons, positive or negative. The figure shows that there is at least one stable nucleus for every mass number except numbers 5 and 8. Plotted horizontally are the mass numbers up to 100 and plotted vertically is the difference between the number of neutrons and the number of protons (this difference is twice the number called T_z on the ordinate axis). There are many nuclei for which this difference is zero; in other words, many of the light nuclei have equal numbers of protons and neutrons. Some have one extra neutron, some two, some three, etc. For certain mass numbers there is more than one stable nucleus. For instance, for the mass number 40, there are two nuclei, calcium and argon, similarly for 58, and so on.

Now the fact that the number of neutrons and the number of

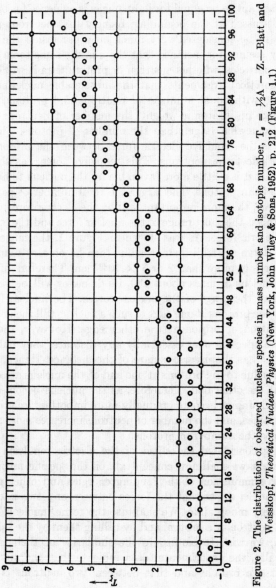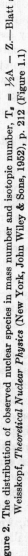

Figure 2. The distribution of observed nuclear species in mass number and isotopic number, $T_z = \frac{1}{2}A - Z$.—Blatt and Weisskopf, *Theoretical Nuclear Physics* (New York, John Wiley & Sons, 1952), p. 212 (Figure 1.1)

protons are apt to be equal for light nuclei is evidence for one of the
points discussed at the beginning, namely that neutrons and protons are to be considered very much on a par inside the nucleus.
One may assume for instance that there is the same force between
any two particles, whether neutron or proton; then it will be found
from theoretical arguments that the most stable nuclei should be
just those with equal numbers of neutrons and protons.

As we go up in atomic weight, the number of neutrons tends to
become somewhat larger than the number of protons. The reason
for this is the repulsive electric force between the protons which
does not affect the neutrons. This repulsive force has the consequence that it is a little more favorable for the nucleus to have more
neutrons than protons. The larger the total number of particles in
the nucleus, the more important will be the electric force. The reason for this is the short range of the nuclear force and the long range
of the electric force. As was shown in Figure 1, the nuclear forces
are very large at small distances but then become extremely weak
at distances of more than 2 or 3×10^{-13} cm. Therefore, if we consider a nucleus of mass about 100, its diameter will be very much
larger than the range of the nuclear forces. The nuclear forces exerted by the protons at one edge of such a nucleus will then not be felt
by a neutron or proton at the other edge. However, the electric
forces are effective over essentially any distance; they only fall off
as $1/r^2$, i.e., as the inverse square of the distance. Hence, the electric forces due to the protons at one end of the nucleus are definitely
"felt" at the other end. Therefore, as the nucleus becomes heavier
the electric forces become gradually more important relative to the
nuclear forces, and the number of neutrons increases more and more
relative to the number of protons.

Having considered the effect of the electric repulsion between
the protons, we shall now concentrate on the specific nuclear force.
A closer examination of the binding energies and other properties
of light nuclei shows that the forces between any two nucleons are
indeed very much alike. We shall use the term "nucleon" to mean
either a neutron or a proton, and by calling them by the same name,
nucleon, we wish to emphasize the similarity of their properties.
Specifically, the experimental data indicate that the nuclear force
between two protons and that between two neutrons is precisely
the same.

The case of the force between neutron and proton is a little bit more complicated. This is because there is an essential difference between a system consisting of two identical particles, e.g., two neutrons, and one consisting of two nonidentical particles, e.g., a proton and a neutron. This difference is the Pauli principle, which forbids that two identical particles be in exactly the same quantum state. This principle means that certain quantum states cannot occur in a system consisting of two protons or two neutrons, whereas they can occur in a system consisting of neutron and proton in which the Pauli principle does not operate. The experimental evidence shows then that in those quantum states which can occur in *all* systems, the neutron-neutron, proton-proton, and proton-neutron forces are the same. In those quantum states which can occur only in the proton-neutron system, the forces are different from those in the former case. Still, we are justified in speaking of the charge-independence of nuclear forces, meaning that the nuclear forces are the same for a neutron (no charge) as for a proton (one unit of charge), because in all those quantum states which do occur for identical as well as nonidentical particles, the force is indeed the same independently of the charges of the interacting nucleons.

The most direct evidence showing that neutron-neutron and proton-proton forces are equal comes from the behavior of so-called mirror nuclei. These are nuclei which are obtained from each other by exchanging the neutrons and the protons. Consider for instance the two nuclei which we discussed previously, carbon 13 and nitrogen 13. These two nuclei are just mirror images of each other. Namely, carbon 13 contains 6 protons and 7 neutrons, nitrogen 13 contains 7 protons and 6 neutrons. Now if the neutron-neutron force and the proton-proton force are exactly the same, then these two nuclei should be exactly alike in energy. We believe the two forces to be exactly the same as far as the nuclear force is concerned, but we must still consider the electric force. The electric force gives a repulsion between two protons and therefore makes the nucleus containing more protons heavier than the nucleus containing more neutrons.

In Figure 3, we find plotted the difference in energy between pairs of mirror nuclei,[1] which therefore represents the energy of the

---

[1] The difference in nuclear mass has been corrected for the difference in mass between neutron and proton.

electric repulsion between the protons. As the figure shows, this energy varies extremely regularly with the atomic weight of the nucleus. The abscissa is related to the mass number, while the ordinate is the energy difference. All the observed energy differences

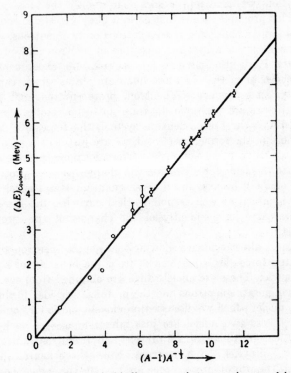

Figure 3. The difference in binding energy between mirror nuclei as a function of $(A - 1)A^{-1/3}$.—Blatt and Weisskopf, p. 228 (Figure 2.1)

(small circles) are seen to fall almost exactly on the same line on this graph.

To examine the meaning of this result, we recall the expression for the electric interaction energy between two charges. This energy is given by Coulomb's law and is

$$W = \frac{e_1 e_2}{r}, \tag{4}$$

if e_1 and e_2 are the two charges and r the distance between them.
Now if we go from carbon 13 to nitrogen 13 we add one more
charge to 6 already existing charges in the carbon nucleus. Hence
e_1 is just the charge of the proton and e_2 is the charge of the carbon
nucleus, which is $Z = 6$ proton charges. Thus,

$$W \propto \frac{Ze^2}{R}, \qquad (5)$$

where R is the radius of the nucleus and the sign $\propto$ means "proportional to."

Now let us assume that the radius of the nucleus, R, is proportional to the cube root of the atomic weight or the mass number.
We shall discuss later the implication of this assumption. For the
present we note that the Coulomb energy difference between mirror
nuclei should be proportional to $ZA^{-1/3}$ where Z is the charge of
that mirror nucleus which has the lesser charge, which can easily
be seen to be $Z = 1/2(A - 1)$. We have therefore plotted as the
abscissa of Figure 3 the quantity $(A - 1)A^{-1/3}$. The figure shows
that the measured energy differences are indeed proportional to
this quantity, within very narrow limits. This shows two things.
First, our assumption that the nuclear radius is proportional to
$A^{1/3}$ appears to be correct. Second, there does not seem to be any
other source of a difference in binding energy between mirror nuclei.
Now of the two mirror nuclei, e.g., N^{13} and C^{13}, one N^{13} has an
extra pair of protons which the other does not have; the other
C^{13} has instead an extra pair of neutrons. The agreement between
experiment and the straight line of Figure 3 thus shows that the
nuclear force between two protons must be (within experimental
error) equal to that between two neutrons, which is what we wanted
to prove. Each of these two forces is quite large, as is shown for
the proton-proton force by direct experiments on the scattering of
protons by protons.

We shall now consider the implications of our result that the
nuclear radius is proportional to $A^{1/3}$. This means that the *volume*
occupied by a nucleus is proportional to the number of particles,
just as it is in ordinary matter. Two ounces of any solid or liquid
material occupy just twice as much space as one ounce of the same
material. It is the same with nuclei, as is shown by the fact that
the measured energy differences fit the straight line in Figure 3.

In addition to proving this interesting qualitative law, Figure 3 can be used for a quantitative determination of the nuclear radius. If we include some corrections which were discovered only in 1953, we find that the radius of a nucleus is given by 1.2×10^{-13} times the cube root of the mass number.

Size and Shape of Nuclei

There are several other ways to determine the radius of the nucleus. The most accurate method at present is by electron diffraction. Experimentally, a beam of very high-energy electrons is directed at a target containing the nuclei to be investigated, and the angular distribution of the scattered electrons is measured. The most accurate experiments of this kind have been done at Stanford University by Hofstadter and collaborators, mostly in 1953 and 1954. The interpretation of these experiments is based on two facts: namely, (1) the electrons have a de Broglie wave length h/p, where p is the momentum and (2) they have an electric interaction with the protons in the nucleus and otherwise no appreciable interaction. The first fact tells us that electrons will be scattered by a nucleus in a manner very similar to that by which X rays are scattered by a crystal or by a liquid; we obtain a diffraction pattern, and from an analysis of this pattern we can deduce how the scatterers are arranged in space. The second fact tells us that the scatterers are the protons in the nucleus; thus the experiment will show the distribution of the protons in the nucleus. Furthermore, we know that electric forces are weak compared with nuclear forces; therefore an electron has only a relatively weak interaction with the nucleus; this in turn means that an electron penetrates easily through the nucleus and thus explores the entire charge distribution in the nucleus at once. We shall see later that this is not the case if neutrons are used instead of electrons.

If we wish to explore the structure of the nucleus, the de Broglie wave length of the electron, $\lambda = h/p$, should be of the order of magnitude of the nuclear radius. Since the radii of nuclei are of the order of 10^{-12} cm, we must give the electron an energy of about 160 Mev. Indeed, the Stanford experiments were carried out with electron energies of from 80 to 200 Mev. The experimental results were analyzed with the help of high-speed computing machines. The first result of this analysis was an exact determination of the nuclear radius; it is indeed $R = 1.2 \times 10^{-13} A^{1/3}$ with an accuracy of a few per cent. The most accurate measurements were done mostly with heavy nuclei, but at least one light nucleus, helium 4, was found to have a radius exactly obeying the formula, 1.9×10^{-13}. However, helium may be exceptionally small because of its very strong binding.

In addition to measuring the nuclear radius, the electron diffraction experiments also give information on the shape of the nucleus, i.e., on the radial distribution of the protons. In Figure 4

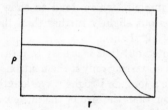

Figure 4. Distribution of protons in the nucleus of gold.—Yennie, Ravenhall, and Wilson, *Phys. Rev.*, **95**, (1954), 502

the density of protons is plotted against the distance from the center of the nucleus. It is seen that this density does not drop abruptly at the surface of the nucleus but goes to zero gradually. This is in fact expected from quantum mechanics. The exact shape of the proton distribution cannot be determined at present from the Stanford experiments, but the "thickness" of the surface layer, suitably defined, can be measured and is about 2×10^{-13} cm. It is probably about the same for all nuclei, independent of A.

Still another way of determining the nuclear size, and a very old one, is from the interaction of fast neutrons with nuclei. Those neutrons which collide with a nucleus either will be scattered or will cause some nuclear reaction. Now in contrast to electrons, neutrons (and also protons) have an exceedingly strong interaction with the nucleons in the nucleus. Therefore, as soon as they hit the surface of a nucleus they will immediately do something. Either they are reflected back, or they penetrate into the nucleus and become part of it. Therefore, it is not too surprising that the size of the nucleus as measured by neutron scattering is somewhat larger than that deduced from electron scattering or from mirror nuclei.

It is about

$$R_n = (1.2 \, A^{1/3} + a) \times 10^{-13} \, \text{cm.} \tag{6}$$

The quantity a is between 1 and 1.5. The explanation for formula 6 is that the neutron interacts strongly even with the outer fringes of the nucleus, i.e., it feels the presence of the nucleus as soon as it arrives at the outer edge of the nucleon distribution shown in Figure 4. There may also be a slight contribution to the constant a from the fact that the neutron interacts with neutrons as well as with protons while the electron interacts only with protons, and there are some arguments which tend to show that the neutron distribution reaches out slightly further than the proton distribution (by 0.5 to 1×10^{-13} cm).

It should be pointed out that it is easy to measure the size of the nucleus by neutron scattering only if the neutrons have high energy. Slow neutrons have a long de Broglie wave length, $\lambda = h/mv$, comparable to or greater than the size of the nucleus. One then obtains diffraction effects which make it impossible to interpret the measured cross section simply as the geometrical size of the nucleus. Because of the strong interaction between neutron and nucleus, the interpretation of diffraction effects for neutrons is not as straightforward as for electrons. Nevertheless, many interesting conclusions have been drawn from the scattering of relatively slow neutrons, of energy one million electron volts or less, by nuclei. Similarly, the "diffraction" scattering of protons has given valuable information.

Comparison of the Energy of Isobars

We shall now consider a more detailed feature of nuclear structure. In Figure 5 has been plotted schematically the energy of various nuclei of the same mass number A. Such nuclei are called isobars, and we have seen that all isobars contain the same total number of nucleons, A. They are conveniently distinguished from each other by a quantity which is denoted by T_z and is often called the isotopic number; it is defined as one-half of the difference between the number of neutrons and the number of protons. Thus $T_z = 0$ means a nucleus which has just as many neutrons as protons (let us call it the symmetric nucleus). $T = 1$ is a nucleus which has one neutron more and one proton less than the symmetric nucleus, etc. If we had only nuclear forces, the symmetric nucleus should have the lowest energy, and the energies of other nuclei should be larger by an amount approximately proportional to T_z^2; in other words, the curve in Figure 5 should be a parabola with its minimum at $T_z = 0$. The energy of electric repulsion between the protons shifts the minimum of the energy toward positive T_z, corresponding to more neutrons than protons, and this is shown in the figure.

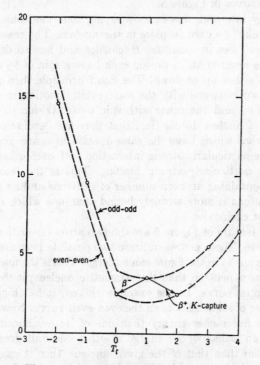

Figure 5. The energy of various isobars of a nucleus with even mass number.—Blatt and Weisskopf, p. 246 (Figure 4.4)

However, the figure shows two further phenomena. The first is a kink at $T_z = 0$. This is a phenomenon which requires a rather elaborate theory given by Wigner. It cannot be explained now, but the reader is referred to the excellent book by Blatt and Weisskopf, *Theoretical Nuclear Physics*, where will also be found further information on all the other topics discussed here. The second feature of

Figure 5 is that there are two curves rather than one. Now in constructing the figure, the mass number A was chosen to be even. Then there are two possibilities: Either the numbers of neutrons and of protons are both even or they are both odd. Now the observed nuclear masses show that the energy in the latter case is consistently higher than in the former, and this experimental fact is the reason why we have *two* curves in Figure 5.

We may interpret this fact by saying that neutrons as well as protons "like" to exist in pairs in the nucleus. The reason for this "preference" lies in quantum mechanics and has to do with the fact that a neutron and a proton each have a spin of ½ unit which can point either up or down. The Pauli principle then permits us to have two neutrons with the same orbital motion in space, one with spin up and the other with spin down. Owing to a peculiar property of nuclear forces (i.e., that they are "exchange" forces), two neutrons which have the same motion in space and opposite spins have particularly strong interaction with each other and give, therefore, particularly strong binding. This is the reason why a nucleus containing an even number of neutrons and an even number of protons is more strongly bound than one which has an odd number of each type.

A final feature of Figure 5 are the two arrows near the minimum of the curve. These arrows indicate two possible beta decays which one of the nuclei in the figure can undergo. This is the nucleus which has one more neutron than the symmetric nucleus; it therefore lies on the upper curve. In the example chosen, it has higher energy than either of its neighbors on the even-even curve. Now, whenever a nucleus has higher energy than one of its neighboring isobars, meaning an isobar whose charge is either one unit greater or one unit smaller than that of the given nucleus, then it can transform into that neighboring isobar by emitting either a positive or a negative electron, as the case may be. This transformation is the beta decay which we discussed before in connection with the transformation of N^{13} into C^{13}. In our example the nucleus $T_z = 1$ has higher energy than *both* its neighboring isobars so that it can undergo beta decay either with emission of a positive charge, going to $T_z = 2$, or of a negative charge, going to $T_z = 0$. These two possibilities are indicated by the two arrows in Figure 5.

The loss of a negative charge always means the emission of an ordinary, negatively charged electron by the nucleus. On the other hand, the nucleus can lose a *positive* charge in two different ways. One way is by the emission of a positive electron. The other way is to absorb one of the electrons which surround the nucleus. In this case, instead of emitting a positive charge, the nucleus absorbs a negative one. The atomic electrons which are most likely to be captured are those in the innermost Bohr orbit, which is called the K shell. The process is therefore known as K electron capture. Whether the nucleus chooses to emit a positron or to capture a K electron depends on the circumstances, especially on the available energy: In order to emit a positron, this particle must first be created, which requires an energy of mc^2, according to Einstein's relation. The K electron, on the other hand, delivers to the nucleus its mass energy mc^2. Thus the emission of a positron requires a greater energy than the K capture, by an amount of about $2mc^2$, or roughly one million electron volts. If the energy of our nucleus $T_z = 1$ exceeds that of $T_z = 2$ only slightly, K capture will be the only form of beta decay possible; if the excess of energy is large, then positron emission is preferred.

The Shell Model

Thus far we have considered those properties of nuclei which are common to all of them. We shall now discuss some of the more detailed features which are different for different nuclei. We have learned about these detailed features only after World War II, particularly through the work of Maria Mayer in Chicago and of Jensen and others in Germany. These workers discovered that the structure of nuclei is similar to a considerable extent to that of the electron shells of atoms. In the atom, the electrons are classified by their quantum numbers. We have electrons in the 1s shell, the 3d shell, and so on. Similarly, inside the nucleus, we also can classify the nucleons according to quantum numbers. There are two important quantum numbers, both in the electron shells of the atom and inside the nucleus: one is the principal quantum number, usually denoted by n, the other is the quantum number usually called l, which denotes the angular momentum of the particle in its orbital motion (either about the nucleus in the case of the electrons or about the center of the nucleus in the case of the nucleons). It turns out that the orbital momentum of nucleons in the nucleus can be very large indeed, up to six units, whereas the orbital momentum of electrons around the nucleus is never greater than three.

By assigning quantum numbers to the electrons in the atom, we can understand the periodic system of the elements, that is, we can explain why the chemical properties of atoms follow a regular sequence and then start all over again. Similarly, we could define a periodic system of the nuclei according to the nucleon shells in the nuclei. Unfortunately, it is much harder to detect these periodicities in nuclei than it is among atoms. That is why it took nuclear physicists about fifteen years to discover this property. The change in the binding energy of the last electron from a noble gas to the alkali atom following it is about a factor of four. The corresponding change in binding energy of nuclei is only about 20 per cent, which is very difficult to detect, especially since it may be obscured by other variations of binding energy of the same order of magnitude. Moreover, only very recently have the binding energies of nuclei been measured with sufficient accuracy for this purpose. But we are now quite sure that the "periodic system" of nuclei is a reality.

The atoms in which the electrons are most strongly bound are the noble gases. Their counterparts among the nuclei are called "magic nuclei." In a noble gas, the electrons fill a certain number of "shells" completely, a shell being defined by the orbital momentum and the principal quantum number of the electrons. There are no electrons outside these complete shells. Likewise, in a magic nucleus either the neutrons or the protons just fill a number of complete shells. There are a few nuclei for which *both* neutrons and protons fill complete shells: these are called "doubly magic." Just as the electrons in a noble gas atom are particularly strongly bound to the atom, so also do the magic nuclei have particularly large binding energies. This in turn causes them to behave in a peculiar way with regard to all sorts of nuclear transmutations. They have, for instance, very small cross sections for capturing an additional neutron; in fact, this is one way of finding magic nuclei.

Whether a nucleus is magic or not has of course nothing at all to do with the position of the corresponding atom in the chemical periodic system of the elements. The so-called magic numbers, that is, the number of nucleons which make up a closed shell, are given as follows: 2, 8, 20, 28, 50, 82, and 126—very strange numbers (28 is not very strongly "magic"). On the other hand, the magic numbers for the electrons in the atom which determine the periodic system are 2, 10, 18, 36, 54, 86. One can see that there is no relation between the two sets of numbers. It can be understood why the two sets are so different but we will not go into this.

As has been pointed out, we can ascribe to each nucleon in the nucleus quantum numbers, angular momentum, principal quantum number, etc. In fact, one is invariably surprised at the accuracy with which this description seems to work. Then, knowing the quantum numbers of the nucleons, one can predict observable nuclear properties such as the spin of a nucleus, i.e., its total angular momentum. With less assurance, one can predict its magnetic moment and the position and properties of its low-lying energy levels. For instance, a magic nucleus has only very few excited energy levels up to quite high energies. A nucleus midway between magic numbers, on the other hand, has very many closely spaced energy levels. This is very similar to the spectroscopic behavior of atoms: In a noble gas atom, the first excited state lies extremely high, about 10 volts. On the other hand, an atom with many electrons in an incomplete shell, such as a rare earth atom, has hundreds of energy levels within the first 5 electron volts. The behavior of the energy levels of nuclei and atoms is thus very analogous.

Nuclear Transmutations

Having considered the structure of nuclei, we can now look at their transmutations. In Table 4 some typical nuclear transmuta-

Table 4. Some possible nuclear reactions, showing reaction energies

$$N^{14} + H^2 = C^{12} + He^4 + 13.570 \text{ Mev}$$
$$N^{14} + H^2 = N^{15} + H^1 + 8.609 \text{ Mev}$$
$$N^{14} + H^2 = O^{15} + n^1 + 5.121 \text{ Mev}$$
$$O^{15} = N^{15} + \beta^+ + 2.705 \text{ Mev}$$
$$N^{14} + H^2 = O^{16} + \gamma + 20.718 \text{ Mev}$$
$$N^{14} + n^1 = C^{13} + H^2 - 5.316 \text{ Mev}$$

tions are listed, each represented by an equation. In the transmutation equation the total mass number and the total charge must balance on the two sides. This implies conservation of protons and neutrons. In each transmutation some energy is either set free or absorbed. The amounts of transmutation energy set free are given in the equations in the table. The energy set free may, for instance, be deduced from the atomic masses.

Looking at Table 4 in detail, one can see that the first three reactions are all produced by the interaction of the same nuclei, namely, a deuteron and N^{14}. This interaction can lead to three different results, which are given on the right-hand side of the three equations. In each case a different amount of energy is set free. The fourth reaction shown is a beta decay. The fifth reaction is a somewhat unusual one; instead of leading to two nuclei in the end, it leads to the combination of *all* the particles present in one nucleus, in this case O^{16}. In a reaction of this type, a mechanism must be provided to dispose of the energy set free. The easiest way to accomplish this is by emitting electromagnetic radiation. The radiation which comes from nuclei is usually called gamma radiation. Emission of radiation in a nuclear collision is considerably less likely than is a reaction leading to the formation of two nuclei, such as the first three reactions of Table 4. This is due to the relatively small interaction between charged particles and radiation. This interaction is measured by the well-known fine structure constant $2\pi e^2/hc$, which is 1/137. Roughly speaking, the probability of having a reaction of Type 5, in which a gamma ray comes out, is about one per cent of the probability of having one of the first three reactions. Finally, the last reaction in Table 4 is one in which energy is consumed, the amount being 5.3 Mev in this case. This reaction can proceed only if energy is supplied to start with; then the outgoing particles will have less kinetic energy than the incident particles.

Reaction Energies

The reaction energy, let us say in the first reaction, can be measured by determining the kinetic energy of the incoming deuteron H^2 and the kinetic energy of the outgoing He^4. The customary way to do this used to be a measurement of the range of the outgoing particle in, let us say, air. This method was introduced by the Cavendish Laboratory in the 1920's. Nowadays, the measurement can be done far more accurately, using quite elaborate methods of electric or magnetic deflection of the particles produced in the reaction, the most usual method being electrostatic deflection. A few laboratories in this country have specialized in this work, particularly Massachusetts Institute of Technology and California Institute of Technology, and have obtained exceedingly great accuracy in measuring reaction energies. The numbers given in Table 4 are no exaggeration; one really gets the reaction energies accurate to kilovolts when the total energy is 15 Mev.

Table 5. Determination of the energy difference between neutron and proton from nuclear transmutations*

Cycle	Mass difference from experimental Q (Mev)
$n(\beta^-)H^1$	0.783 ± 0.013
$H^3(p, n)He^3$, $H^3(\beta^-)He^3$	0.7822 ± 0.001
$C^{13}(p, n)N^{13}$, $N^{13}(\beta^+)C^{13}$	0.781 ± 0.005
$C^{14}(p, n)N^{14}$, $C^{14}(\beta^-)N^{14}$	0.783 ± 0.004
$O^{18}(p, n)F^{18}$, $F^{18}(\beta^+)O^{18}$	0.796 ± 0.015
$H^2(d, p)H^3$, $H^2(d, n)He^3$, $H^3(\beta^-)He^3$	0.7845 ± 0.010
$C^{12}(d, p)C^{13}$, $C^{12}(d, n)N^{13}$, $N^{13}(\beta^+)C^{13}$	0.782 ± 0.007
$B^{10}(n, \alpha)Li^7$, $Be^9(d, \alpha)Li^7$, $Be^9(d, p)Be^{10}$, $Be^{10}(\beta^-)B^{10}$	0.780 ± 0.013

Weighted mean of $n - H^1 = 0.7823 \pm 0.001$
$(p_e = 0.24$ kev, $p_i = 0.95$ kev, $p_e/p_i = 0.25)$

* Source: Lauritsen *et al.*, *Phys. Rev.*, **83** (1951), 512

Table 5 shows the manner in which the measurement of nuclear reaction energies may be used to get relations among the masses of different nuclei. The particular problem here is to determine the difference between the masses of the neutron and the proton. Each line of the table corresponds to a "reaction cycle" such that one starts with a neutron and ends with a proton plus an electron while all other nuclei remain unchanged in the end. Consider, for example, the second-to-last cycle; we start with C^{12} and bombard it with a deuteron, producing a neutron and a N^{13} nucleus, and measure the reaction energy Q_1. Then we allow the N^{13} to decay into C^{13} and a positive electron, in which process an energy Q_2 is set free. Next we bombard the C^{13} with a proton to yield C^{12} and a deuteron, plus energy $-Q_3$. (In practice, this experiment is done in the reverse manner: C^{12} is bombarded with deuterons, yielding C^{13} and a proton and releasing the energy Q_3.) Thus we have recovered C^{12} and the deuteron and have in effect consumed a proton and obtained instead a neutron and a positron. In this process the energy $Q = Q_1 + Q_2 - Q_3$ is set free. Therefore, the difference in energy between a hydrogen atom (proton plus electron) and a neutron is $Q + 2mc^2$, where m is the mass of an electron or positron. This same difference in mass can be obtained by means of eight different cycles, all of which are listed in Table 5. The experimental result, as shown by the table, is that the neutron is heavier than the hydrogen atom by 0.782 Mev, with the eight different cycles agreeing well within experimental error. This will give an idea of the amount of work and the amount of mutually supporting evidence which go into the determination of the relation between the masses of different atoms.

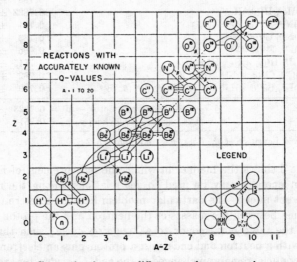

Figure 6. Connection between different nuclear masses by measured reaction energies.—Lauritsen *et al.*, *Phys. Rev.*, **83** (1951), 512

Further evidence of the same sort is shown in Figure 6. Each line in this figure indicates that the masses of the connected nuclei can be related to each other by means of some nuclear reaction whose energy has been accurately measured. Solid lines represent reactions involving nuclear particles, dotted lines, beta decays. For instance, the atomic weights of Li^7 and B^{10} may be connected by a reaction in which an alpha particle enters the Li^7 and a neutron comes out. They may also be connected by converting Li^7 first to Be^7 by a (p, n) reaction and then converting Be^7 to B^{10} by a (p, α) reaction (proton in, alpha particle out), etc. All the measured reaction energies can be fitted together to give a consistent set of nuclear masses. With the good instruments now available, the various reaction cycles used to obtain the difference of two atomic masses give results which agree within a few kilovolts. One can further compare these mass differences obtained from nuclear reactions with the mass spectrograph measurements of the masses of the nuclei involved. Again we get agreement, and this may be considered as a check on the Einstein relation between mass and energy. Altogether this relation has been checked by at least 100 different reaction cycles.

Aside from giving an experimental proof of the Einstein relation, the comparison between reaction energies and mass spectrograph measurements establishes two points: one is the accuracy of the mass spectrograph method, and the second is the correct interpretation of the nuclear reactions which have taken place. Unfortunately, there is at present a slight discrepancy, of the order of 10 kev, between the mass spectrograph masses and the nuclear reaction energy measurement. The reason for this discrepancy is unknown, and until it is resolved, it is probable that the reaction energy measurements are somewhat more accurate than those with the mass spectrograph.

Rate of Nuclear Transmutations

Now we come to perhaps the most important point about nuclear transmutations, their classification. We have already discussed two kinds of nuclear transmutations. The first kind is the spontaneous transmutation, the spontaneous decay of a nucleus into smaller parts. Examples of this are the beta decay, i.e., the emission of positive or negative electrons or K electron capture, and the alpha decay, such as the decay of uranium. The second kind is a transmutation initiated by a collision, such as the reactions listed in Table 4 (with the exception of the beta decay of O^{15}). To obtain this second kind of transmutation, we must first bring two nuclei together. The spontaneous transmutations, on the other hand, take place in a single nucleus.

Table 6. Typical times involved in nuclear reactions (in seconds)

Collisions	Spontaneous	
Fast particles........$10^{-20} - 10^{-18}$	Neutrons............10^{-21}	
Slow neutrons.......$10^{-16} - 10^{-12}$	Alpha particles.......$10^{-8} - 10^{+19}$	
Gamma rays.........$10^{-17} - 10^{-14}$	Gamma	
	Allowed...........$10^{-15} - 10^{-13}$	
	Forbidden.........$10^{-13} - 10^{+7}$	
	Beta	
	Allowed...........$10^{-2} - 10^{+9}$	
	Forbidden........ $1 \quad - 10^{+16}$	

In Table 6 the nuclear reactions are classified first into these two kinds, collisions and spontaneous disintegrations, and then divided further according to the type of particle which is emitted in the transmutation. If the particle emitted is a neutron, it is useful to distinguish further between fast and slow neutrons.

Table 6 also lists the time that it normally takes for a nuclear transmutation of a given type to occur. Considering first the time for collisions, we see that it takes the shortest time if the collision leads to the emission of fast particles, which may be fast neutrons, fast protons, deuterons, alpha particles, etc. In any of these cases, the time required for the complete process is usually between 10^{-20} and 10^{-18} second. On the other hand, a collision leading to the emission of slow neutrons takes considerably longer. This time is in the first approximation proportional to the velocity of the neutrons coming out. Another type of transmutation is one leading to the emission of gamma rays. It has already been mentioned that such transmutations are considerably less likely than those leading to the emission of nuclear particles; accordingly, it takes considerably longer before the gamma rays come out and before the whole process is completed than if fast particles can be emitted. Experimentally, the time required for such "radiative" collisions is something like 10^{-17} to 10^{-14} second.

On the right-hand side of Table 6 are listed the spontaneous nuclear disintegrations. First of all there is the possibility of a nucleus which is unstable against the emission of a neutron. Such a nucleus cannot live very long, only about 10^{-21} second, which is almost as short as the time required for a neutron to go once across the nucleus. There is one example of such a nucleus, namely, helium 5.

We have already seen that every mass number from 1 to 250 exists except the number 5. No nucleus of number 5 exists because that particular nucleus decays in a very short time into a neutron and a helium 4 nucleus. Next is the possibility for the nucleus to emit fast charged particles, particularly alpha particles. This emission takes different lengths of time, depending on the circumstances. The decay by charged particle emission is governed by the penetration of a potential barrier; according to the energy of the particle which comes out and the height of the potential barrier, the lifetimes may range all the way from 10^{-8} second to 10^{+19} seconds. Lifetimes anywhere within these limits have actually been observed. In addition, there are certainly nuclei which *could* decay with emission of alpha particles as far as their energy is concerned, but which would have still longer lifetimes. But this can never be known because the number of alpha particles emitted would be too small to be observed with even the most sensitive detector. Moreover, 10^{19} seconds is quite a lot longer than the past life of the universe (about 10^{17} seconds).

The emission of gamma rays can take place not only during a collision but also spontaneously. The reason for this is that a collision leading to emission of nuclear particles will not always leave the residual nucleus in its ground state but very often in an excited quantum state. Consider for instance one of the transmutations we discussed earlier, such as $N^{14} + H^2 = C^{12} + He^4$. Then the C^{12} may be left behind in an excited quantum state. The only way in which the nucleus can go from this excited quantum state to the ground state is by emission of gamma rays. This process will take times varying from about 10^{-16} second on up.

Gamma ray transitions are classified into allowed and forbidden transitions. A transition is called allowed if the nucleus can radiate like an electric dipole; whether this is possible depends on the angular momenta of the nucleus in the initial and final states, just as for the optical spectra of atoms. If electric dipole emission is not possible, the transition can take place only by the emission of higher multipole radiation. Such forbidden transitions are observed in many nuclei. In particular, it often happens that the first excited state of a nucleus has a completely different angular momentum from that of the ground state; for instance, this occurs frequently among the rare earth elements. The ground state may have an angular momentum of $\frac{1}{2}$ and the first excited state one of $5\frac{1}{2}$. Then *five* units of angular momentum must be disposed of and have to be given to the gamma ray. It can easily be shown theoretically that whenever one has to dispose of a large amount of angular momentum, then the optical emission is very unlikely. This is why such transitions are called highly forbidden. The lifetimes of excited nuclear energy levels which can decay only by forbidden gamma emission are extremely long. This then makes it possible to observe such excited states as separate nuclear species; they are known as nuclear isomers.

The lifetimes for forbidden gamma ray transitions are given in Table 6, somewhat arbitrarily, as varying between 10^{-13} and 10^{+7} seconds, the latter figure being close to a year. If a nuclear isomer is formed, it will remain for a time of the order of its lifetime and look to all intents like the same nucleus in its ground state, until it finally emits a gamma ray. Isomers may be considered as nuclei which have a pure gamma radioactivity. If a certain number of isomeric nuclei are produced initially, that number will subsequently decrease exponentially with time, just as in the familiar radioactive decay. Many experimental and theoretical investigations have been made of the lifetimes of isomers, and these have given much information on the structure of nuclei.

Finally we consider the emission of beta rays, that is, electrons. We have seen that this is even less likely a process than gamma ray emission. The physical constant which describes the coupling between beta ray emission and nucleons is exceedingly small, much smaller than the number $1/137$ which is characteristic for the coupling with electromagnetic radiation and hence for gamma ray emission. Thus beta ray emission will, in general, not occur unless *every* other possibility has been exhausted. Among the beta transitions there are again allowed ones, which are characterized by the fact that the angular momentum of the nucleus does not need to change or changes only by one unit, and forbidden transitions, which involve a considerable change in the angular momentum of the nucleus. The allowed transitions have different lifetimes according to the energy which is available to the beta rays. This lifetime goes about as the inverse fifth power of the energy available for the beta ray emission. According to Table 6 the lifetime ranges from 10^{-2} to 10^{+9} seconds. The longest "allowed" lifetime known is that of tritium, the superheavy hydrogen of mass 3 which lives for 12 years; the shortest is B^{12} with a life of 1/50 of a second. If we consider forbidden transitions, we find that their lifetimes range from about one second to 10^{16}. This limit is set by our ability to observe weak beta ray activities. There are presumably other beta ray transitions which have even longer lifetimes which we cannot observe.

Potential Barriers

Let us now consider some transmutations in detail, beginning with the emission of alpha rays, because this is probably the most familiar process. The theory for this process was given by Gamow in 1929. Figure 7 illustrates the idea schematically. It shows the potential energy of the interaction between the emitted alpha particle and the remaining nucleus. At large distances, the potential energy is simply due to the electrostatic repulsion between these two particles and varies inversely as the distance between them. On the other hand, we know that the alpha particle can be bound in the nucleus and therefore we must assume that at very small distances there is a *negative* potential energy between alpha particle and nucleus. This is represented by the potential well in the middle of Figure 7. The figure also shows a broken horizontal line which

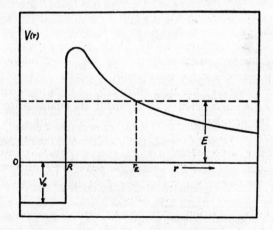

Figure 7. Potential barrier in alpha decay

represents the energy of the alpha particle. According to classical mechanics, the alpha particle could either move inside the nucleus or it could move entirely outside the nucleus, more precisely outside the point r_E. It cannot, in classical mechanics, ever move from the inside to the outside. The fact that the potential energy, for some distances r, exceeds the total energy E, presents an absolute barrier to the particle. However, in quantum mechanics, the alpha particle *can* leak through such a potential barrier. The probability with which it "leaks out" depends on the height and the width of the barrier and can be calculated from these factors.

The result of this calculation is shown in Figure 8, which gives the relation between the lifetime and the energy of the alpha particle. This figure corresponds to the natural alpha-radioactive nuclei, i.e., the nuclei at the end of the periodic table which are energetically capable of emitting alpha particles. The abscissa in Figure 8 is the energy in millions of electron volts, while the ordinate gives the reciprocal of the lifetime on a logarithmic scale. Zero corresponds to a lifetime of one second; thus the scale ranges from 10^{20} seconds at the bottom to 10^{-8} second at the top. The circles correspond to observed lifetimes and energies. We can see that the lifetime varies tremendously, by some 24 decades, while there is only a rather small variation of energy, by scarcely more than a factor of two. The theory of Gamow and of Condon and Gurney explains this remarkable fact. Indeed, the three solid curves in Figure 8 are the predictions of the theory for different radii of the nucleus. The agreement with observation is remarkably good. Further, the theory permits us to deduce the nuclear radii from the observed relation between lifetime and energy. One finds, among other things, that the different radioactive families have slightly different nuclear radii, corresponding to the three curves. Furthermore, we have here another method of determining the radius of the nucleus in addition to those we have discussed before. It is a rather accurate method, and historically it was the first accurate determination of the nuclear radius.

Next we shall consider nuclear collisions. Collisions induced by neutrons have already been discussed. For fast neutrons, the cross section is about the geometric size of the nucleus; for slow neutrons we find, in general, much larger cross sections. This is one of the reasons why the neutrons are slowed down in an atomic energy pile: they will then react more easily with the uranium nuclei.

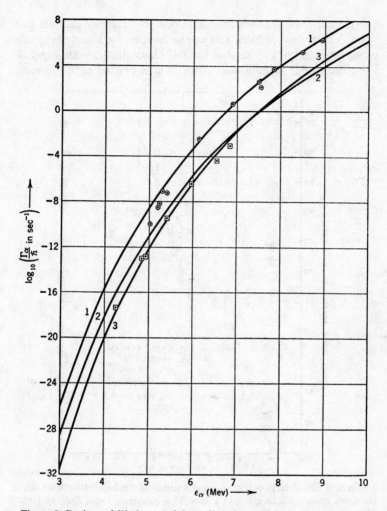

Figure 8. Reciprocal lifetime of alpha-radioactive nuclei vs. the energy of the α particle. Circles and Curves 1 and 2 correspond to $Z = 82$ for the daughter nucleus, Curve 1 is for a radius $R = 9.3 \times 10^{-13}$ cm, Curve 2 for $R = 7.9 \times 10^{-13}$. Squares and Curve 3 correspond to $Z = 90$ and $R = 9.6 \times 10^{-13}$.—Blatt and Weisskopf, p. 575 (chap. 11, Fig. 3.1)

We shall now discuss those reactions produced by charged particles. Their cross section, just as the lifetime for alpha decay, depends strongly on the potential barrier. This is illustrated in Figure 9. Here the energy in million electron volts is plotted as the abscissa,

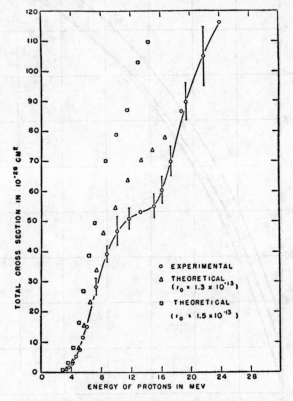

Figure 9. Total cross section for the reaction of protons with Cu[63] (sum of the three cross sections given in Figure 13).—Ghoshal, *Phys. Rev.*, **80** (1950), 941

and the cross section in units of 10^{-26} cm^2 as the ordinate. The two curves are obtained by calculation, and both refer to the same charged particle reaction. In both cases the cross section increases very rapidly with increasing energy. This is due to the fact that the penetration of the potential barrier of the nucleus becomes easier.

Now the height of the potential barrier depends on the radius of the nucleus, and this therefore provides another method to determine the radius of the nucleus. The two curves in the figure correspond to two different assumptions about the radius of the nucleus. Since we have seen earlier that the nuclear radius R is proportional to the cube root of the mass number, it is convenient to write it in the form

$$R = r_0 A^{1/3}, \tag{7}$$

and then we can examine the value of r_0. The two curves in Figure 9 correspond to $r_0 = 1.3 \times 10^{-13}$ cm and 1.5×10^{-13} cm, respectively. It is seen that the 1.3 curve fits much better than does the 1.5 curve. The 1.3 curve corresponds to a higher potential barrier, which gives less penetration and therefore smaller cross sections, and this is what is observed. Now the figure 1.3 is still somewhat larger than 1.2, which is now believed to be the most accurate value of r_0. The reason for this is that the proton which was used as a projectile to bombard the nucleus interacts with it even when it is still somewhat outside the nucleus. We have already discussed a similar effect for neutrons.

Table 7. Height of potential barrier for protons and cross section

	Z	A	R	B(Mev)	σ(barns)
H	1	1	1.2	0.6	.18
C	6	12	2.8	2.1	.50
Al	13	27	3.6	3.9	.72
Cu	29	64	4.8	7.0	1.13
Ag	47	108	5.7	9.8	1.50
U	92	238	7.5	15.2	2.38

Table 7 gives the height of the potential barrier for protons interacting with a few nuclei. In the first column the familiar chemical symbol is given, in the second column the nuclear charge, next the mass number, then the radius of the nucleus according to Formula 7, next the barrier height in millions of electron volts for protons. Thus the barrier ranges from 500,000 volts for a proton-proton collision to 15 million volts for the uranium nucleus. One requires protons of 15 million volts if they are to go over the top of the potential barrier of the uranium nucleus. Almost half as much is required to get over the top of the barrier around the copper nucleus, although that nucleus has less than a third of the nuclear charge of uranium and about a quarter of the atomic weight.

The last column of Table 7 gives the geometric cross section of nuclei in barns. The barn is a unit of 10^{-24} cm². It is a very useful unit for nuclear physics, being of the same order as the geometrical cross section of a medium-size nucleus. The heaviest nuclei have geometric cross sections of somewhat over two barns. Copper has about one, and carbon about 0.5 barn. These geometric cross sections represent approximately the actual cross sections for the collision of a fast neutron (let us say, 50 Mev) with the respective nuclei. From the collision cross sections we find that neutrons are able to go through solid matter, such as iron or uranium, for a distance of the order of 5 or 10 cm before making a collision. This "mean free path" of neutrons gives us an idea of the size of a piece of matter required to "contain" neutrons, for instance, the minimum size of a nuclear reactor. In such a reactor, one must of course have a large number of collisions of the neutron, so that the size must be several times 10 cm.

The next subject is only vaguely connected with our main discussion.

Table 8. Reactions in stars

H + H = D + ϵ^+	10^{10}yr.		C^{12} + H = N^{13} + γ		$2 \cdot 10^6$ y
D + H = He^3 + γ	4 sec		N^{13} = C^{13} + ϵ^+		12 min.
He^3 + He^3 = He^4 + 2H	$4 \cdot 10^5$yr.		C^{13} + H = N^{14} + γ		$5 \cdot 10^4$ y
			N^{14} + H = O^{15} + γ		$4 \cdot 10^6$ y
			O^{15} = N^{15} + ϵ^+		2 min.
			N^{15} + H = C^{12} + He^4		20 y

Table 8 shows the nuclear reactions which take place in a star and which generate its energy. They are all charged-particle reactions, and the reason why these reactions involve protons is that the potential barrier repelling any heavier nucleus is too high. Therefore all the reactions occurring in ordinary stars involve protons. On the right-hand side of Table 8 is given the carbon cycle. This is the common reaction in the larger stars. On the left-hand side the proton-proton reaction chain is shown. While not a cycle, this set of reactions is mainly responsible for the energy production in the lighter stars, from the sun down to the red dwarfs. The proton-

proton cycle starts with a very unusual reaction, namely, one in which a positive electron is emitted in a *collision*. This is an exception to the rules we have given and can become important only under the unusual conditions prevailing in stars, and only when extremely long times are available. At the high temperatures and densities inside stars, a great many protons will make close collisions all the time, but even under these conditions, it requires some 10^{11} years for an average proton to undergo this reaction because the beta decay is such an extremely unlikely process. The other reaction chain, the carbon cycle, takes a much shorter time to be completed, in spite of the fact that there is a much higher potential barrier between a carbon nucleus and a proton than between two protons. The reason is that the carbon cycle reactions are ordinary reactions in which nuclear particles are emitted rather than positive electrons. The second and the fifth reactions in the carbon cycle are spontaneous, not collisions; they are spontaneous beta disintegrations in which a positive electron is emitted.

The Compound Nucleus

We shall now discuss what happens to a nucleus after it has been hit by a particle. This is described by the theory of the compound nucleus. This theory was suggested by Bohr in 1935 and states that a nuclear particle which hits a nucleus becomes completely amalgamated with it. Particle and nucleus form a "compound nucleus" which will stay together for a considerable time on the nuclear scale, maybe for 10^{-16} second. After the compound nucleus has been formed, it is supposed to "forget" the way in which it was produced, and its subsequent disintegration will depend only on its energy. Its ultimate disintegration, in one or another possible way, completes the nuclear reaction.

The theory of the compound nucleus was conceived originally in order to explain certain phenomena known as resonances. It is observed that most nuclear reactions have cross sections which are not smooth functions of the energy, except at very high energies (about 10 Mev or higher). At lower energy there are usually a number of irregularities. An example of this is shown in Figure 10, which gives the results of measurements of the cross section of a certain nuclear reaction as a function of energy. The reaction is that between aluminum and protons, leading to the emission of gamma

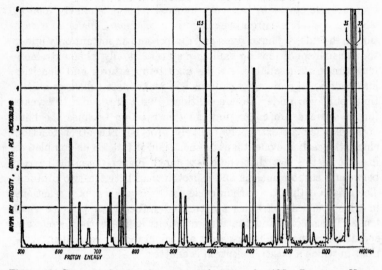

Figure 10. Cross section for the capture of protons by Al[27].—Brostrom, Huus, and Tangen, *Phys. Rev.*, **71** (1947), 661

rays. The ordinate is the gamma ray intensity as a function of the kinetic energy of the bombarding proton. As the proton energy goes from 500 to 1400 kev, there are tremendous fluctuations in cross section, including very sharp, narrow maxima. To interpret these, we assume that the compound nucleus has a set of energy levels, just as any stable nucleus or atom. Whenever the energy of the incident proton, plus the energy of the target nucleus, agrees with the energy of one of these levels, we obtain a "resonance." The incident proton is then "eager" to enter the nucleus and form the compound, and a large cross section results.

Figure 11 shows the same phenomenon at much lower energies. This figure refers to the capture of *neutrons* by the element lutetium. The experiment is performed by means of a neutron velocity selector. The neutron energy in this case ranges from 1/100 of an electron volt to 100 electron volts. One can see that there are many resonance levels, separated by only a few volts, in this energy region.

One of the important problems in nuclear theory is that of finding a good theory of the density of energy levels, i.e., how many levels will be found, on the average, in an energy interval of, say, 1000

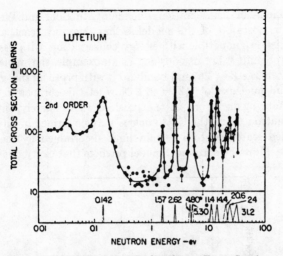

Figure 11. Neutron capture by lutetium.—Foote, Landon,
and Sailor, *Phys. Rev.*, **92** (1953), 656

volts. Quite a few theories have been proposed. The best so far is
that due to Claude Bloch, a young Frenchman who worked at
California Institute of Technology. This theory seems to explain
fairly well the energy level density which has been observed in
neutron velocity selector experiments as a function of the mass
number of the nucleus. The heavier the nucleus, that is, the more
nucleons it contains, the denser are the energy levels because there
are more and more ways of distributing the energy of the nucleus
among the nucleons. This theoretical prediction is well confirmed by
experiment. Indeed, Figure 10, which referred to Al, of mass number
27, showed on the average about four levels for every 100,000 electron
volts, while Figure 11, referring to the heavy nucleus Lu, of mass
number 175, shows about equally many levels for each interval of
10 electron volts. Another result of both theory and experiment
is that the levels become denser at higher excitation energy of the
nucleus.

Having discussed the cross section for the formation of the compound nucleus and its interesting resonance maxima, we ask next
in which way the compound nucleus will disintegrate, that is, what
particles will come out of it. This is described by the so-called sta-

tistical model of disintegration, due mainly to Bohr and Weisskopf. The main postulate of this model is that one may reach any final state which is compatible with energy conservation, with essentially equal probability. Let us consider, as an example, the nucleus Fe^{56} (nuclear charge $Z = 26$) and bombard it with protons; this gives the compound nucleus Co^{57} ($Z = 27$). Now let this compound nucleus disintegrate again in one of the possible ways, namely, into Co^{56} plus a neutron. Then the Co^{56} nucleus may be formed in any one of its excited states up to a certain limit determined by the energy available. Now the statistical model predicts that every one of these

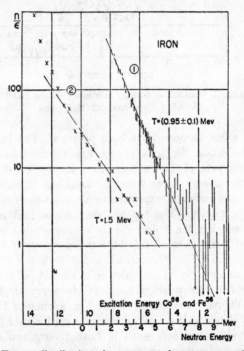

Figure 12. Energy distribution of neutrons and protons emerging when Fe^{56} is bombarded with protons of 16 Mev. Curve 1, which is derived from the neutron distribution in the reaction Fe^{56} (p, n)Co^{56}, indicates the distribution of level density in the residual nucleus Co^{56} and corresponds to a "temperature" of 0.95 Mev for that nucleus. Curve 2, derived from the energy distribution of the inelastically scattered protons from the reaction Fe^{56} (p, p)Fe^{56} indicates the level density in the nucleus Fe^{56}.—Gugelot, *Phys. Rev.*, **81** (1951), 51 (Figure 9)

levels will be reached with equal probability, apart from such factors as statistical weights and the probability of penetration through a potential barrier which was discussed earlier.

Figure 12 gives some experimental results, obtained by Gugelot at Princeton, on the energy distribution of neutrons resulting from this nuclear reaction. The upper curve, 1, gives the energy distribution of neutrons which come out of the proton bombardment of Fe^{56}. The ordinate is the number of neutrons observed divided by their energy. It is plotted on a logarithmic scale against the neutron energy. It is seen that lower energy neutrons are emitted with much higher probability than higher energy neutrons. The reason for this is that the less energetic neutrons leave more excitation energy in the nucleus. As we have mentioned, when a nucleus has more excitation energy, the number of levels per unit energy is much higher. Since each level is reached with equal probability, the likelihood that the excitation energy left in the residual nucleus is between E and $E + dE$ will be much greater for high E than for low E.

The experiment also shows quantitatively how the level density increases with increasing excitation energy. The increase is approximately exponential, i.e., the logarithm of the number of emitted particles varies linearly with the energy of the neutron. Thus the energy distribution of emitted particles is given somewhat as follows:

$$N(\epsilon) \propto e^{-\epsilon/T}, \tag{8}$$

where $N(\epsilon)$ is the number of particles of energy ϵ emitted and T is a constant characteristic of the nucleus and the total energy available. The higher the kinetic energy ϵ, the fewer particles are emitted. Formula 8 is just the Boltzmann distribution which is familiar from the kinetic theory of gases. The constant T which appears in the formula is analogous to the temperature in kinetic theory, except that in nuclear physics we measure the temperature directly in energy units. Curve 1 in Figure 12 corresponds to a value of the "temperature" of about one million volts.

By doing experiments on the energy distribution of the emitted neutrons, then, one can determine the temperature of a nucleus as a function of the energy originally supplied to it. When this is done, rather surprising results are found; namely, the temperature is surprisingly low for most compound nuclei which are formed by bombarding a target nucleus with a neutron of 14 Mev. This result is not quite understood, but it seems to be an experimental fact that the temperature does not change very much with the energy supplied to the nucleus. Whether one gives the nucleus an excitation energy of 5 million volts or 50, the temperature always seems to be about one million electron volts. Before these experiments were performed, it was believed, rather naturally, that the nuclear temperature would rise steadily with the excitation energy. Why this assumption is false makes a very interesting puzzle.

The measured energy distributions of the outgoing particles do show, however, that the residual nucleus tends to retain as much energy as possible, in agreement with theoretical expectation. Now if a large amount of energy is supplied to the compound nucleus, e.g., in the form of kinetic energy of the incident particle, then, according to this rule, the residual nucleus is apt to retain a very large fraction of it as excitation energy. This being so, the residual nucleus often has enough energy to emit an *additional* particle, after the first particle has left the nucleus. Whenever there is enough energy in the residual nucleus, the additional particle is likely to be emitted. This is so because a reaction leading to the emission of nuclear particles is nearly always more probable than a reaction leading to the emission of gamma rays, as we have seen.

Figure 13 illustrates these considerations. It shows the results of experiments carried out at Berkeley by Ghoshal in which Cu^{63} was bombarded with protons. The compound nucleus Zn^{64} is formed (of nuclear charge 30 and mass number 64). The normal way for this nucleus to decay is by emission of a neutron, leaving the residual nucleus Zn^{63}. The nuclear reaction is then

$$Cu^{63} + H^1 = n^1 + Zn^{63} - 3 \text{ Mev} . \qquad (9)$$

The reaction energy of about -3 Mev can be deduced from the energy of the positrons, which the beta-radioactive nucleus emits subsequently. This radioactivity makes the formation of the nucleus Zn^{63} easy to observe. The lower curve on the left of Figure 13 gives the cross section for the formation of Zn^{63} as a function of the energy of the incident protons. In the beginning, this curve behaves exactly as we might expect from elementary theory: The cross section is negligibly small at 3 Mev proton energy and then rises steeply with increasing energy, indicating the increasing probability for the penetration of the incident proton through the potential barrier.

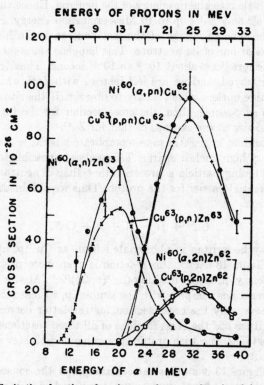

Figure 13. Excitation function of various nuclear reactions involving the compound nucleus Zn^{64}.—Ghoshal, *Phys. Rev.*, **80** (1950), 940

However, at about 13 Mev proton energy a phenomenon happens which would be very surprising to us if we did not know about the statistical model of the nucleus; namely, the cross section for the formation of Zn^{63}, suddenly begins to decrease at 13 Mev and becomes quite small at proton energies above 22 Mev. On the basis of the statistical model, we are able to explain this as follows: Of the 13 Mev proton energy, 3 Mev are absorbed in the nuclear reaction (9). The remaining 10 Mev are then shared between the excitation energy of the residual nucleus Zn^{63} and the kinetic energy of the outgoing nucleon. But we know from our previous arguments that most of the energy goes into excitation of the residual nucleus and very little into kinetic energy of the neutron. Hence the residual nucleus Zn^{63} may have up to 10 Mev excitation energy. But this is exactly the binding energy of the last neutron in Zn^{63}. Therefore Zn^{63} can emit one of its neutrons. This happens spontaneously and in a very short time, about 10^{-18} to 10^{-20} second. Thus the nucleus Zn^{63} is destroyed, and we are left instead with Zn^{62}, which is also a radioactive nucleus which is easy to observe. If the situation were as simple as possible, then, the cross section for the formation of Zn^{62} would rise at the expense of that for Zn^{63}.

The situation is slightly more complicated because Zn does not have a very high nuclear charge. This makes it possible to have the second outgoing particle a proton rather than a neutron, in spite of the potential barrier for the proton. Thus we obtain the alternative reaction

$$Cu^{63} + H = H + n + Cu^{62}, \tag{10}$$

which may be written in abbreviated form as $Cu^{63}(p, np)Cu^{62}$. In fact, as Figure 13 shows, this reaction is even more probable than the previously discussed reaction $Cu^{63}(p, 2n)Zn^{62}$. At any rate, both of these reactions compete with the simple (p, n) reaction, and this is the reason why the cross section for the latter decreases above 13 Mev. If we *add* the cross sections of all three reactions, the total continues to increase with proton energy beyond 13 Mev and finally flattens out.

Thus Figure 13 is an illustrative example of the consequences of the statistical model of nuclear reactions and of the competition between various possible nuclear reactions. Of course, in those cases where Zn^{63} remains in the end, it must get rid of its excitation energy by the emission of gamma rays. Figure 13 shows further that at still higher energies, above 24 Mev proton energy, the cross sections for the (p, np) and $(p, 2n)$ reactions also begin to decrease, undoubtedly because emission of three particles from the compound nucleus becomes important.

Figure 13 shows still another point which demonstrates the essential validity of the concept of the compound nucleus. Our compound nucleus Zn^{64} can be formed in at least two different ways, either from Cu^{63} by adding a proton or from Ni^{60} by adding an alpha particle. Both of these experiments were done by Ghoshal. Figure 13 was drawn in such a way that the same abscissa corresponds to the same energy of the compound nucleus. To achieve this, the alpha particle must have 7 Mev more kinetic energy than the protons. We see that the cross section for the reactions starting with alpha particles depends on the energy of the compound nucleus essentially in the same way as does the cross section of the reactions starting with protons. The curves drop at the same point and rise at the same point. This is to be expected because the same competition occurs between the various modes of disintegration of the compound nucleus. The curves in Figure 13 demonstrate that the compound nucleus really does not "know" how it was formed and that the relative probability of its various modes of disintegration is independent of the manner in which the nucleus was formed.

All the points about nuclear reactions which we have discussed may be combined to yield predictions of the cross sections of various nuclear reactions. The probability of penetrating the potential barrier can be calculated. One can also calculate by statistics the relative probabilities of emitting one neutron, two neutrons, a neutron and a proton, etc. So we are in a rather good position to predict, for any arbitrary nuclear reaction which has never been observed, the cross section as a function of energy. We can predict what product will come out, what the ratio will be between various nuclear reactions, and how that ratio will depend on energy.

Beta Decay

Finally, we should consider the process of beta decay, which has been mentioned so often. In this process a certain energy is available for the emission of the electrons. Figure 14, curve a, shows what is observed: It is found that electrons come out with all sorts of energies, and the figure shows a typical momentum distribution of the emitted electrons. The distribution extends up to a maximum momentum p_{max}, and it can be shown experimentally that the energy of an electron of momentum p_{max} is exactly equal to the total energy available for the disintegration. In most cases, however, as is shown by Figure 14a, the electron comes out with much less energy than is available.

For this and other reasons, Pauli suggested in 1934 that not *one*

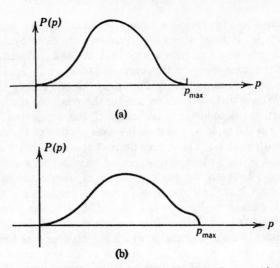

Figure 14. Momentum distribution of the electrons in beta disintegration.—Blatt and Weisskopf, p. 676 (chap. 13, Fig. 2.1)

particle comes out in beta decay but two, namely, an electron and a neutral particle which is not observed. This suggestion was made into a quantitative theory by Fermi, who named the neutral particle the neutrino. Electron and neutrino share the available energy, but it is not arbitrary *how* they share it. Fermi's theory predicts accurately the distribution in energy of the electrons. The calculated distribution curve is shown in Figure 14 and has been shown to agree with the observed distribution in dozens of examples.

Fermi's theory has been much elaborated in the last 20 years. An important point is the change of angular momentum of the nucleus in beta decay. If there is no change, or if the angular momentum changes by one unit, the beta transition is in general "allowed." It then takes place rather fast, and the energy distribution of the electrons is as shown in Figure 14a. If the angular momentum changes by more than one unit, the lifetime of the radioactive nucleus is much longer and the energy distribution is different, again in a predictable way. The very long lifetimes of beta-active nuclei are all due to large angular momentum change; for instance, K^{40}, which has to change its angular momentum by four units in order to go to Ca^{40}, has a lifetime of about a billion years.

In spite of all the exploration of beta decay, it still has not been possible to observe the neutrino directly. However, we know most of its properties. Its mass is probably zero; at least we know that the mass is extremely small compared to that of an electron. If it were not zero, the energy distribution of the electrons would correspond to curve b in Figure 14, while the observed energy distribution corresponds to curve a. The neutrino has a spin of $\frac{1}{2}$; it has, as far as we can tell, no interaction with matter except the beta-decay interaction. Since we know that it can be emitted together with electrons, we must conclude that it can also do the reverse, that is, that it can *induce* beta-ray processes. If, for instance, a neutrino hits a proton, it may convert it into a neutron and a positive electron. This prediction follows from the general principles of statistical mechanics and quantum mechanics which also permit us to predict the cross section for this process. It is exceedingly small, about 10^{-45} cm^2. In spite of this small number, Reines and Cowan of the Los Alamos Laboratory are attempting an experiment to observe the neutrino. They plan to use the Savannah River atomic pile, which emits large numbers of beta rays and therefore many neutrinos also, and hope to carry this experiment out in the near future.

Added in proof: Recent reports indicate that these investigators have been successful in their search for direct evidence of the neutrino.

Elementary Particles

V. F. WEISSKOPF

The physics of the elementary particles is one of the most interesting and also one of the most philosophic parts of modern physics.
As we all know, the aim of philosophy and science is to reduce the
variety of phenomena which we see to some simple principle, some
simple fact. This is, no doubt, the essence of what we mean by an
explanation in science. The elementary particles have played a very
important role in this.

One always has thought that matter, as we know it, or all phenomena, as we know them, are fundamentally the effects of simple
movements or other actions of elementary entities which one usually
regards as elementary particles. In many ways this has been found
to be truer than one had any reason to hope for. The idea is very
old and has been ascribed to Democritus, the Greek philosopher,
who said that all matter consists of atoms, particles of some fundamental nature. The word atom implies the indivisibility of that
elementary part of matter.

This lack of subdivision has always intrigued the scientists as
well as some philosophers. When one has introduced some entity,
some particle, some atom, one is almost inevitably led to ask questions concerning the structure of that atom, in spite of the fact that
one has introduced it as an indivisible thing in the first place.

Let us now proceed directly from Democritus in Greece to the
nineteenth century, when the idea of the atom as the indivisible
unit of matter was taken up again. Perhaps the most obvious realization of the fact that matter should consist of separate atoms is
found in the kinetic theory of gases, which was developed in the
middle of the last century. What do we assume if we want to describe the mechanics of gases? We assume that the atoms (or
molecules; the difference will not be stressed here) move independently of each other and collide from time to time as they come
near one another. It is possible to describe the properties of gases
by making the assumption that the atoms are bodies of approxi-

115

mately (sometimes exactly) spherical shape, which collide just like billiard balls. That is, the assumption of spherical units moving and colliding is the basis of our picture of what happens in a gas. As a matter of fact, one may say that the heat energy contained in the gas is nothing but the kinetic energy of the atoms which is exchanged at random by collisions. It is important that we assume that any internal structure the atoms may have is unaffected by the collisions, that is, the atoms act as perfect spheres.

At this point an interesting question arises which we will meet at every step of our development. The problem pointed out by Boltzmann is the following: If these atoms have internal structure, then it is not quite clear why the heat energy which is put into this gas is visible only in the form of kinetic energy of the atom. (Perhaps it should be pointed out that, from the calculation of the pressure of the gas, one can easily see that the heat delivered to the gas is all in the kinetic energy of the particles.) Boltzmann said that one cannot quite understand why, during these collisions, some of the energy does not go into the internal movements of the atoms. In other words, why does the heat energy not excite the internal degrees of freedom of the atoms? Boltzmann argued along the following lines: The atom must have some internal structure and therefore must be able to perform some kind of internal motion. From the general laws of Newtonian mechanics, one would then expect that the collisions should transfer some of the kinetic energy into these internal modes of motion and therefore take energy away from the heat motion. This, however, has not been observed; in fact, the specific heat of gases indicates that the heat energy is only kinetic. In other words, an atom in a gas at normal temperature behaves as if it had *no* internal structure. Hence the atom behaves, at least in these phenomena, as if it were an elementary particle.

Of course, we know that this is not so. As is well known, the atom does have internal structure. The reason this structure does not show up in the mechanics of gases was unknown to Boltzmann but is known to us now: It is explained by the quantum nature of the mechanical properties of the atom. The quantum nature requires that a system the size of an atom cannot accept energy in indefinitely small portions. It may accept energy only in finite amounts. Hence, if the first step in the atomic spectrum is high enough, higher than the average kinetic energy involved in the collisions, then it is just impossible to excite the internal motions of the atom. Therefore, if we have to deal with energies below the first excitation potential of the atom, the atom may, within this range of phenomena, be considered as an elementary particle. This is an enormously important fact of nature whose importance cannot be overstressed. If atomic systems did not have the quantum properties, progress toward an understanding of these complex mechanisms would probably not be possible. It is just these quantum steps which make it possible to separate the very complicated mechanisms into tractable, simpler constituents. For example, to explain the behavior of gases we need not know the special mechanism within the atom, simply because that mechanism does not come into play; the excitation energy is too high. In the same way it was possible to study atomic phenomena without knowing anything about the nucleus, since the nuclear mechanism does not come into play at those energies which are important in atomic phenomena.

With this guiding idea, we would now like to study the phenomena in nature's microcosmos by going down to smaller and smaller particles. This is equivalent to going to higher and higher energies because there is a fundamental law in quantum mechanics which says that the energies necessary to get a mechanism into play are connected with the size of the system. This law says that the smaller the system, the higher this energy. Hence if we want to investigate very small systems, we need very high energies. We therefore order our material according to decreasing size or increasing energy.

Let us start with phenomena in which only energies below, say, one electron volt play a role. Let us call this energy Region I. In this region we have good reason to believe atoms will not be excited; for these energies atoms are indivisible and act like elementary particles. The kinetic theory of gases belongs to this region, since at room temperature the kinetic energy of a gas atom is about one-fortieth of an electron volt. This is much less than the smallest quantum of energy required to excite an atom. In this energy region we are justified in saying that our elementary particles are the atoms as such. In other words, below one electron volt, in the region we have called Region I, the old idea of Democritus is correct—the atoms are the elementary particles.

We must now transgress this energy limit, because almost all the phenomena which surround us in daily life have to do with energy transfers between particles which are larger than one electron volt. By simply tapping a pencil, one can deliver to the atoms an energy of the order of one electron volt. Phenomena like flames or electric discharges surely deal with energy exchanges of much larger value. Therefore we must introduce the next region of energy, Region II, which will include the most important phenomena of practical life. This is the region between one electron volt and, say, 1000 or 10,000 electron volts. This is a region of great interest to physics and even more so to chemistry, since for these energies the structure of the atom comes into the open. The energies are high enough so that the electrons in the atom are excited and the theory of atomic structure comes into play. We then find that the atom consists of a heavy atomic nucleus at the center surrounded by the electrons. The picture is very close to that of the planetary system, with the nucleus playing the role of the sun and the electrons that of the various planets.

Without entering into a discussion of atomic structure here we shall summarize the situation in this region from the point of view of elementary particles. At this stage the list of elementary particles contains the electron and all the different atomic nuclei. In this energy region the nuclei present themselves to us as indivisible particles whose internal degrees of freedom are not only unknown to us but do not even play any role. The nuclei act as elementary indivisible particles, just as the atoms did in the very low-energy region we called Region I. They are "billiard balls" endowed only with a mass, a charge, and sometimes a magnetic moment.

In order to get into the structure of the nuclei themselves, we must open up a region of higher energy and come to the phenomena in Region III, belonging to energies roughly between 10^5 and 10^7 electron volts. Energies of this magnitude can be produced only by modern high-tension machines, like cyclotrons, van de Graaff generators, etc. Under the impact of these energies, even atomic nuclei can be excited and their structure revealed.

We shall now simply state some important empirical facts concerning nuclei; the establishment of these facts is the fruit of a long period of experimental research. First, and perhaps most important, it was demonstrated that the nucleus is made up of two kinds of particles, and no others. These are the proton and neutron. The proton has a charge equal, but opposite in sign, to the electron, while the neutron is uncharged. The proton and neutron mass are almost equal and almost two thousand times the electron mass. In a neutral atom the number of electrons is equal to the number of protons in the nucleus; in addition, the nucleus will contain neutrons, in fact, usually more neutrons than protons.

We see now that all matter can be composed of the nuclear particles, the neutrons and protons plus the electrons in the orbits surrounding the nucleus. We see then that we now have three elementary particles, the proton, the neutron, and the electron.

As soon as we discover that the nucleus contains only protons and neutrons, we come upon a new problem: How does the nucleus hold together? This was no problem in the atom, since the electrons are attracted to the nucleus by the electrostatic forces which tend to bring opposite charges together. But in the nuclear case, we put a large number of positively charged particles, the protons, into a very small region, and from our knowledge of electricity we would expect such a system to fly asunder. Clearly, we must therefore postulate the existence of attractive forces of a nonelectric nature which are able to fuse the elementary particles within the nucleus together. So new kinds of forces will have to be investigated here. From the experiments we know that these forces must be very strong, since it is found that one needs very high energy to remove a particle, say a proton or alpha particle (two protons and two neutrons bound together), from the nucleus. In fact, energies of several million electron volts (Mev) are needed. So the forces that hold the protons and neutrons together are very strong indeed, far stronger than forces of an electric nature.

Now let us review the energy regions once again. First there was the region of the kinetic theory of gases, and second there was that of atomic physics. It should now be pointed out that one of the triumphs of atomic physics is the demonstration that the forces which surround us in daily life, the forces of chemical binding, the forces which keep a pencil together, etc., are all manifestations of, and may be reduced to, the electric forces which act between electrons and nuclei. (There is, of course, one other force which physics has had to deal with, the gravitational force, but this will not play any role in our considerations.) So, to repeat, in Regions I and II, that of gas theory and atomic physics, the only forces which we must consider are electric forces. Now the electromagnetic forces have been studied for some 100 to 150 years, and so we have become very familiar with them. We know about the attraction between unlike charges, the repulsion between like charges, and the fact that the force is inversely proportional to the square of the distance. These are all familiar phenomena because we may observe them on a macroscopic scale. But, as we have seen, when we come to Region III, into the realm of nuclear physics, we are faced with something entirely new. For the first time in well over a century we have a new kind of force, a nuclear force.

We may learn a most important property of nuclear forces from the analysis of experiments on the scattering between nuclear particles. From such an analysis we find that the nuclear force does not reach very far; more precisely, the moment the two particles (say a proton and a neutron) are a little farther apart than the radius of a typical nucleus, there will be no force at all between them. So we now have a somewhat better picture of our nuclear force: It is extremely strong and acts only over a very short distance. Owing to this short range of action, however, nuclear forces cannot manifest themselves in our everyday, macroscopic world. By the time we are at a distance of one-hundred billionth of a centimeter from the nucleus, the nuclear forces are already undetectable. We therefore realize that not only are we faced with a completely new type of force, but, unlike the electromagnetic case, we have no hope of becoming acquainted with it in the macroscopic domain.

Besides baring the nuclear forces, the energies available in Region III also enable us to begin an investigation of the internal structure of the nucleus. Associated with the motion of this internal structure there is a whole host of new and fascinating phenomena: nuclear transmutations, nuclear reactions, and the phenomena of fission and fusion. The last two can, perhaps unfortunately, be applied on a large scale.

There are, however, other phenomena which belong to this energy region and which are of special interest to us since we are concerned with the elementary particles. These phenomena are connected with the existence of the positive electron, the positron. So far we have dealt only with the normal, common electron which, as we know, has a negative charge. When we go into this high-energy region (over one million electron volts), we come upon a most interesting new phenomenon: pair creation. This is a phenomenon in which one can produce electrons out of the vacuum, that is, out of nothing. (We do not refer to this as the creation of matter because electrons by themselves are not matter in the everyday sense of the word. As was pointed out earlier, the matter which surrounds us is made up of atoms, which contain protons and neutrons as well as electrons.*) The experimental fact is that one can produce electrons from light. If one has light whose frequency is sufficiently great so that it has an energy of more than one million electron volts (according to Planck's relation, Energy $= h\nu$, where ν is the frequency and h Planck's quantum constant), then under certain conditions this light can be transformed into a pair of electrons. Now, of course, these electrons have mass, and the light does not; this is, therefore, an example of Einstein's famous law that energy may be transformed into mass. If both these electrons were of the usual, atomic variety with which we are so familiar, we would immediately come to a contradiction. For light bears no charge, and a pair of ordinary electrons would have two negative charges, so that charge would not be conserved in the act of pair creation. What happens in fact is that one of the electrons of the pair is of the old-fashioned negative kind, while the other has the same mass but is positively charged: the positron.

Now let us have a closer look at this surprising phenomenon of pair creation; Figure 1 is a schematic illustration of what happens. It should be understood that in order for light to be transformed into a pair, the region in space where the process occurs must be under *tension*, that is, a force field must be present. The reason for this requirement is well understood, but we shall not attempt an explanation here. This tension, or force field, is most suitably supplied by the electric field of an atomic nucleus. Thus in the illustration we see a light quantum passing in the immediate neighborhood of a nucleus and being transformed there into an electron and a positron. This phenomenon can actually be observed directly in the laboratory. The most striking manifestation of pair creation is ob-

---

* *Added in proof:* Since this article was written, a group of physicists at the University of California in Berkeley, Chamberlain, Segrè, Wiegand, and Ypsilantis, succeeded in creating pairs of positive and negative protons (protons and antiprotons) out of the vacuum. They used a proton beam of 6 billion electron volts. This represents actual creation of matter.

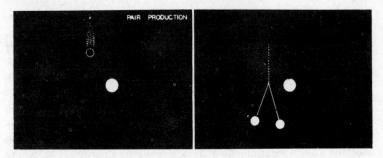

Figure 1. Schematic diagram showing pair production

served in the cosmic radiation, and to understand this we will first have to discuss two further processes involving light and electrons.

The first of these is the inverse of pair creation and is called pair annihilation. What happens here is that a positron (positively charged electron) collides with an ordinary electron, and the two annihilate each other with the simultaneous appearance of light. It is evident that this is just pair creation turned around. This is again an illustration of Einstein's law, only this time mass is transformed into energy, the energy of the light quanta.

The second process concerns the radiation of light, or, in other words, the emission of light quanta. This is illustrated in Figure 2. Here we have a charged particle, say an electron, passing in the vicinity of a nucleus. Because of the electric field of the nucleus, it is deflected. An acceleration is associated with this deflection, and we know from the theory of electricity that the acceleration of a charge is accompanied by the radiation of light. Thus, as can be

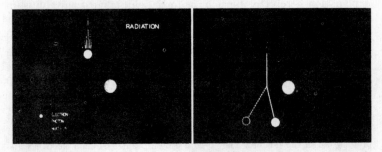

Figure 2. Schematic diagram showing the radiation of light (*Bremsstrahlung*)

seen in the illustration, the deflected electron emits a quantum of
light.

If we now combine these three processes, pair creation, pair annihilation, and the emission of light quanta, we are led to the phenomena of cosmic-ray showers. What happens can be described
as follows: First an ultra-high-energy particle, say an electron,
enters the earth's atmosphere. It is deflected by an atomic nucleus
in the atmosphere and emits a very-high-energy quantum of light
(called a photon). This photon, as it passes some other nucleus,
creates a pair; the electron and positron then are deflected in turn
and emit more photons, which in turn create more pairs. The positrons created may annihilate with atomic electrons, thus producing

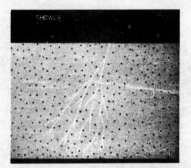

Figure 3. Schematic diagram showing formation of a shower

more photons. We now have an avalanche effect, an avalanche of
electrons, positrons, and photons. Such an avalanche is called a
shower. Now, of course, this process cannot continue forever because eventually the energy which the emitted photons have is too
low to enable them to go on and create pairs. When this point is
reached, the shower ceases to grow. This effect is illustrated in
Figures 3 and 4. Figure 3 illustrates schematically what happens
when a cosmic-ray particle initiates a shower in the atmosphere.
A cosmic-ray particle is a particle which enters the atmosphere
from interstellar space and then produces avalanches of the type
described above. Figure 4 shows an actual photograph of a shower
in a cloud chamber. The thin, dark, horizontal regions are metal
plates in the chamber which place a great many atomic nuclei in
the path of a cosmic-ray particle. This means that the shower de-

velops much faster than it would in the atmosphere. This is then an example wherein a very large number of pairs have been produced by photons passing near the nuclei in the metal plates. The picture is a striking illustration of how quickly and dramatically this avalanche develops.

Figure 4. Cloud chamber photograph showing the formation of a shower

We now have increased our number of elementary particles to four: the electron, the positron, the neutron, and the proton. Before leaving the energy region of nuclear physics, the region we have called Region III, we should mention another process which involves electrons and nuclear particles and which brings yet another particle into the picture. This process is called beta decay. It is connected with the surprising fact that the neutron is not a stable system but that it lives on the average for only 10 minutes or so, after which time it disintegrates into a proton and an electron. It must be stressed that, in general, this can happen only for a free neutron; if the neutron is in a nucleus, it may or may not be able to disintegrate as described. The reason for this will be explained below.

Let us now focus our attention on the decay of the free neutron and see how this new particle arises. To begin, we know that the neutron is a little heavier than the proton, and this mass difference has been measured quite accurately. Now we must bear in mind that the Einstein law is a precise statement that any decrease in mass is directly proportional to an increase in energy, $(\Delta E) = -(\Delta m)c^2$, where ΔE is the change in energy and (Δm) the change in mass, while c is the velocity of light. This law has been verified in a great variety of nuclear experiments, and we would abandon it only under great duress. Let us apply it to the beta decay of the neutron. Before the disintegration we have a neutron, and afterward we have a proton and electron. We know the masses of all the particles involved precisely, and so we know that the electron plus proton are somewhat lighter than the neutron. There has been a decrease of mass therefore, and so we would expect this to appear in the form of kinetic energy for the proton and electron. More precisely, we would expect the proton and electron to leave the site of the disintegration with a well-defined amount of kinetic energy, as given by the Einstein formula when Δm is made equal to the difference in mass between the neutron and the proton plus electron. When we do the experiment, however, we find to our amazement that the proton and electron do not always have this value of the kinetic energy; what we find in fact is that this kinetic energy can be anything between zero and the value we would have expected it to be in each and every disintegration. We are now faced with a difficult decision: We must either abandon the concept of conservation of energy (Einstein's law) or we must assume that we have not given a full description of the beta decay of the neutron; that is, that we have left something out of the picture, and so we get an apparent violation of basic principles. In physics, when we are faced with such a choice, we always try not to abandon a successful basic principle, such as Einstein's law; for if we did abandon it just because of one experiment, we would be faced with the terrible problem of explaining a vast number of other experiments which appear to vindicate the principle. Hence we take the other alternative, if possible, and assume that our description of the process, in this case beta decay, is incomplete. What we do in fact is to postulate that, when the neutron disintegrates, not only the proton and electron result, but a third particle is emitted as well. This other particle carries off just the amount of energy required to satisfy the Einstein relation:

$$\text{(mass of neutron)}c^2 = \text{(mass of proton plus electron plus third particle)}c^2$$
$$+ \text{(kinetic energy of proton plus electron plus third particle)}.$$

From considerations which will not be discussed here, this postulated particle would have to have a mass far smaller than that of the electron, and at present the experimental data indicate that the mass could, in fact, be zero. Clearly this particle would have to be uncharged, since the sum of the charges of the proton and the electron already equals that of the neutron (zero). This particle is called the neutrino. Owing to the fact that it has no charge, it cannot ionize the gas in the cloud chambers, and so it is not observed directly.

Before leaving the subject of beta decay, let us look briefly into the beta decay of nuclei. Thus far we have considered the disintegration of the free neutron, but now we come to the question of when a neutron inside a nucleus can undergo beta decay. Consider for a moment the history of such an event; to begin with we have a nucleus with Z protons and N neutrons. If a neutron decays, we are left with a nucleus of $(Z + 1)$ protons and $(N - 1)$ neutrons plus an emitted electron (and neutrino). Just as in a chemical reaction, this process will occur spontaneously only if the residual nucleus with $(Z + 1)$ protons and $(N - 1)$ neutrons is more stable than the original one; otherwise, the process cannot take place. In nuclei, however, another interesting beta-type decay process can go on. This is the case where one proton disintegrates into a neutron, positron (positively charged electron), and neutrino. In such a reaction, a nucleus which originally had Z protons and N neutrons is transformed into one with $(Z - 1)$ protons and $(N + 1)$ neutrons.

As before, this process will occur only if the residual nucleus is more stable than the original one. Now it should be noted that a free proton, like the one in the hydrogen atom, cannot decay into a neutron plus positron plus neutrino, simply because the proton is lighter than the neutron. If the proton finds itself within a nucleus, however, this mass deficit can be made up by the kinetic energy of the other protons and neutrons in the nucleus, and so the positron emitting beta decay becomes possible. As a last word on the subject of beta decay, it should be mentioned that in all beta-decay processes, whether the observed emitted particle be a positron or electron, the energy balance requires the existence of a third neutral, extremely light particle, the neutrino. Indirect evidence concerning the existence of the neutrino may be obtained from studying the direction in which the nucleus recoils during the disintegration. Experiments of this type give a strong indication that a third particle, which we have called the neutrino, participates in the beta-decay process.

In order to explain the next chapter in the story of the elementary particles, it will be necessary to return for a moment to the electromagnetic field and its light quanta, the photons. Let us consider two fundamental aspects of the electromagnetic field. First of all we know that if we have a stationary charge, such as a proton sitting still, it is surrounded by an electric field whose strength decreases as the inverse square of the distance from the proton. The proton is said to be the source of the electric field. Now the second aspect which we want to consider is the field without a charge, such as a radio or light wave, which can propagate in a region where there are no charges present. Here we see the field as something independent of a source charge. How is this field produced in the first place? Well, we had said before that a charge in acceleration will radiate a light quantum (see Figure 2). In an antenna, the oscillating voltage accelerates billions of electrons and these in turn emit vast numbers of quanta, which combine to form the radio wave. We can then say that the quanta, or photons, are pieces of electromagnetic field which have made themselves independent. They are the basic building blocks of the electromagnetic field, and all electromagnetic phenomena may be explained in terms of their behavior, just as one could explain the behavior of gases in terms of atoms.

Now we may consider once again the nuclear forces which bind the neutrons and protons in the nucleus. It is tempting to describe the nuclear force also as a kind of force field around nuclear particles as sources, just as we had the electric force field around charges. This force field should surround both neutrons and protons; it should also be very strong and extend only for a short distance away from the source particle. At this point the famous Japanese physicist, Yukawa, asked the following question: Let us extend this analogy with the electromagnetic field; what are then the quanta of this nuclear force field? Further, if we strongly accelerate a proton or neutron, will it then emit (radiate) a quantum of the nuclear force field? This is a very daring conjecture, but Yukawa went even further, in a way which is difficult to explain without mathematics. It will be noted that an important difference between the electric and nuclear fields is that the former is inversely proportional to the square of the distance, while the latter vanishes for extremely small distances. Now Yukawa found that this characteristic difference manifests itself also in the field quanta. While the quanta of the electromagnetic field have no mass, Yukawa found that the quanta of a short-range field must have mass. In fact, Yukawa found that the value of the rest mass has a direct connection with the range (i.e., the greatest distance at which the force acts) of the nuclear force: if μ is the mass of the quantum, h is Planck's constant, c the speed of light, and d the range, then $\mu = h/dc$. Since one knows d fairly well, one finds that μ is some 200 to 300 times the electron mass. According to the Einstein relation, this field quantum of Yukawa would have a rest energy of 100 to 150 Mev, and so a proton which has more energy than this should be able to emit the field quantum during a severe deflection such as it would suffer upon impinging on a nucleus. The great triumph of Yukawa's speculation occurred when shortly afterward (1937) particles of mass 200 were found in the cosmic-ray showers. These particles were, of course, tentatively identified as Yukawa's meson.

A word of caution is necessary at this point. It will be noted that we have now left the region of several million electron volts and have gone up to 100 Mev and more. In the lower energy region, most of what has been described above is fairly well established, and we really know a considerable amount about electrons, positrons, photons, protons, neutrons, and neutrinos. But what we have just said about mesons and what will be discussed below is of a very tentative nature. In a discussion of this sort it is always difficult to distinguish clearly between what is well established and what is still in the speculative stage of development.

With this in mind let us return to Yukawa. It was pointed out that a particle of about 200 (electron masses) was found in the cosmic radiation. We shall call this particle the μ-meson. Yukawa also predicted that these mesons should be charged. This is quite different from the photons, which are uncharged. The meson of Yukawa should therefore ionize the vapors in the cloud chamber and be deflected by electric and magnetic fields. These properties make detection much easier than if they were uncharged. The μ-mesons, first found in 1937, were charged, and their discovery was considered to be a great triumph for Yukawa's analogy between the electromagnetic and nuclear force field. But, unfortunately, things were not nearly so simple. The remainder of this discussion will consist of a description of new complications and unexpected phenomena. New unexplained problems will be raised, and it will be evident that the solutions to these problems are not in sight as yet.

To begin with, let us return to the μ-mesons. One would expect them to be produced by a cosmic-ray proton striking a nucleus in the atmosphere. Since the protons have the greatest energy at the highest altitudes, and since more mesons should be produced in an energetic collision, one would expect that the intensity of mesons should increase with altitude. This was found to be so. If these μ-mesons are actually quanta of the nuclear field, we would expect to observe the inverse process to emission, namely, absorption. That is, a μ-meson hitting a nucleus should be absorbed just as an atom can absorb a light quantum. We would therefore expect μ-mesons to be strongly absorbed in matter. At this point we come to the first failure of the theory. It was that μ-mesons were not absorbed at all in matter. As a matter of fact, they are extremely penetrating and may even be detected in mines far below the earth's surface. Thus we are apparently faced with the first breakdown of Yukawa's theoretical picture; although these μ-mesons are produced in energetic nuclear collisions, they are not absorbed by nuclei.

This mystery concerning the μ-meson has now been cleared up to a certain extent. The clarification occurred in 1947 and is due to an English physicist, Powell, who was studying cosmic-ray events in photographic emulsions exposed at very high altitudes. Powell discovered that when a cosmic-ray proton hits a nucleus, charged particles of approximately 300 electron masses are emitted. After about 10^{-8} second, these particles suddenly change their path in the emulsion, and the track they then leave is thinner. By studying the second part of the track one finds that the particle now has about 200 electron masses. This second part of the track is left by a particle which we now identify as the μ-meson and which we have already considered. The first part of the track is left by some new particle which is now called the π-meson. Clearly, then, the particle people had been observing before Powell, the μ-meson, is not produced itself during the nuclear collision. What is produced is the π-meson. This π-meson also has been shown to exhibit another very important property: It is found to be very readily absorbed by atomic nuclei. Hence, it is just this π-meson, and not the μ-meson, that is produced in nuclear collisions, and it is absorbed by nuclei.

Figure 5 shows an example of the absorption of a π-meson. On the left we have a nucleus which has exploded after being struck by a cosmic-ray particle. It emits several π-mesons, one of which strikes another nucleus before it decays. This is seen in the lower part of the picture; the absorption of the π-meson has caused this nucleus to be highly excited, and this excitation has been dissipated by the emission of other particles, including π-mesons, which are seen in the emulsion.

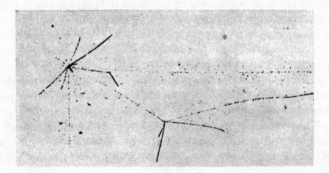

Figure 5. Nuclear emulsion showing production and absorption of π-meson

This explains why one saw only μ-mesons before: The π-meson is easily absorbed, and if it should survive absorption, it decays into a μ-meson after 10^{-8} second. Now it should be pointed out that the π-meson cannot decay into a μ-meson alone, since this would not conserve energy and momentum. Some other particle must be emitted during the decay. Since the charge of the μ-meson equals that of the π-meson, this other particle must be neutral and we believe it to be the neutrino. However, the story is not yet complete. It has been found that the μ-meson is also unstable, and after about one-millionth of a second it decays into an electron (and probably neutrinos in order to conserve momentum).

Figure 6. Nuclear emulsion showing decay of π-meson to μ-meson,
with subsequent decay of μ-meson to electron

In Figure 6 we can see the entire chain of events in the life history of the mesons, with the π-meson playing the role of grandfather and the electron that of grandson. In this actual photograph we see a rather heavy track left by a slow π-meson traveling upward; it then decays into a μ-meson which travels to the right, leaving a somewhat lighter track; after about one-millionth of a second the μ-meson decays and sends the grandson, the electron, off in the upward direction.

The experimenters have now discovered positively and negatively charged π- and μ-mesons. Moreover, they have found a neutral π-meson which decays into two light quanta after the extremely short time interval of 10^{-15} second. This neutral π-meson is also produced in nuclear collisions and, like its charged brothers, is very easily absorbed by nuclei. The properties of the various mesons are given in Table 1.

Let us now take stock of the meson situation. We have seen that the π-meson family (charged and neutral ones) is easily produced in very energetic nuclear collisions; the π-mesons are also absorbed

quite readily by nuclei. The mass of these particles agrees quite
well with the predictions of Yukawa. So one is very tempted to say
that the π-mesons are actually the quanta of the nuclear force field.
But the analogy with the electromagnetic field is really quite weak
now because these π-mesons are very unstable (we have seen that
they live for 10^{-8} or 10^{-15} second, depending on their charge),

Table 1. Properties of elementary particles

Particle	Charge	Mass	symbol	Lifetime if isolated	Decay scheme
Photon.......	0	0	ν	Infinite	
Neutrino.....	0	0	ν	Infinite (?)	
Electron......	-1	1	e^-	Infinite	
Positron......	$+1$	1	e^+	Infinite	
Proton.......	$+1$	1836	p	Infinite	
Neutron......	0	1839	n	10 minutes	$n \rightarrow p + e^- + \nu$
μ-Meson......	$+1$	207	μ^+	10^{-6}second	$\mu^+ \rightarrow e^+ + 2\nu$
μ-Meson......	-1	207	μ^-	10^{-6}second	$\mu^- \rightarrow e^- + 2\nu$
π-Meson......	$+1$	273	π^+	10^{-8}second	$\pi^+ \rightarrow \mu^+ + \nu$
π-Meson......	-1	273	π^-	10^{-8}second	$\pi^- \rightarrow \mu^- + \nu$
π·Meson......	0	265	π^0	10^{-15}second	$\pi^0 \rightarrow 2\gamma$
τ-Meson......	$+1$	966	τ^+	10^{-8}second	$\tau^+ \rightarrow 2\pi^+ + \pi^-$
τ-Meson......	-1	966	τ^-	10^{-8}second	$\tau^- \rightarrow 2\pi^- + \pi^+$
θ^0-Meson.....	0	966	θ^0	10^{-10}second	$\theta^0 \rightarrow \pi^+ + \pi^-$
$\theta^\pm$-Meson.....	± 1	~950	$\theta^\pm$	10^{-8}–10^{-9}second	$\theta^\pm \rightarrow \pi^\pm + \pi^0$
κ-Meson......	Charged	~920	κ	10^{-8}second	$\kappa^\pm \rightarrow \mu^\pm + \nu$
Λ^0 Particle...	0	2180	Λ^0	10^{-10}second	$\Lambda^0 \rightarrow p + \pi^-$
Σ Particle....	$+1$	2330	Σ^+	10^{-10}second	$\Sigma^+ \rightarrow p + \pi^0$
Σ Particle....	-1	2330	Σ^-	10^{-10}second	$\Sigma^- \rightarrow n + \pi^-$
Cascade particle....	-1	~2600	Y^-	?	$Y^- \rightarrow \Lambda^0 + \pi^-$

while the quanta of the electromagnetic field are perfectly stable.
So there seems to be a certain amount of truth in Yukawa's original
proposal, but it is extremely difficult to say just how much. After
all, why do the π-mesons decay into μ-mesons? And, furthermore,
what role do these μ-mesons play? They are the corpses of π-mesons
which have lost their ability to interact with nuclei; after a microsecond they decay into an electron and a pair of neutrinos. It is not
clear why nature needs these particles; as far as we can see they play
a completely superfluous role in the whole scheme. These last few

questions are certainly among the most important ones which physics is attacking today, and their resolution is not in sight.

The phenomena we have just described take place in the region of a few hundred million electron volts. Suppose we now consider what takes place at still higher energies. Until recently our knowledge of this region was entirely due to the cosmic-ray people, but the Brookhaven cosmotron now enables us to reach such energies in the laboratory. In this ultra-high-energy region, quite a few new types of particles have been found. Some of them have been seen only a very few times, and very little is known about them. However, two types of particles are known somewhat better than the others, although it should be pointed out once more that everything we know about these phenomena is very tentative.

The first group of particles have a mass of about 1000 times that of the electron. There are charged and neutral ones, and they decay in various ways. One, in particular, is called a τ-meson and decays into three π-mesons after a life of about 10^{-8} second.

The second group of particles are also unstable, and they decay into protons or neutrons. The best known of these is the Λ^0 particle. The designation Λ (inverted V) is because of the way it looks in the cloud chamber pictures, and the zero because it is uncharged. To the best of our very limited knowledge, the Λ^0 particle is an excited proton which, after 10^{-10} second, decays into a proton and a negatively charged π-meson. The appearance of such a particle could mean that we have now reached energies sufficiently high so as to excite the internal structure of the neutron and proton.

It will be recalled that at sufficiently low energies, atoms, nuclei, etc., all looked like elementary particles. As soon as the energy is sufficient to excite the first quantum state of the system, we have to take its internal structure into account. Now we could, by analogy, say that the Λ^0 particle is actually the first quantum state of the proton. This then decays by the emission of a field quantum, the π-meson, just as the excited state of an atom decays by the emission of a light quantum. One should not think that this is the correct description of the Λ^0 particle; it is simply a rough idea. In fact, if the Λ^0 particle were just an excited proton, one would expect it to have a much shorter life than the observed value. Thus, there are many unsolved problems here.

We turn now to two photographs showing the decay of the

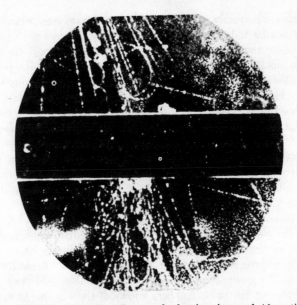

Figure 7. Cloud chamber photograph showing decay of Λ^0 particle

Figure 8. Cloud chamber photograph showing decay of Λ^0 particle into a proton
and a negative π-meson. Cloud chamber in magnetic field

Λ^0 particle. In the first one (Figure 7) a cosmic-ray particle has initiated a nuclear explosion in the lead plate inserted in the cloud chamber (dark horizontal region). A Λ^0 particle is emitted in the explosion, and in the lower right-hand part of the photograph, one can see the Λ-shaped decay of this particle into a proton and π-meson. In Figure 8 we again see the decay of a Λ^0 particle. This cloud chamber has been placed in a magnetic field, and, as we know, charged particles have circular orbits in such fields. The direction of the curvature is determined by the sign of the charge, and the magnitude by its mass and velocity. In Figure 8 the lighter track which curves to the right is a negatively charged π-meson, while the heavier track is the proton. The proton is seen to curve slightly to the left. This picture shows that the two particles have opposite charge, as required by the fact that the Λ^0 particle is electrically neutral.

To summarize then, these new particles present us with a wealth of unsolved problems. We have the π-mesons, which bear some resemblance to Yukawa's nuclear field quanta, but we do not understand why they remain active only for 10^{-8} second and then decay into the inactive μ-mesons. The μ-mesons are even more mysterious particles. Unstable themselves, they play an unknown role in nature. Moreover, we have found a host of other unstable particles: The particles of mass near 1000 electron masses, of which the τ-meson is an example, and the Λ^0 particles of a mass larger than that of a proton or a neutron, which decay into a proton or a neutron with the emission of a π-meson.

All these particles are formed by collisions of very-high-energy particles with the neutrons and protons in atomic nuclei. Surely these processes are indications of an internal structure of the elementary particles, proton and neutron. It is again the same step which we have observed so often: At low energies (less than one electron volt) atoms act as elementary particles until an energy is reached (one electron volt) at which their internal structure responds. It was found to consist of electrons and nuclei. At still higher energies ($>$ one million electron volts) the internal structure of the nuclei begins to respond and the nuclei cease to act like elementary particles. We find protons and neutrons bound by nuclear forces in different configurations. When energies greater than 100 Mev come into play, the internal structure of the protons and neutrons reveals itself in a way which is as yet not understood. New particles, mesons of different character, are created, which decay according to a mysterious pattern. This pattern contains the answers to many questions regarding the nature of our elementary particles, but we have not yet learned how to read it.

Electronuclear Machines

LELAND J. HAWORTH

Introduction

Electronuclear machines, more generally called particle accelerators, have played a vital role in the development of nuclear science and technology. Although we shall be concerned primarily with the basic principles, the design, and the performance of the machines themselves, it will be useful to begin with a brief description of this role.

Although it is possible to glean much information by observing the interactions of whole nuclei with atomic and with externally applied electric and magnetic fields, detailed knowledge of internal structure, the forces between constituent elementary particles, the internal energy states, etc., can best be studied by methods in which nuclei are disturbed internally, either spontaneously or by bombardment with energetic particles or photons. It is the function of the particle accelerators to provide these bombarding particles.

Before the advent of particle accelerators, intranuclear experiments were confined to the use of naturally radioactive substances and cosmic rays. Detailed observations had been made of the various radioactive chains of the heavy elements by Becquerel, the Curies, Rutherford, and many others. Energetic particles derived from radioactive sources had also been used for secondary purposes, notably Rutherford's scattering experiments leading to the Rutherford-Bohr atom and observations of artificial transmutation of elements, also first accomplished by Rutherford in 1919. A mass of observational data had been acquired through cosmic rays, but they are few in number and complex in composition, and they cannot be controlled arbitrarily. It was difficult or impossible to perform controlled and quantitatively accurate experiments, and the neutron, a fundamental constituent of compound nuclei, had not yet been discovered. By analogy with the extranuclear case, and from the observations already made, it was recognized that a source of controlled high-energy particles in sufficient quantities would be extremely useful in nuclear experiments. From theoretical considerations heavy nuclear particles, especially protons, gave most promise of results. Since they are positively charged, very high energies seemed essential to enable them to surmount the Coulomb barrier presented by the repulsive forces between like charges and to penetrate the nucleus. Numerous workers were endeavoring in various ways to achieve the required energies, believed to lie in the millions of electron volts. Fortunately, however, as a result of a nuclear model due primarily to Condon, it was suddenly realized that in accordance with principles of quantum mechanics there is a finite probability that the Coulomb barrier will be penetrated by a particle having insufficient energy to surmount that barrier. Taking advantage of this fact, Cockcroft and Walton at the Cavendish Laboratory modified a more ambitious plan, constructed a transformer-rectifier high-voltage source which accelerated protons to approximately 200 kv,[1] and thereby achieved in 1932 the disintegration of lithium 7 into two alpha particles. At about the same time, Van de Graaff at Princeton University devised the electrostatic generator which now bears his name, and Ernest Lawrence at the University of California originated the cyclotron, the forebearer of all modern magnetic accelerators. The era of electronuclear machines was born.

Accelerators are now used in three different ways: first, to observe the direct and immediate effects resulting from bombardment of nuclei by the accelerated particles, such as electrons, protons, deuterons, and alpha particles; second, to produce secondary particles, such as gamma rays, neutrons, and mesons, which are in turn used in direct experiments; third, to produce radioactive nuclei by transmutation or excitation, these product nuclei being studied, often at remote locations, as they decay toward stable states.

Accelerators come in diverse shapes and sizes, determined by the experiments to be performed, the technical possibilities and limitations of the machines themselves, and, increasingly, the purse strings of the builder. They are characterized by a number of parameters, among them the type of accelerated particles and the numbers accelerated; the maximum energy achievable and the flexibility of

---

[1] The units will be defined in the following pages.

its control; the homogeneity and the focal properties of the particle beam; the geometrical arrangement, particularly as it applies to the required location of the targets; the level of background radiation compared to that utilized in the actual experiments; and the time dependence of the beam, whether continuous or pulsed in character. In attempting to improve these characteristics, the greatest effort over the past two decades has been to increase the particle energy, since it is this parameter which determines the variety of possible phenomena. We will, therefore, consider the technology, with energy as the central theme. Furthermore, since the search for higher and higher energies has followed a natural progression from simple to more and more complex machines, it will be both interesting and instructive to follow the historical development.

Particle Electrodynamics

Before discussing the technical designs of the various accelerators, let us consider certain of the applicable equations of particle dynamics. Since the velocities of our particles in general will not be negligible compared to the velocity of light, we must use the precise equations of relativity theory and utilize the familiar approximations of classical dynamics only under special circumstances. Although it is not within our scope to develop relativity theory, it will be helpful to derive the specific equations we need in terms of familiar concepts. Let us, then, assume without proof the familiar equation of Einstein, expressing the equivalence of mass and energy:

$$E = mc^2, \tag{1}$$

where c is the velocity of light. By this equation, a particle at rest possesses a "rest" energy

$$E_0 = m_0 c^2, \tag{1a}$$

where m_0 is the "rest" mass. When in motion, the particle has a total energy

$$E = mc^2 = E_0 + T = m_0 c^2 + T, \tag{2}$$

where T is the kinetic energy. Thus the mass is not constant but varies in accordance with

$$m = m_0 + \frac{T}{c^2}.$$

In ordinary terrestrial mechanics, T is so small compared to m_0c^2 that the change in mass can be neglected and $m \cong m_0$. For example a projectile traveling at 1500 fps has a kinetic energy which is only about one billion billionth of its rest energy.

Newton's laws of motion are fully valid in any system, providing this change in mass is borne in mind. In particular, by the second law, Force = time rate of change of momentum

$$F = \frac{dp}{dt} = \frac{d(mv)}{dt} = m\frac{dv}{dt} + v\frac{dm}{dt}. \tag{3}$$

(Note that this gives the classical approximation $F = ma$ when the change in mass can be neglected.)

By the definitions of work and energy, Force $\times$ distance = work = change in kinetic energy = change in total energy, or

$$Fds = dT = dE,$$

whence

$$F\frac{ds}{dt} = Fv = \frac{dT}{dt} = c^2\frac{dm}{dt}. \tag{4}$$

From (3) and (4),

$$v\frac{dp}{dt} = \frac{dE}{dt}.$$

Multiplying by $m = E/c^2$,

$$mv\frac{dp}{dt} = p\frac{dp}{dt} = \frac{E}{c^2}\frac{dE}{dt}.$$

Integrating

$$\tfrac{1}{2}p^2 \Big|_0^p = \tfrac{1}{2}p^2 = \frac{E^2}{2c^2}\Big|_{E_0}^{E} = \frac{1}{2c^2}(E^2 - E_0^2),$$

whence

$$p = mv = \frac{1}{c}\sqrt{E^2 - E_0^2}$$

$$= \frac{1}{c}\sqrt{(E_0 + T)^2 - E_0^2} = \frac{1}{c}\sqrt{T(2E_0 + T)}, \tag{5}$$

an extremely importance equation in particle accelerators.

For the classical case of $T \ll E$,

$$p = mv \cong m_0 v \cong \frac{1}{c} \sqrt{2 E_0 T} = \frac{1}{c} \sqrt{2 m_0 c^2 T} = \sqrt{2 m_0 T}, \quad (5a)$$

whence

$$T = \frac{p^2}{2 m_0} = \tfrac{1}{2} m_0 v^2.$$

At the other extreme, when $T \gg E_0$.

$$p = mv \cong \frac{E}{c} \cong \frac{T}{c}. \quad (5b)$$

Thus in the classical case T is quadratic in the momentum, and in the completely "relativistic" case the relationship is linear.

Certain alternative forms of Equation 5 are useful. Solving for v,

$$v = \frac{1}{mc} \sqrt{E^2 - E_0{}^2} = \frac{c}{E} \sqrt{E^2 - E_0{}^2}$$

$$= c \sqrt{1 - \left(\frac{E_0}{E}\right)^2} = c \sqrt{1 - \left(\frac{E_0}{E_0 + T}\right)^2}, \quad (6)$$

which approaches c as an upper limit when T is very large compared to E_0. It is often convenient to deal with $\beta = v/c$, i.e., to measure velocity relative to that of light. Values of β are plotted as a function

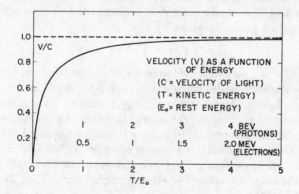

Figure 1. Values $\beta = v/c$ for the proton and the electron plotted as functions of kinetic energy, T, measured in Mev and in units of T/E_0.

of *kinetic* (not *total*) energy for the electron and the proton in Figure 1. We see that the velocity of light is closely approached by electrons of a few Mev (million electron volts) energy, but by protons only in the Bev (billion electron volts) range.

Returning to Equation 5,

$$m^2v^2 = \frac{1}{c^2}(E^2 - E_0^2) = c^2(m^2 - m_0^2),$$

whence

$$m = \frac{m_0}{\sqrt{1 - (v/c)^2}} = \frac{m_0}{\sqrt{1 - \beta^2}} \text{ and } E = \frac{E_0}{\sqrt{1 - \beta^2}}, \qquad (7)$$

expressing the mass and the energy as functions of velocity. It is clear that to achieve the velocity of light completely would require infinite energy and would result in infinite mass.

In the classical case of $v \ll c$ (i.e., $\beta \ll 1$), $m \cong m_0$ and is essentially constant. In the case of our projectile, for example, $\sqrt{1 - \beta^2} \cong 1 - (1.1 \times 10^{-12})$, confirming our previous calculation.

In accelerators we are primarily concerned with the behavior of charged particles under the influence of electric and magnetic fields. In all cases the kinetic energy results from the force exerted on the particle by an electric field. This force is given by

$$F = eX,$$

where e is the charge on the particle and X is the strength of the electric field. The kinetic energy, T, imparted to a particle in moving between two points is given by

$$T = \int F dx = \int eX dx = eV, \qquad (8)$$

where V is the potential difference between the points in question; T is measured in joules when e is in coulombs and V is in volts. In nuclear physics, however, the energy is commonly expressed in "electron volts," that is, the energy acquired by an electron (or an equally charged proton) in passing through a potential difference of one volt. In our field of interest, energies·are usually measured in thousands of electron volts (Kev), millions of electron volts (Mev), or, in the extreme, billions of electron volts (Bev). Then Equation 8 can be written

$$\overline{T} = \bar{e}V, \qquad (8a)$$

where $\bar{e}$ is measured in units of the electronic charge and $\overline{T}$ is in terms of units corresponding to those in which V is measured. Often the world electron is omitted for brevity, and we speak of volts, millions of volts, billions of volts, etc.

A charged particle *moving* in a magnetic field experiences a force which is perpendicular to the direction of the field and to the direction of motion of the particle. This force is given by

$$F = Hev, \qquad (9)$$

where v is the velocity of the particle and H is the component of the magnetic field which is perpendicular to the motion. Since the force is perpendicular to the motion, no work is accomplished and the particle gains no energy. Instead, it is deflected in a circular path and by the laws of mechanics:

$$F = Hev = \frac{mv^2}{\rho}, \qquad (10)$$

where ρ is the radius of curvature and mv^2/ρ is the centrifugal force. Recasting and using Equation 5,

$$H\rho = \frac{mv}{e} = \frac{p}{e} = \frac{1}{ce} \sqrt{E^2 - E_0{}^2} = \frac{1}{ce} \sqrt{T(2E_0 + T)}, \qquad (11)$$

an extremely important equation for magnetic accelerators. For the "classical" approximation at low energies,

$$H\rho \cong \frac{1}{ce} \sqrt{2E_0 T} = \frac{1}{e} \sqrt{2m_0 T}. \qquad (11a)$$

For the completely relativistic case,

$$H\rho \cong \frac{E}{ce} \cong \frac{T}{ce}, \qquad (11b)$$

the first approximation being more accurate than the second.

$H\rho$ is plotted as a function of kinetic energy for protons and for electrons in Figure 2.

In a uniform field the particle revolves in a circle with a frequency

$$f = \frac{v}{2\pi\rho} = \frac{He}{2\pi m} = \frac{Hec^2}{2\pi E} = \frac{Hec^2}{2\pi(E_0 + T)}, \qquad (12)$$

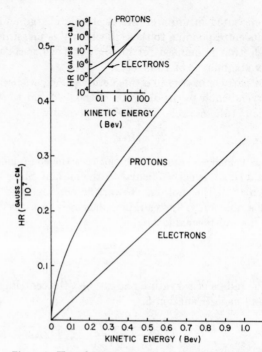

Figure 2. $H\rho$ vs kinetic energy for protons and electrons.
(Note logarithmic scales in insert.)

which decreases with increasing kinetic energy. In the extreme of $T \ll E_0$ we have

$$f \cong \frac{He}{2\pi m_0} = \frac{Hec^2}{2\pi E_0}. \tag{12a}$$

That is, to a high degree of approximation, f is constant.

Any consistent set of units such as those of the cgs or the M.K.S. systems will, of course, satisfy the above equations. It is often convenient for numerical calculations, however, to use certain units peculiar to particle dynamics. Table 1 indicates the conversions we will make from the cgs system and the symbols that will be used.

Some of the equations which will be used numerically are given in Table 2 in combined cgs and nuclear units. The velocity of light in centimeters per second (3×10^{10}) has been substituted for c where it appears.

TABLE 1

e (electromagnetic units) $= \dfrac{e}{10}$ (coulombs) $= \bar{e}$ (electronic units) $\times 1.6 \times 10^{-20}$

E, E_0, T (ergs) $= \bar{E}, \bar{E}_0, \bar{T}$ (Mev) $\times 1.6 \times 10^{-6}$

m (grams) $= \bar{m}$ (atomic units) $\times 1.66 \times 10^{-24}$

v (cm/sec) $= \beta \times 3 \times 10^{10}$

H (gauss) $= \bar{H}$ (kilogauss) $\times 10^3$

TABLE 2

$$\bar{E} = 931\bar{m} \tag{1'}$$

$$\beta = \sqrt{1 - (\bar{m}_0/\bar{m})^2} = \sqrt{1 - (\bar{E}_0/\bar{E})^2} = \sqrt{1 - (\bar{E}_0/(\bar{E}_0 + \bar{T}))^2} \tag{6'}$$

$$\bar{m} = \bar{m}_0/\sqrt{1 - \beta^2} \qquad \bar{E} = \bar{E}_0/\sqrt{1 - \beta^2} \tag{7'}$$

$$\bar{T} = \bar{e}\bar{v} \tag{8'}$$

$$\bar{H}\rho = \frac{3.11\bar{m}\beta}{\bar{e}} \times 10^3 = \frac{10}{3\bar{e}}\sqrt{\bar{E}^2 - \bar{E}_0^2} = \frac{10}{3\bar{e}}\sqrt{\bar{T}(2\bar{E}_0 + \bar{T})} \tag{11'}$$

$$\bar{H}\rho = \frac{10}{3\bar{e}}\sqrt{2\bar{E}_0\bar{T}} = 0.0432\sqrt{\bar{m}_0\bar{T}} \qquad \text{when } \bar{T} \ll \bar{E}_0 \tag{11a'}$$

$$\bar{H}\rho = \frac{10^4}{3\bar{e}}\bar{T} \qquad \text{when } \bar{T} \gg \bar{E}_0 \tag{11b'}$$

$$f = \frac{1.54\,\bar{H}\bar{e}}{\bar{m}} = \frac{1435\,\bar{H}\bar{e}}{\bar{E}} = \frac{1435\,\bar{H}\bar{e}}{\bar{E}_0 + \bar{T}} \text{ Megacycles/sec.} \tag{12'}$$

TABLE 3

	Electron	Proton	Deuteron
$\bar{e}$ (electronic units)............	-1	1	1
$\bar{m}_0$ (atomic units).............	5×10^{-4}	1.008	1.016
$\bar{E}_0 = m_0 c^2$(Mev)	0.51	938	1877

The constants of the particles of principal interest are given in Table 3.

Constant Potential Accelerators

In the simplest—and historically the first successful—accelerators, the particles are accelerated inside a highly evacuated tube (Figure 3) with a particle source at one end and the target at the other, the requisite electric field being produced by a d-c potential difference applied between source and target.

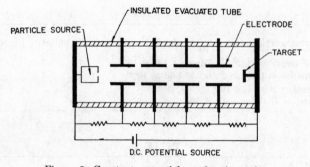

Figure 3. Constant potential accelerating tube.

In an electron accelerator the source is a hot cathode. In a heavy particle (proton, deuteron, etc.) accelerator, an electrical discharge in an appropriate gas produces the desired stripped nuclei, some of which pass through a fine channel in a gas-containing barrier and into the accelerating tube proper.

The electrode structure along the tube serves several purposes— to shield the tube walls, to distribute the potential difference more or less uniformly along the tube and hence reduce the breakdowns from large, localized gradients, and to focus the particles into a beam. The desired potential distribution is achieved by appropriate resistor networks or by corona discharges between points outside the accelerating tube.

The focusing action of the electric field between electrodes is illustrated in Figure 4. As can be seen, to the left of the central plane of the gap the electric field has a component toward the axis and, to the right, a component outward. A particle passing down the axis is undeviated. In any other position, the particle is deflected *toward* the axis until it reaches the central plane and away from the axis thereafter. Since, however, the particle has been accelerated in the

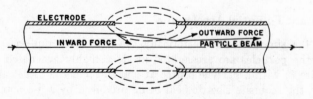

Figure 4. Principle of electrostatic focusing.

process, the time duration of the *outward* force is less than was that of the *inward* force, resulting in a net converging effect, analogous to that of a converging optical lens. (The reverse would, of course, be true of a decelerating field.) Hence a series of accelerating gaps behaves like a series of lenses and may be used to produce a sharply focused beam at the target.

Direct-current potential differences have been applied to such accelerating tubes by two general methods, transformer-rectifiers and electrostatic generators. Cockcroft and Walton used a voltage-multiplying transformer-rectifier set for the first successful nuclear studies with laboratory accelerated particles. Their original 200-Kev machine, and improved versions at the Cavendish Laboratory and elsewhere, contributed much to early work in the field and many are still in useful operation. The upper energy limit has been, however, in the range from a few hundred kilovolts to approximately one million volts.

Of more lasting importance has been the electrostatic generator, originally devised by Van de Graaff, which establishes a potential difference by mechanically transferring electrostatic charges between points through the medium of a nonconducting belt driven by a motor. As illustrated in Figure 5, charge is sprayed onto the belt from needle points raised to a potential of several kilovolts by a transformer-rectifier source. On arriving inside the hollow metal electrode at the opposite end of the belt arrangement, the charge is

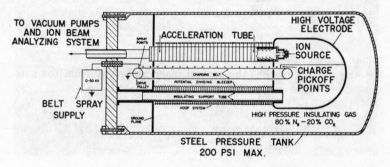

Figure 5. Schematic of electrostatic (Van de Graaff) generator. The "hoop system" consists of circular metal rings surrounding the tube and belt and serves to distribute the electric field uniformly. Permission of Brookhaven National Laboratory

removed by a second electrode and, in accordance with well-known processes, passes to the outside of the sphere and raises its potential. In the absence of a useful load, the potential is finally limited by breakdown along the accelerating tube, the belt, and the supporting structure, and by corona discharge into the surrounding air. The potential can be very accurately controlled through the rate of charging of the belt and by the use of controlled corona discharges.

The potential realizable in an open Van de Graaff generator is limited to a value of one or two million volts, depending on the size and design of the machine. Consequently, since the very early days, most such accelerators have been enclosed in large steel tanks, pressurized to several atmospheres by nitrogen (air involves a fire hazard) together with some discharge inhibiting vapor such as Freon. Under these conditions the upper potential limit is usually fixed by discharges inside the accelerating tubes. Up to several million volts it is possible to operate satisfactorily with a tube gradient of about one-half million volts per foot. For reasons not entirely understood, however, a sufficiently uniform gradient has not yet been achieved for total potentials of more than seven or eight million volts. A typical Van de Graaff generator is pictured in Figure 6.

Figure 6. Four Mev proton Van de Graaff generator used as injector for Brookhaven cosmotron. The large cylinder, serving as an equipotential surface at an intermediate voltage, conceals the high electrode and part of the voltage column. Permission of Brookhaven National Laboratory

Charging currents of many milliamperes have been achieved by the use of multiple belts. Comparable beams of accelerated electrons have been produced. In heavy particle accelerators, however, useful currents have been restricted to a very few milliamperes by the limitations of positive ion sources so far developed.

The Van de Graaff generator has been and continues to be an extremely important tool in nuclear physics. Within its energy range, it produces much the most uniform, constant, and precisely controllable particle beams available to the nuclear physicist, the energy spread and the variability being in many cases less than 0.1 per cent.

Resonance Acceleration

Linear Resonance

Contemporarily with Cockcroft-Walton and Van de Graaff, another type of accelerator was being considered that was a bit more sophisticated. It was realized that there would be definite upper limits to the potential difference which could be maintained continuously across an accelerating tube. Suppose instead that alternate electrodes are connected to opposite terminals of an oscillating potential source as shown in Figure 7. Then, during one half of the radio frequency cycle, the field will be in a given direction in the odd-numbered gaps and during the other half in the even-numbered gaps. Under the proper relationship between electrode length, particle velocity, and radio frequency, a particle can, therefore, be accelerated in a given gap, "drift" through the field free region inside the next electrode, and arrive at the following gap a half cycle later to be accelerated again, and so on. The total energy is given by NeV, where N is the number of gaps and V is the value of the gap voltage averaged over the various transits. Hence in principle it is possible to accelerate particles to high energies by *successive* energy

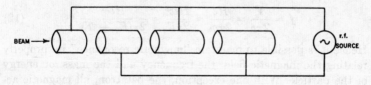

Figure 7. Principle of linear resonance acceleration.

increments without the necessity of maintaining correspondingly high potential differences. Unfortunately, in the early days practical difficulties arose. Clearly the number of electrodes required to achieve a given energy is inversely proportional to the radio frequency voltage; the length of the electrodes is inversely proportional to the frequency. (Note that the electrodes must increase in length as the particles move faster.) The radio-frequency art of those days could not provide adequate combinations of high frequency and high voltage for a practical accelerator. Furthermore, difficulty was anticipated in maintaining proper phase of the particles at each successive gap for systems with very large numbers of electrodes. Hence, although some success was achieved for very heavy ions (v being relatively small, since kinetic energy = $\frac{1}{2}mv^2$), attempts to develop such a radio-frequency "linear accelerator" were abandoned in favor of more promising methods. As will be described later, subsequent technological developments have more recently brought about a revival of radio-frequency linear accelerators.

Magnetic Resonance

Although not of direct practical importance, the early attempts at a linear "resonance" accelerator nevertheless led to the most important single step taken in the entire development of high-energy accelerators. It occurred to Dr. Ernest Lawrence of the University of California, one of the leading workers in the field, that it might be possible to avoid the need for a very long linear device by using repetitive accelerations of particles revolving under the influence of a magnetic field. Crudely put, the linear accelerator might be wrapped into a circle and the same electrodes used over and over again by establishing resonance between the orbital revolution frequency and that of the oscillating field. Fortunately, the equations of electrodynamics are favorable to this concept.

From Equation 11 the revolution frequency is given by

$$f = \frac{V}{2\pi\rho} = \frac{He}{2\pi m} = \frac{Hec^2}{2\pi E} = \frac{Hec^2}{2\pi(E_0 + T)}. \tag{12}$$

Hence it is possible to maintain "magnetic resonance" by properly relating the magnetic field, the frequency and the mass, or energy of the particle. With one exception, the betatron, all magnetic accelerators utilize this principle.

Fixed Magnet Accelerators

The Cyclotron

In considering the possibility of magnetic resonance accelerators Lawrence noted the extremely important fact (Equation 12) that in a uniform magnetic field particles revolve at an essentially constant frequency so long as the kinetic energy is small compared to the rest energy and the mass is essentially constant. Such a condition obtains for heavy particles at the energies of a few million electron volts that Lawrence was endeavoring to attain. As such particles gain energy in a uniform field they travel in larger and larger circles, the radius increasing essentially in proportion to the velocity so that the period of revolution and, hence, the frequency remain essentially constant. In the case of a proton, $\Delta f/f = \overline{T}/931 \cong 0.001\overline{T}$.

Lawrence's accelerator, based on this principle and now familiarly known as the cyclotron, is illustrated schematically in Figure 8. Between flat, cylindrical poles of an electromagnet is placed a pair of hollow electrodes, shaped as though a flat cylindrical copper box had been cut into two semicylinders. The electrodes, called "Dees" from their shape, are driven by a power source of the resonant frequency, which, from Table 2, is approximately 23 megacycles per second for protons in a field of 15,000 gauss. Ions formed in an arc discharge at the center are pulled into a Dee during its negative ex-

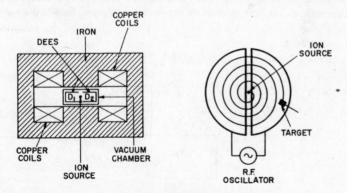

Figure 8. Schematic of the cyclotron. (The plan view is enlarged in comparison with the vertical section.)

cursion. Deflected by the magnetic field, they subsequently enter the gap between Dees and are further accelerated by the field, which has meanwhile reversed. During each successive half cycle of the radio frequency they traverse a semicircle in the field free region within a Dee, re-entering the gap at the proper phase to receive further acceleration. As their energy increases, so does the radius of curvature so that a spiral path is traversed toward the periphery of the magnet. At the edge of the useful magnetic field the particles impinge upon an appropriate target or, in some cyclotrons, pass outside of a thin metal septum beyond which an appropriate electric field deflects them entirely out of the magnet.

Since the path traversed is fairly long, often a hundred or more revolutions, a slight upward or downward component of velocity would, if uncorrected, result in loss of the particle against the Dee wall. Fortunately this correction is fairly straightforward. If the magnetic field has a slight negative gradient outward, the lines of force are concave inward as shown in Figure 9. Under this condition the deflecting force on a particle not on the central plane will have a component toward that plane which increases with distance from the plane. Slightly misdirected particles will, therefore, oscillate about the central plane. By careful design, using tapered poles, it is possible to provide sufficient gradient to thus "focus" most of the particles without departing disastrously from the resonance condition.

Lawrence's first cyclotron, built in 1931, had a diameter of 11 inches and in its first operation accelerated protons to 80,000 volts.

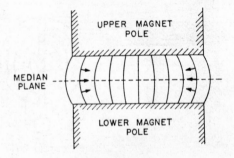

Figure 9. Principle of vertical focusing in the cyclotron. The curvature of the magnetic lines of force is exaggerated.

Since then numerous machines of increasing size and energy have been built at Berkeley and elsewhere, the largest completed having a diameter of 60 inches. Improvements in techniques have increased the internally circulating currents to as much as several milliamperes, and those available outside to hundreds of microamperes. The particles are used to study the immediate reactions in target nuclei, to produce secondary particles, especially neutrons, which are themselves used for bombardment, and to produce artificially radioactive isotopes. Protons, deuterons, and, to some extent, alpha particles and other more complex nuclei are used in the direct studies. Deuterons are most important in producing neutrons and radioactive nuclei.

By the advent of World War II the cyclotron as originally conceived was approaching an upper energy limit of 15 to 20 Mev for protons and 25 Mev for deuterons because of the relativistic change in mass. The obvious corrective measure of increasing the magnetic

Figure 10. The Brookhaven 60-inch cyclotron magnet before introduction of vacuum chamber. Courtesy of Brookhaven National Laboratory

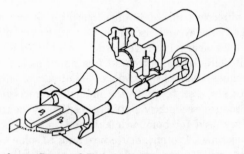

Figure 11. Cyclotron Dees and Dee stems. The latter provide support and the radio-frequency connection. Permission of Brookhaven National Laboratory

field radially to offset the increasing mass was of course not possible because of the focusing requirement described above. A theoretically possible alternative was to change the frequency cyclically, in such a manner that, during an interval of decreasing radio frequency, resonance would be maintained with a group of particles spiraling outward with decreasing revolution frequency. This would, of course, require a very precise relationship between the rate of change of radio frequency and the rate of change of energy, determined by the energy increment per gap. Since this precision seemed, at best, achievable for only a very few particles happening to reach the gap at just the right phase of the radio frequency, no serious attempt was made prior to World War II to exploit this possibility. Rather, workers in the field strove for higher and higher radio frequency voltages in order to reduce the number of requisite revolutions and therefore the total phase lag of the particles with respect to the fixed radio frequency. In an ambitious project at the University of California, Lawrence was building a machine with a pole diameter of 184 inches that was expected to utilize approximately 1,000,000 volts of radio frequency. While the magnet was under construction, the United States entered World War II and all cyclotron developments ceased at Berkeley and elsewhere. By the end of the war, new ideas were brought forward which will be described in the following sections.

Phase Stability

We have seen that in any radio-frequency accelerator the frequency of the driving voltage must not depart significantly from the transit frequency of the particles over a large number of successive transits. Prior to 1945 this was considered a substantial difficulty for linear accelerators and an almost insurmountable obstacle to frequency modulating the cyclotron. Fortunately, in 1945, a new principle, enunciated independently by McMillan in California and Veksler in the U.S.S.R., showed that under proper conditions the requisite synchronism would be brought about automatically by the particles themselves.

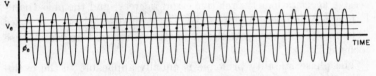

Figure 12. Principle of phase stability.

To understand this principle, let us return briefly to the linear accelerator. Assuming the correct radio frequency, a particle entering the first gap at precisely the correct time with precisely the correct velocity will receive an increment of energy and an increase in velocity just sufficient to time its arrival properly at the next gap, and so on. In general the particles will not fulfill these idealized or "equilibrium" conditions. In Figure 12, which plots the radio-frequency voltage against time, let V_e be the equilibrium voltage and ϕ_e the equilibrium phase on the rising voltage wave form. Consider a particle entering a gap with the equilibrium velocity but at a phase which is later than ϕ_e. Because of its excess in energy increment and hence in velocity, it will reach the next gap in less than one full cycle, advancing in phase toward equilibrium. Additional excessive energy increments in the successive gaps will accelerate the rate of phase advance. After several transits the particle will have reached equilibrium phase but with a substantially excessive velocity. The phase advance will therefore continue, but now the energy increments will be less than in equilibrium and the velocity excess will decrease. At some subsequent time equilibrium velocity will again be reached, but the phase lead will be substantially as large as the original lag. The process then reverses, the phase retards, and the velocity increments become larger and larger until the original condition is again reached and the cycle repeats. There is, therefore, a stable oscillation about the equilibrium phase, so that we have a condition of automatic "phase stability." Since the cycle has included all combinations of phase lag, phase lead, velocity excess, and velocity deficit, we see that all types of initial error are acceptable within, of course, certain quantitative limits. (It is obvious that no stability exists about the corresponding point on the *falling* side of the wave form, since, for example, an initial phase lag is *increased* by the resulting *deficit* in energy increment and vice versa.)

As the energy and velocity of the particles increase through successive accelerations the relative errors decrease and the phase oscillations are damped in amplitude. The result is a phase and space "bunching" of the particles, sometimes referred to as "phase focusing."

The phase stability principle is equally applicable to the cyclotron. However, since in a given magnetic field an *increase* in energy results in a *decrease* in frequency (Equation 12) the stable phase occurs on the falling rather than the rising side of the voltage wave form. Since the particles tend to keep automatically in phase with the radio-frequency voltage, they can be made to follow relatively slow changes in the frequency and maintain the resonance condition as their mass increases. The action is as follows: The frequency is decreased slowly through the initial resonance condition so that a group of particles is captured and bunched at the center of the magnet. As the frequency continues to decrease, the particles continue to oscillate about the equilibrium phase that corresponds to a rate of energy increase just sufficient to maintain the resonant condition of Equation 12. They therefore spiral outward, maintaining on the average that energy and that radius of curvature appropriate to the frequency at the moment. The phase focusing is unaffected by the radial decrease in magnetic field provided for the vertical focusing, the only effect being to increase slightly the pitch of the spiral path. It is important to note that since the particles maintain the requisite phase stability indefinitely there is no longer any need for excessive radio-frequency voltages to hold down the total number of orbital revolutions.

The Synchrocyclotron

Following the announcement of the phase stability principle, it was quickly applied to the 184-inch cyclotron magnet previously erected at Berkeley. The radio-frequency source was modulated by a rotating condenser, as indicated in Figure 13. Since high radio-frequency voltage was no longer a problem, only one Dee was excited, resulting in considerable simplification of the radio-frequency circuits. Deuterons were accelerated to 190 Mev in 1946, and the machine was subsequently modified to produce protons of 350 Mev, requiring a frequency modulation of 30-odd per cent. Because of the synchronous control of the particles, similar to that of the rotor of a synchronous motor, the instrument is usually called a synchro-

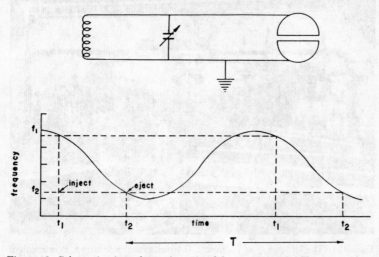

Figure 13. Schematic of synchrocyclotron and frequency-modulation wave form

cyclotron. It is also sometimes called the frequency-modulated or f-m cyclotron.

Numerous other synchrocyclotrons have since been built. The highest energy particles yet produced are 450-Mev protons at the University of Chicago.[2] Plans are under way to rebuild the 184-inch magnet at Berkeley to give higher magnetic fields and ultimately produce protons of approximately 700 Mev. The Council for European Nuclear Research (C.E.R.N.), a laboratory in Geneva

---

[2] In July 1955 Russian scientists announced the successful operation some time before of a 670-Mev proton synchrocyclotron.

jointly operated by 12 European countries, will soon commence construction of a 600-Mev proton machine.[3]

The synchrocyclotron was the first accelerator delivering particles sufficiently energetic to produce mesons. It has therefore been primarily utilized to study interactions between fundamental nuclear particles or nucleons (i.e., protons and neutrons) and only secondarily to study complex nuclei. Among the important types of experi-

Figure 14. The University of California 184-inch synchrocyclotron. Permission of University of California Radiation Laboratory

ments are nucleon-nucleon scattering, studies of meson production processes, and secondary studies of the mesons produced.

Because of the frequency modulation cycle, the synchrocyclotron delivers particles in pulses rather than continuously, so that the average current is only about 1/1000 of that in the cyclotron, i.e., a very few microamperes. Fortunately, up to the present this has not been too serious a handicap, since many of the experiments involve Wilson cloud chambers, which also operate discontinuously, or photographic emulsions in which intensity is often not a problem.

---

[3] As of July 1955 the construction of this accelerator was well under way.

However, as the newer phenomena which are being studied are better understood, requirements are increasing for precise measurements involving much larger numbers of events and the need for experiments involving counters is increasing. The lower intensity will therefore be an increasing handicap in the future.

The synchrocyclotron has no such technical limitation on its achievable energy as that provided by the relativistic frequency change in the standard cyclotron. Indeed, the size of such machines could, from a technical standpoint, be increased almost indefinitely. There are, however, serious economic limitations on size. The magnet of the Berkeley synchrocyclotron, for example, incorporates some 4000 tons of steel and hundreds of tons of copper. Assuming its future energy of 700 Mev, we see from Figure 2 that future increases in energy would involve almost proportional (to total energy) increases in linear dimensions. For example, at 3 Bev the particle radius would be increased by a factor of 2.8, requiring a $(2.8)^3$-fold increase in massiveness of the magnet, or approximately 92,000 tons of steel. For reasons of cost, it therefore seems unlikely that synchrocyclotrons will be built much larger than those already contemplated. Fortunately, as we shall see later, other methods are available for achieving higher energies.

Pulsed Magnet Electron Accelerators

Modern ultra-high-energy accelerators are all descendants of the cyclotron family. Let us now turn to another development beginning in about 1940 which has provided the other side of the ancestral tree.

So far we have been concerned principally with heavy particle accelerators and have said little about electrons. They are, in general, somewhat less useful for nuclear research than are protrons, deuterons, and other nuclear particles, especially at the very low energies provided by d-c machines. The cyclotron is, of course, not adaptable to electrons because of their large relativistic change of mass with energy. Nevertheless there has always been a need for high-energy electrons, both for direct experiments and as sources for high-energy gamma rays. The search for methods of producing them led to a whole new class of accelerators.

Among the early ideas advanced for achieving high-energy electrons was that of accelerating them by magnetic induction, that is, by the electric field that surrounds a region in which a magnetic field is changing with time. Electrons made to circulate properly about such a region would receive a continuous acceleration and the problems of radio-frequency synchronization would be avoided. Sporadic attempts to utilize this principle were made without success by Wideroe in Germany in 1928 and Walton in England in 1929 and occasionally by others in the 1930's. The idea was later revived by Kerst at the University of Illinois and put into successful practice in 1940 in an accelerator which he called the "betatron." Although the induction acceleration principle is limited in its application at high energies, certain other principles which Kerst developed have been of transcendent importance.

In the cyclotrons the *magnetic field* is *held fixed* and the particles circulate in orbits of *increasing radius* as their energy increases. In the induction accelerator it was clearly more appropriate to keep the orbit *radius fixed* by *increasing* the *magnetic field* with time in proper proportion to the increasing energy (Equation 11). The guiding field need then cover only an annular ring in the region of a doughnut-shaped vacuum tube surrounding the fixed orbit.

The electrons will travel a very great distance while being accelerated, and it is required that they do so on or near a given circular path. The slightest error in initial trajectory or minute disturbances resulting from machine imperfections could prevent their doing so unless some form of constraining or "focusing" force is provided. The development of a two-dimensional focusing method (with R. Serber) and of the pulsed magnet technique constituted the great contributions of Kerst.

Betatron Focusing

We have seen in the cyclotron how the magnetic field itself can be made to provide vertical focusing, but we also require radial focusing. For reasons to be described later, magnetic fields alone cannot be made to provide simultaneous focusing in two dimensions; indeed, focusing in one plane can be provided only at the expense of defocusing in the other. Fortunately, as Kerst and Serber pointed out, it is possible to combine vertical focusing by the magnetic field with radial focusing making use of the centrifugal force.

For a particle to remain on or near the desired orbit requires that restoring forces be present if it strays away from that orbit. Under our conditions two types of radial force are present, the magnetic force Hev directed inward and the centrifugal force mv^2/ρ directed outward. These forces are plotted as functions of ρ in Figure 15. Consider first the case of uniform magnetic field (Curve 1). The equilibrium orbit will be established at the radius ρ_e where the opposing forces are equal. From the diagram we see that a net inward

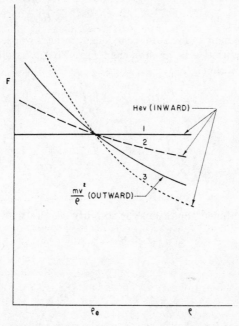

Figure 15. Radial forces on particles in a magnet field. Curve 1; n = 0
Curve 2; 0 < n < 1   Curve 3; n > 1.

force exists for regions outside ρ_e and a net outward force for regions inside ρ_e. This condition still obtains for the radially decreasing field needed for vertical focusing, providing the rate of decrease is not too great (Curve 2). Should, however, the rate of decrease of the magnetic force be made greater than that of the centrifugal force (Curve 3), a condition of instability results in which a particle outside the equilibrium orbit will be pushed still farther outward and vice versa. Thus, the negative radial gradient necessary to achieve vertical focusing tends to weaken and, if extreme, will actually destroy the inherent radial focusing. Conversely, the use of a positive radial gradient to strengthen the radial focusing would produce vertical defocusing.

The limits on the gradient which will allow both vertical and radial focusing are easily expressed. Let the equation

$$\frac{dH}{d\rho} = -n\frac{H}{\rho} \qquad \text{or} \qquad n = -\frac{\rho}{H}\frac{dH}{d\rho} \qquad (13)$$

define the gradient index number n. Then, to have vertical focusing, it is necessary that n be greater than zero. To have radial focusing it is necessary that

$$-\frac{d}{d\rho}(Hev) < -\frac{d}{d\rho}\left(\frac{mv^2}{\rho}\right)$$

$$-ev\frac{dH}{d\rho} < \frac{mv^2}{\rho^2},$$

or, since $Hev = mv^2/\rho$,

$$n < 1.$$

Thus our combined conditions for stability require that

$$0 < n < 1.$$

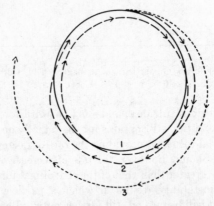

Figure 16. Particle orbits for various magnetic gradients.
Curve 1; n = 0   Curve 2; 0 < n < 1   Curve 3; n > 1.

The physical result can be seen in Figure 16. A particle directed down its equilibrium orbit will continue on that orbit (solid circle) unless disturbed by some external force. On the other hand, a particle on the equilibrium orbit but slightly misdirected in, say, an outward direction will move into a region of decreased field, and hence its radius of curvature will increase. Under the condition represented by Curve 2 of Figure 15 it will execute the precessing orbit indicated in the dashed curve. The net effect is therefore an oscillation about the equilibrium orbit. If, however, the field falls off too rapidly, as was the case for Curve 3 of Figure 15, the orbit will be a continuing spiral and the particle will be lost. The converse effect will, of course, be felt by a particle straying inward.

The frequency of the vertical and the radial oscillations can be computed as follows:

For the vertical case the restoring force F_z is given by

$$F_z = ev(H_\rho)_z = ev \frac{dH_\rho}{dz} z,$$

where $H\rho$ is the radial component of field and $(H\rho)_z$ is its value at a distance z from the central plane. From magnetic theory,

$$\frac{dH_\rho}{dz} = -\frac{dH_z}{d\rho}.$$

Whence

$$F_z = -ev \frac{dH_z}{d\rho} \cdot z \cong -ev \frac{dH}{d\rho} \cdot z = -nev \frac{H}{\rho} z.$$

This is an equation for simple harmonic motion where the stiffness coefficient $k = nev\, H/\rho$.

Hence the frequency of vertical oscillation

$$f_z = \frac{1}{2\pi} \sqrt{\frac{k}{m}} = \frac{1}{2\pi} \sqrt{\frac{nevH}{m\rho}} = \frac{1}{2\pi} \sqrt{\frac{nv^2}{\rho^2}} = \frac{v}{2\pi\rho} \sqrt{n}.$$

But $v/2\pi\rho$ = the orbital frequency, which we shall call f_0. Then

$$f = f_0 \sqrt{n}. \qquad (14a)$$

In the radial case, let $\Delta\rho$ be distance from the equilibrium orbit.

Then

$$F_\rho = \frac{d}{d\rho}\left(\frac{mv^2}{\rho} - Hev\right)\Delta\rho = \left(-\frac{mv^2}{\rho^2} - ev\frac{dH}{d\rho}\right)\Delta\rho$$

$$= \left(-\frac{mv^2}{\rho^2} + nev\frac{H}{\rho}\right)\Delta\rho$$

$$= \left(-\frac{Hev}{\rho} + n\frac{Hev}{\rho}\right)\Delta\rho = -\frac{Hev}{\rho}(1 - n)\,\Delta\rho,$$

whence, by analogy with the vertical case,

$$f\rho = f_0\sqrt{1 - n}. \tag{14b}$$

Thus we see that the frequencies of these "free" or betatron oscillations are lower than the orbital frequency, that they bear a constant relationship to it, and that, therefore, their "wave length" remains constant in an accelerator of constant orbital radius and constant n.

The value of n must be chosen so that there are no low-order harmonic relationships between $f_0, f_e,$ and f_z in order to avoid resonances which, by coupling, may disastrously blow up the amplitude of one of the oscillations. For example, the point at which $n = 0.2$ is that point at which

$$f_z = f_0\sqrt{0.2}\;;\;\;f_\rho = f_0\sqrt{0.8} = 2f_0\sqrt{0.2} = 2f_z$$

marks the maximum usable radius in a synchrocyclotron, since there the large radial oscillation energy that is always present couples into and blows up the vertical oscillation.

The amplitude of the free oscillations depends, of course, on the disturbances which caused them. Unfortunately the restoring forces are rather weak so that substantial allowance must be made in the vacuum chamber. As will be seen later, this has important economic effects in the larger accelerators.

The Betatron

The betatron utilizes a magnet looking much like that of a cyclotron except for the central core and gap, which are shaped as shown in Figure 17. Within the ring-shaped gap is placed a vacuum chamber of glass or porcelain called the "doughnut." At one point near the periphery of the doughnut is placed a hot cathode which can be pulsed negatively to a few tens of kilovolts by an appropriate source. The magnet, which must, of course, be laminated, is excited with a sinusoidal wave form, either by an a-c source or by the discharge of a bank of condensers through a switch tube. There is, therefore, through the central core an increasing flux and within the doughnut an increasing magnetic field. Electrons ejected into the doughnut experience an accelerating electric field, resulting from the change in flux, and are deflected in a circular path by the field

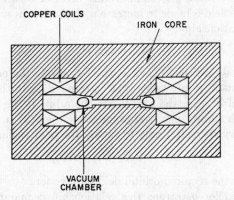

Figure 17. Schematic of the betatron.

in the doughnut. Fortunately an extremely simple and easily attainable relationship exists between the flux change and the field required to hold the electrons in a circular path of constant radius.

By elementary principles the kinetic energy acquired by the particles in one turn is given by

$$\Delta T = e \frac{d\phi}{dt} = 2\pi\rho F = 2\pi\rho \frac{dp}{dt},$$

where $d\phi/dt$ is the rate of change of flux inside the orbit and dp/dt is the rate of change of momentum. Integrating,

$$p - p_0 = \frac{e}{2\pi\rho}(\phi - \phi_0),$$

so that the change of momentum is proportional to that of the flux.

For a particle starting from rest

$$p = \frac{e}{2\pi\rho}\,\Delta\phi,$$

where $\Delta\phi$ is the total change in flux. To hold the particle in the orbit requires a magnetic field defined by Equation 11.

$$H\rho = \frac{p}{e} = \frac{\Delta\phi}{2\pi\rho}.$$

Hence there exists an "equilibrium" orbit of constant radius ρ_o, provided the field is made to increase with the flux in such a manner that the relationship

$$\Delta\phi_e = 2\pi\rho_e{}^2 H_e$$

is continuously satisfied. That is, the flux inside the orbit must be made to grow at a rate twice that corresponding to the rising of a uniform field H_e over the area inside the orbit. If the particles are injected with a finite energy appropriate to the field at that instant, it is necessary thereafter only to satisfy the relationship

$$\Delta\phi_e = 2\pi\rho_e{}^2 (H_e - H_e{}^0),$$

where $H_e{}^0$ is the required orbital field at injection.

In the smaller betatrons this relationship is maintained by so choosing the gap in the central core as to provide the appropriate magnetic reluctance. In the largest machines, however, the flux is swung from a negative to a positive value i.e., it is initially "biased") in order to increase the total change and hence the maximum orbital field. In that case separate magnets are used for the flux and the guide field. By driving them in parallel a constant relationship is maintained between dH/dt and $d\phi/dt$ and hence between H and $\Delta\phi$. This phenomenon is known as "flux forcing."

Starting with his original 2.3-Mev betatron, Kerst has built successively larger machines up to a 300-Mev accelerator with a 1000-ton magnet. Numerous other betatrons have been built elsewhere at energies up to 100 Mev, mostly to serve as high-energy X-ray sources. At energies below say 100 Mev, the betatron is operationally the simplest and most reliable of all accelerators, having among electron machines only the drawback of all magnetic types: that the beam does not emerge naturally.

Both technical and economic factors limit the maximum energy achievable in betatrons. As the electrons achieve higher and higher energies, the radial acceleration results in an energy loss through radiation which is proportional to E^4/ρ. Since E is approximately proportional to the maximum radius, the loss per turn at maximum energy varies approximately as the cube of that energy. Clearly this loss must come from the energy received through acceleration and hence "uses up" part of the magnetic flux, destroying the linear relationship of Equation 15 and forcing corrective measures. Although not appreciable at low energies, the loss is already ~ 650 volts per turn in Kerst's large betatron, compared with an accelerating voltage of approximately 2500 volts per turn. As the size of the machine is increased, the available flux increases as ρ^2 and therefore as E^2_{max}, whereas the radiation loss increases as E^3_{max}, so that an ever larger proportion of the available flux change is required merely to overcome the radiation losses. This effect will reduce the maximum guide field that can be matched to the flux and force an additional increase in size. Hence the linear dimensions would be somewhat greater than linear with E, the weight would have more than an E^3 dependence, and the magnet would soon be prohibitively expensive. Since better high-energy methods are available, it is unlikely that additional large machines of this type will be built.

The Synchrotron

So far we have described three great discoveries. In historical sequence, they are the magnetic resonance principle of Lawrence, the pulsed magnet and "betatron" focusing of Kerst and Serber, and the phase stability principle of Veksler and McMillan. Together they constitute adequate elements for constructing very-high-energy accelerators.

We shall consider next the marriage of the betatron and the cyclotron to produce a new class of accelerators that combine the pulsed, ring-type guiding magnet and doughnut-shaped vacuum chamber of the former with the phase-stabilized radio-frequency acceleration of the latter. This step was first taken in an electron accelerator proposed by McMillan and named by him the "synchrotron" (Figure 18).

As we have noted earlier, electrons acquire velocities very near that of light at energies of only a very few million electron volts, for

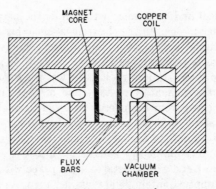

Figure 18. Schematic of synchrotron.

Figure 19. McMillan's 300-Mev synchrotron at the University of California. Permission of University of California Radiation Laboratory

example, $\beta = 0.95$ at one million electron volts and $= 0.98$ at 2 Mev. Once they have achieved such an energy the radius of their orbits changes very little when synchronous with a fixed radio frequency. In order to take advantage of this fact in the design and construction of the radio-frequency circuits, synchrotrons utilize some other method of achieving this requisite initial velocity. In many of them betatron acceleration to a few million electron volts is provided by small bars of iron, called flux bars, passing through the orbital plane. Having achieved its purpose of providing flux for the initial acceleration, this iron is allowed to saturate so that it provides only a small drain on the magnet power supply. In other synchrotrons, a high-voltage pulse transformer is used to pulse the cathode to one million electron volts or so. Still others use an external accelerator in the form of a Van de Graaff generator, or a transformer-rectifier set. The tuned radio-frequency circuits made possible by this method are used to drive a resonant cavity placed at one point within the doughnut, an electric field across a gap on the inner wall of the cavity providing the accelerating field.

Since the magnet is ring-shaped, it requires far less iron than either the cyclotron or the betatron and is proportionally cheaper to construct. It is usually excited by switching a charged condenser bank across the coils, giving a sine wave excitation of a few milliseconds duration.

Numerous synchrotrons have been constructed in this country and elsewhere, the most common energy among the larger machines being 300 Mev. One such accelerator at the California Institute of Technology has operated for some time at 500 Mev and will soon be converted to a 1-Bev machine.

The synchrotron suffers the same difficulty from radiation losses as does the betatron, but it is not so limited by this effect since it is technically feasible to compensate fairly large losses by additions to the radio-frequency accelerating system. It has recently been suggested, for example, that a synchrotron of 5 Bev could be constructed by using multiple driving circuits kept in proper phase by a common master oscillator. Such an accelerator would, however, probably be near the upper limits of economic feasibility for synchrotrons used for accelerating electrons.

Linear Accelerators

To this point we have considered accelerators delivering particles in the range of hundreds of millions of electron volts. We have seen that the cyclotrons accelerating heavy particles are limited by economics to energies of not more than one billion electron volts and that the electron synchrotrons become increasingly difficult and expensive at much above that energy. Before considering the development of higher energy magnetic accelerators, let us return briefly to the original concept of a resonance accelerator, that is, the linear accelerator.

Two important developments during and since World War II combined to make linear accelerators feasible; they are the phase stability principle already described and the remarkable development in ultra-high radio-frequency components and techniques brought about by the emphasis on military radar. The higher powers available at a few hundred megacycles have led to successful accelerators for protons, and the extension into the microwave region (3000 megacycles) has done the same for electrons. We shall describe both kinds very briefly.

Linear accelerators have the very great advantage that external particle beams are readily available with full intensity and adequate focusing. Not only can experimental equipment be readily used, but background radiation is small and shielding problems are minimized. Their principal disadvantage is high cost. Since that cost increases only as the first power of the energy in contrast to the E^3 dependence of any given type of magnetic accelerator at relativistic energies, it has often been hoped by the supporters of linear accelerators that, as energy ranges increase, they will become economically more practical. So far, however, successive new developments in magnetic accelerators have kept the latter in ascendancy.

The Proton Linear Accelerator

Encouraged by the wartime technical developments mentioned above, Alvarez in 1946 at the University of California began construction of a proton linear accelerator, originally planned to utilize surplus radar equipment and to achieve proton energies of 300 Mev. An accelerator producing protons of 32 Mev was constructed as a first step and the technical feasibility proved. Because of the development of the synchrocyclotron and the synchrotron, the unit has never been extended. Alvarez' accelerator, now used as an effective research tool, is illustrated in Figure 20. The accelerating electrodes or "drift tubes," thirty in number, are enclosed in a large copper-lined steel tank, resonating at the 200-megacycle driving frequency to produce a standing wave. The phase velocity is made infinite so that all parts of the tank are in phase and the entire accelerating voltage (28 Mev) appears across the tank. The drift tubes are spaced at intervals $v \cdot f = \beta\lambda$ so that the protons travel between gaps during one complete oscillation, or twice that in the machines described earlier. The sections between drift tube centers resonate as subunits, each being driven by its own coupling loop. The different length sections are matched by varying the diameter of the individual drift tubes. The tank is excited by thirty 17-kw

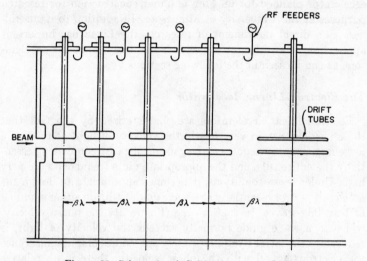

Figure 20. Schematic of California proton Linac.

oscillator tubes synchronized by a master oscillator and pulsed 1000 times per second for 2 microseconds. Constant phase is maintained by the tight coupling between the individual tank sections which they excite. Protons are injected from a 4-Mev Van de Graaff and the Linac proper adds an additional 28 Mev to give a total of 32 Mev.

A troublesome focusing problem is present in the Linac. In accordance with the phase focusing principle, the particles pass through a gap during a rising phase of the voltage wave form. Consequently, the field increases during the time of transit, and the defocusing force on the particle after it passes the central plane in the gap is greater than the previous focusing force. This effect was overcome by placing a grid arrangement over the entrance of each drift tube so that the lines of force terminate at that point and only focusing forces are present. Unfortunately, although great care was taken to minimize the grid structure, many of the particles strike it and are lost, causing a severe reduction in intensity.

The California Linac, delivering as it does a well-focused and reasonably homogeneous beam externally, has been extremely useful for a wide variety of precise experiments. A second proton linear accelerator planned for 68 Mev is under construction for research purposes at the University of Minnesota. In addition to its usefulness as a direct instrument of research, the Linac has important application as an injector for ultra-high-energy magnetic accelerators, as can be seen in the following sections.

The Electron Linear Accelerator

Electron linear accelerators are characterized by the fact that these particles attain very nearly the velocity of light at relatively low energies. In consequence, the gap spacings are equal along essentially the entire tube and the appropriate radio frequencies are very high. Under these conditions, it becomes appropriate to design the accelerating tube essentially as a wave guide utilizing either standing or traveling waves. In such a tube (Figure 21) the phase velocity, which in a wave guide normally exceeds the velocity of light, is reduced to the latter by appropriately spaced iris diaphragms. Since the electrons travel with the phase velocity, there is no relative phase shift and the defocusing problem of the proton synchrotron is not present.

A number of electron linear accelerators of relatively low energy

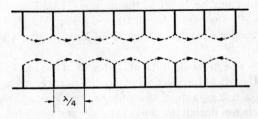

Figure 21. Schematic of electron linear accelerator tube.

have been built, some using standing and some traveling waves. The only machine at very high energies has been constructed at Stanford University by Hansen (now deceased), Ginzton, Panofsky, and others. In its final form, this accelerator will be driven by 22 klystrons, each developing 17 megawatts of power at 3000 megacycles. At the present time, approximately 16 such tubes are in place, sufficient to accelerate electrons to 600 Mev. Like its proton counterpart this accelerator is pulsed, there being sixty 2-microsecond pulses per second. The average current is approximately one microampere. There is, of course, no reason other than economics not to extend the energy of this machine indefinitely. It is however, difficult at the present time to predict what the additional rate of cost will be after the components become standardized.

The Proton Synchrotron

By 1946–1947 the principles of the synchrocyclotron and the synchrotron were well worked out, and there were under construction various machines of both types which would accelerate particles to hundreds of millions of electron volts. Since there was, however, a clear-cut need for particles of energies in the billions of electron volts, physicists cast about for methods of achieving these still higher energies. For technical and economic reasons neither the synchrocyclotron nor the synchrotron seemed feasible for the purpose. In principle, the linear accelerator could be extended indefinitely in energy but appeared economically prohibitive in the multibillion volt range. About this time, groups at the University of Birmingham, England, and at the University of California and the Brookhaven National Laboratory, in the United States, began to consider the possibility of synchrotrons for accelerating protrons.[4]

In principle such an accelerator is no different from the electron synchrotron, but there is one important practical difference. Whereas it is relatively easy to accelerate electrons to a velocity approximating that of light in order to use constant frequencies in the synchronous acceleration, to do so with protons would require an initial

---

[4] The first suggestion for such an accelerator seems to have been made by M. L. Oliphant in a report to the British Government in 1943, but the fact was not disclosed until much later. W. M. Brobeck at the University of California began to study the possibility independently in 1946.

energy itself in the billion electron volts range. It is therefore necessary to use frequency modulation in a proton synchrotron. In spite of the technical difficulty which this would introduce and the engineering complexity and economic cost of machines in the desired energy range, all three groups mentioned above were encouraged by their studies to proceed; machines were designed and constructed and are now in useful operation. The Birmingham synchrotron delivers protons at one billion electron volts, the Brookhaven accelerator at 3 Bev, and the California accelerator at 6 Bev. All are similar in principle but differ in engineering detail. We will therefore devote our principal attention to the Brookhaven machine, called the Cosmotron because the energies of its protons overlap those of cosmic rays.

The Cosmotron

As in the electron synchrotron, the magnet of the Cosmotron is ring-shaped (Figure 22) and encloses a flat, doughnut-shaped vacuum chamber with an accelerating electrode at one point. The protons are accelerated to an energy of 3 Mev by a Van de Graaff generator before being injected at a precisely controlled time with respect to the rising magnetic field. Over a period of approximately one second, they receive from the accelerating electrode an average of approximately 1000 volts of additional energy during each of approximately 3 million revolutions, acquiring in the process a total

Figure 22. The Cosmotron. Permission of Brookhaven National Laboratory

energy of 3 Bev while traveling a distance of approximately 150,000 miles. During the acceleration period the velocity of the particles increases by a factor of 11, from 0.09β to 0.96β and the frequency of revolution increases from 0.36 megacycles per second to 4.0 megacycles per second. Most of this change takes place relatively early in the acceleration period, as can be seen by the velocity curve of Figure 1.

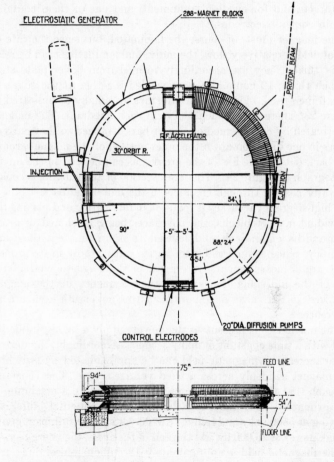

Figure 23. Schematic of Cosmotron. Permission of Brookhaven National Laboratory

A plan view and a vertical cross section of the magnet are shown in Figure 23. Following a scheme introduced into an electron synchrotron by H. R. Crane at the University of Michigan, the magnet of the Cosmotron is split into four quadrants separated by four field-less straight sections. One of the straight sections accommodates the injection apparatus for the initial beam and another the radio-frequency accelerating electrode. The remaining two are utilized for targets and for ejection equipment, and one of them contains certain control electrodes.

The magnet must, of course, be laminated, but since the rate of rise of field is relatively slow, the individual laminations can be relatively thick. They are accordingly formed from boiler plate steel $\frac{1}{2}$ inch thick; 12 laminations are welded together at the edges to form 6 inch-thick blocks which are stacked radially as indicated in Figure 23. There are 72 such blocks in each quadrant. The magnet is activated by coils formed of copper bars arranged so that current passes in one direction down the inner portion of the magnet groove and back outside the lips of the groove, as can be seen in the model photograph of Figure 24. The inner section of the winding is cooled by water passing through channels in the individual bars.

A high degree of accuracy is required in fabricating and placing the individual magnet blocks, the pole faces being machined to a few thousandths of an inch and leveled to approximately the same accuracy. Since commercial steel varies considerably in its properties, careful measurements were made of the magnetic characteristics of the individual blocks and their sequence in the magnet arranged so that near neighbors tend to compensate each other's differences.

The magnet coils present to the power supply a highly inductive load with a time constant of many seconds. Accordingly, the desired linear increase in magnetic field can be approximated by switching the magnet suddenly across a fixed voltage source. The constants are such that the required rate of rise of current to a maximum of approximately 7000 amp is achieved by a potential difference starting at 5500 volts and falling to 3700 volts under full load, giving a peak power of 26,000 kw. At the end of the cycle, the energy stored in the magnetic field is approximately 12 million joules. Since it is clearly not feasible to pulse power lines at such high levels, some means of energy storage is necessary. Condensers such as those used

with the smaller magnets of electron synchrotrons would be prohibitively expensive. Energy is therefore stored in a large rotating
flywheel driven by a slip-phase motor. Connected to the same shaft
as the motor and flywheel is a 12-phase, 60-cycle generator, the output of which is rectified by 24 triggered ignitron rectifier tubes con-

Figure 24. Model of Cosmotron magnet quadrant. End view showing cross section of magnet and vacuum chamber. Small tubes on right are for water cooling.
Permission of Brookhaven National Laboratory

nected in parallel to the magnet coils. In operation, these tubes are
switched on sequentially near the peak of their voltage waves, giving
approximately a d-c voltage with a 720-cycle first harmonic ripple
content. At the end of the excitation cycle, the phasing of the
ignitron triggering is reversed so that the current, which continues
to flow because of the inductance of the magnet, does so against the
voltage of the generator, converting the latter to a motor and restoring energy to the flywheel. About 75 per cent of the original

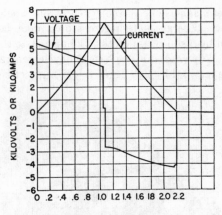

Figure 25. Voltage and current wave forms in Cosmotron magnet; injection takes place at approximately 15 milliseconds. Permission of Brookhaven National Laboratory

Figure 26. Cosmotron magnet power supply. Permission of Brookhaven National Laboratory

energy is thus recovered on each cycle. This recovery occupies about one second, after which 3 seconds is devoted to energy storage in the flywheel by the electric motor, before the cycle repeats. The voltage and current wave forms in the magnet are shown in Figure 25 and a photograph of the rotating machinery in Figure 26.

A difficult problem was presented by the frequency modulation requirements on the radio-frequency accelerating system. A master-

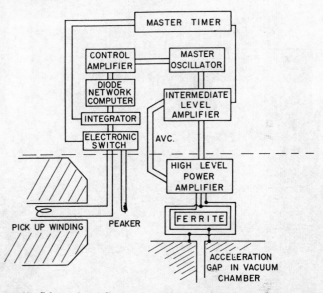

Figure 27. Schematic of Cosmotron radio-frequency system. The "peaker" delivers a signal when the magnet has reached injection field. Permission of Brookhaven National Laboratory

oscillator-power-amplifier method was chosen, the required high precision of tracking the radio frequency with the magnetic field being accomplished as follows: A coil placed within the magnet develops a voltage proportional to dH/dt, which is integrated to provide a voltage proportional to H. After amplification, the latter is fed into an electronic computer, the output of which controls the master oscillator by appropriate saturation of a magnetic ferrite core in the inductance of the tuned circuit.

One of the most difficult problems concerned the accelerating unit and the power amplifier. Since it was not deemed feasible to track a tuned circuit over the required frequency range, a "brute force" method was used. In the appropriate straight section the vacuum chamber is surrounded by a stack of window-frame-like laminations formed of magnetic ferrite (Figure 28), the assembly being excited by a distributed single-turn winding driven by the power amplifier.

Figure 28. Accelerating unit of Cosmotron showing ferrite slabs and rods.
Permission of Brookhaven National Laboratory

In passing through the window of this structure, the protons are accelerated by the induced electric field in a manner analogous to the inducing of a voltage in the secondary winding of a transformer. Since the protons require about 1000 volts per turn to maintain their synchronism in the rising magnetic field, a peak voltage of approximately 2000 volts is used so that the equilibrium phase is at approximately one-half peak amplitude. The peak and average power of the driver stage are approximately 150 and 50 kw respectively.

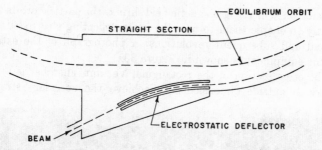

Figure 29. Method of injection into Cosmotron. Permission of Brookhaven National Laboratory

The method of injection is illustrated in Figure 29. A focused beam from the Van de Graaff, approaching the vacuum chamber at a slight angle, is bent by electrostatic deflection and injected in a tangential direction near the edge of the useful magnetic field of the

Figure 30. Injection system of the Cosmotron. Permission of Brookhaven National Laboratory

Cosmotron. The rising magnetic field shrinks the particle orbits sufficiently to enable them to pass the inner deflecting electrode in the
second and subsequent revolutions. A photograph of the exterior
of this equipment is shown in Figure 30.

The cross section of the rectangular vacuum chamber is 9 x 30
inches in outside dimensions. To achieve the necessary strength

Figure 31. Quadrant of the Cosmotron vacuum chamber. Permission of
Brookhaven National Laboratory

from glass or porcelain would require prohibitively thick walls, so
that a metal structure is required. To reduce eddy currents, the top
and bottom walls are formed of one inch wide stainless steel bars
bridging the chamber and insulated at one end from each other
and from the side wall of the chamber. The vacuum is maintained
by a rubber blanket covering the bars (Figure 31) and by an elaborate system of rubber gaskets. Twelve 16-inch oil diffusion pumps
evacuate the system.

Many of the components can be seen in the photograph of Figure

22. In addition to the magnet, it is possible to see the Van de Graaff generator (at the far corner of the room), the power amplifier supply (to the right of center of the ring), and some of the vacuum pumps and other equipment. In operation, the entire foreground region, including the two nearby straight sections used for targets, is enclosed in a massive concrete shield, only part of which is shown, that is perforated by appropriate beam channels at the elevation of the vacuum chamber.

The principal parameters of the Cosmotron are listed in Table 4.

The Cosmotron is used to study: (1) direct interactions of the protons with other nucleons, including the production of mesons (particles of intermediate mass) and hyperons (particles of mass greater than that of nucleons which are presumably formed by ex-

TABLE 4. Basic parameters of the Cosmotron

Injection energy	3.6 Mev
Means of obtaining injection energy	Van de Graaff accelerator
Final energy (with pole-face windings)	2.95 Bev
Orbit radius	30 feet
Orbit circumference	230 feet
Number of quadrants	4
Number of straight sections	4
Length of straight section	Approximately 11 feet
n-Value	0.6
Usable aperture	$6\frac{1}{4}$ inches x 28 inches
Acceleration time	1 second
Repetition rate	12 per minute
Magnetic field at injection	295 gauss
Maximum magnetic field (with pole-face windings)	Approximately 14 Kgauss
Magnet cross-section area	94 inches x 94 inches
Lamination thickness	$\frac{1}{2}$ inch
Total weight of magnet steel	2000 tons
Cross section of copper in windings	62 square inches
Total weight of copper	70 tons
Peak current in magnet coil	7000 amp
Number of turns	48
Peak stored energy in magnet	12×10^6 joules
Radio-frequency swing	330 kc–4.18 megacycles
Weight of ferrite in accelerating core	2800 pounds
Volts per turn required for 3 Bev	1000 volts
Operating pressure	Approximately 5×10^{-6} mm of Hg

citation of the latter), (2) similar interactions of high-energy neutrons formed by protons which lose their charge in passing through a target; (3) interactions of the secondary mesons and hyperons with nucleons, and (4) the fragmentation of complex nuclei when bombarded by fast protons and neutrons. In Figure 32 is shown a cloud chamber picture of the spontaneous disintegration of a type of hyperon, known as a V particle from the appearance of its disintegration track.

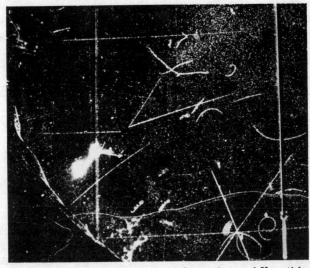

Figure 32. Cloud chamber photograph of decay of neutral V particle formed in the chamber wall, presumably by a fast neutron. Permission of Brookhaven National Laboratory

The proton synchrotron at California, known as the Bevatron (from Bev) has an orbit radius of 50 feet, making possible 6-Bev protons. It differs in design from the Cosmotron principally in the incorporation of: (a) an H-type magnet with two return legs as in the cyclotron, rather than a single-sided C-shaped magnet, (b) an electrostatically driven "drift tube" rather than an induction accelerator, (c) a Linac rather than a Van de Graaf injector, and (d) a different type of vacuum chamber with the magnet pole tips inside. The Bevatron is now in highly successful operation for research purposes at 6 Bev.

The most serious shortcoming of proton synchrotrons is their low intensity, owing to the brevity and infrequency of the pulses which they deliver. In the Cosmotron, for example, the rising magnetic field captures injected protons into stable orbits for a period of only about 50 microseconds during each of the twelve pulses per minute. Since the injected beam is about one milliampere and since less than half of the magnetically captured protons are "bunched" and accelerated by the radio frequency, the average current has a theoretical upper limit of

$$10^{-3} \times 50 \times 10^{-6} \times 1/2 \times 1/5 = 5 \times 10^{-9} \text{ amp} = 0.005 \ \mu a.$$

This corresponds to 6×10^{10} protons per pulse, slightly higher than actual experience.

This intensity is of the order of a few thousandths of the circulating current in a synchrocyclotron and a few millionths of that in a standard cyclotron. Although fairly satisfactory for cloud chamber and nuclear emulsion experiments, it leaves much to be desired in experiments with counters.

The proton synchrotron, like the synchrocyclotron, has no foreseeable technical limitation on ultimate particle energies. (Because of their large rest mass protons will not suffer appreciable radiation losses below some thousands of billions of volts.) There is, however, a very real economic limitation on ultimate energy in proton synchrotrons of the Cosmotron-Bevatron type. Since the maximum magnetic field is fixed by the properties of iron, increasing the energy requires a proportionate increase in the magnet diameter. Starting from an optimized design the width and height of the vacuum chamber must be similarly increased to allow for the proportionate increase in amplitude of the betatron oscillations. Hence the volume and weight of the magnet increase as E^3. In the light of experience the "relative aperture" of the Cosmotron vacuum chamber might conceivably be reduced to, say, 0.7 in linear dimensions or 0.5 in cross-sectional area, thus reducing the magnet iron to ~ 1000 tons. On this basis, the magnet of a 10-Bev Cosmotron would weigh 27,000 tons, that of a 20-Bev machine 216,000 tons, etc., clearly far beyond the feasible limit.

Need for Still Higher Energies

Several devices have been described that accelerate particles to hundreds of million electron volts and one, the proton synchrotron, which achieves several billion electron volts. Unfortunately not all of this energy is available for nuclear excitation processes since the law of conservation of momentum requires that part of it remain in the form of kinetic energy. The pertinent relationship is easily derived.

Consider, for example, the important case of a proton in motion colliding with a proton or neutron at rest. The total energy of the two particles will be $2E_0 + T$. By Equation 5 the momentum of the moving particle will be

$$p = \frac{1}{c} \sqrt{(E_0 + T)^2 - E_0^2}.$$

The energy of excitation, $\mathcal{E}$, is maximized if the collision is inelastic. The two particles momentarily form a single particle of rest energy $2E_0 + \mathcal{E}$, whence, since the total energy is unchanged, the momentum can be written as

$$p = \frac{1}{c} \sqrt{(2E_0 + T)^2 - (2E_0 + \mathcal{E})^2}.$$

Then by the conservation of momentum,

$$\frac{1}{c} \sqrt{(E_0 + T)^2 - E_0^2} = \frac{1}{c} \sqrt{(2E_0 + T)^2 - (2E_0 + \mathcal{E})^2},$$

whence

$$\mathcal{E}^2 + 4E_0\mathcal{E} - 2E_0T = 0$$

and

$$\mathcal{E} = 2E_0 \left[\sqrt{1 + \frac{T}{2E_0}} - 1 \right].$$

When $T \ll E_0$, this reduces to $\mathcal{E} \cong \frac{1}{2} T$, the classical formula for such a case. When $T \gg E_0$, $\mathcal{E} \cong \sqrt{2E_0T}$, that is, the excitation energy increases only as the *square root* of T. Table 5 illustrates the situation.

TABLE 5

T	10 Mev	100 Mev	1 Bev	3 Bev	6 Bev	15 Bev	25 Bev	100 Bev
$\mathcal{E}/T$	0.5	0.49	0.45	0.38	0.33	0.25	0.21	0.12
$\mathcal{E}$	5 Mev	49 Mev	0.45 Bev	1.14 Bev	1.98 Bev	3.75 Bev	5.2 Bev	12 Bev

Thus, large increases in particle energy are required to increase substantially the energy available for excitation when working in the multi-Bev region. It is worthy of note that the design value of 6 Bev for the Bevatron was deliberately chosen in excess of the $2 \times 0.938 = 1.876$ Bev required to create a new pair of nucleons by conversion of kinetic energy into mass.

From the above we see that the excitation energies so far available are not large in comparison to nucleon rest energies. It is highly desirable to extend our scale considerably in order to be well above the threshold for nucleon pair production, to increase the yield of known processes, and to discover any new and unexpected phenomena.

The Alternating Gradient Synchrotron

Mindful of the needs just outlined and encouraged by the success of the cosmotron, physicists began, in 1952, to investigate further energy extensions. For reasons described in earlier sections the prospect was not bright. For technical or economic reasons all accelerators except the proton synchrotron seemed out of the race. Attention was therefore centered on this instrument.

The principal stumbling block was, of course, the rapidly rising cost of the magnet. Except for detailed improvements in design, its linear dimensions must increase in proportion to the energy, since the diameter is fixed by the properties of iron and since no better method than that of the betatron was known for focusing the beam and reducing the requirements of relative aperture. It was hoped that, through careful design and the elimination of certain unnecessary safety factors, the relative aperture could be reduced sufficiently to make economically possible a machine somewhere in the 10- to 15-Bev region, but no more. Fortunately, while studying the various possibilities, a group of scientists at Brookhaven discovered a new and extremely important focusing principle which, in a single step, reduced the aperture requirements manyfold.

Scientists at C.E.R.N. had suggested that, in order to reduce certain engineering problems, the magnet of a larger cosmotron might be divided into sixteen rather than the previous four sections. While studying this proposal, M. S. Livingston suggested that alternate sectors might face in opposite directions in order to average out the distorting effects of magnetic saturation and permit the use of higher fields. He reasoned that, as the magnet saturated, the gradient n would increase to finally exceed unity in half the sectors and decrease to finally become negative in the others but that acceptable results might obtain if the average remained between zero and one. While studying this question, E. D. Courant discovered that gradients which alternate in this manner can indeed be used and, much more importantly, that they can be made to produce very strong focusing. The general theory was subsequently worked out by Courant and H. S. Snyder.[5]

Before studying the principle of "alternating gradient" or "strong" focusing, let us consider briefly some general aspects of magnetic focusing. We recall (Figure 15) that in orbital motion a radial decrease in field provides vertical focusing but radial defocusing and vice versa. In fact, we were able to produce two-dimensional focusing only by utilizing the centrifugal force. This is an example of a more general principle that magnetic forces cannot provide focusing in two planes simultaneously.

For simplicity, suppose we wish to direct a beam of particles along a straight line. Then, to have converging magnetic forces at all points off that line, it is necessary that the magnetic lines of force form continuous closed figures, such as circles, about the line. But such closed patterns exist only around an electric current. Clearly no current-bearing wires can be put in the path of our particles. Any attempt to utilize magnetic poles will have some such effect as that illustrated in Figure 33. The horizontal and vertical gradients combine in such a way that converging forces in one plane are accompanied by diverging forces in the other. A 90° rotation of the poles would reverse the effect in the two planes. A succession of alternately oriented systems gives the alternation of gradients proposed by Courant, Livingston, and Snyder but with the fixed field made zero at the "orbit" so that the latter is a straight line. By properly relating the strengths of the gradients and the lengths of the sectors, this arrangement can be made to provide very "strong" focusing, even though, at first sight, the effects of successive sectors seem to cancel each other.

An exact demonstration of the principle involved is difficult without rather complex mathematical treatment. Let us consider, how-

---

[5] It has since been learned that a similar system had been developed but not published by N. Christofilos of Athens, Greece, in 1950.

ever, the following qualitative argument. In an alternating array, temporarily remove the fields in those sectors which cause divergence in a given dimension. Then the remaining fields will provide strong restoring forces in that same dimension and an oscillation will result. If, now, the diverging fields are restored they will act to push the particle path outward so that in the *converging* sectors the restoring forces will be stronger than they were before. Now reverse the procedure. A certain diverging path will be traced in the absence of the converging fields. Replacement of the latter will reduce the divergence and hence *weaken* the average diverging forces. Thus the

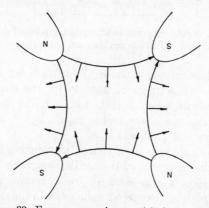

Figure 33. Forces on moving particle in nonuniform
magnetic field.

converging sectors *weaken* the effect of the diverging sectors, but the diverging sectors *strengthen* the effect of the converging sectors. Hence, on the average the converging sectors prevail and a net focusing results. Typical oscillating orbits are illustrated for a hypothetical case in Figure 34. The same conditions apply in the other plane but with the role of the sectors reversed.

In applying the principle to the synchrotron, the alternating gradients are provided by shaping of the pole pieces as shown in Figure 35, so that the field decreases and increases radially in alternate sectors. There are, of course, quantitative requirements on the arrangement. For equal length sectors the gradients must not depart too much from equality lest the diverging forces will prevail in one plane. Also if the gradients are too large for a given sector length, a

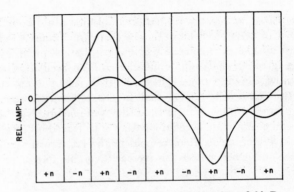

Figure 34. Oscillating orbits in alternating gradient field. Permission of Brookhaven National Laboratory

particle may be lost entirely in the diverging plane before it traverses a complete sector. The limits of stability for the circular case are indicated in Figure 36, where N is the total number of sectors and is thus an inverse measure of the sector length, and n_1 and n_2 are the values of the opposite gradients.

The strong focusing results, of course, in reducing the amplitude and increasing the frequency of the oscillations, both by a factor of approximately $\frac{1}{2} \sqrt{n}$ compared to the constant gradient case. When the principle was discovered, values of n in the thousands were

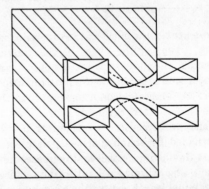

Figure 35. Alternating gradient synchrotron magnet. The dotted lines indicate the pole faces of the magnets of opposite gradient. Permission of Brookhaven National Laboratory

contemplated so that the oscillation amplitude could be reduced to fractions of an inch. Unfortunately there is a practical difficulty which is related to the increase in the oscillation frequency. If the oscillation frequency is an exact multiple of the orbital frequency, any imperfections in the magnet will be encountered on successive revolutions in exactly the same phase of the free oscillations, result-

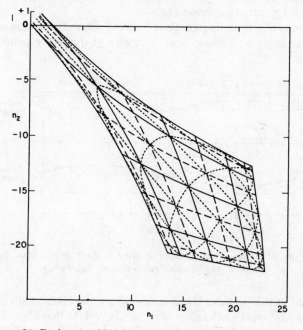

Figure 36. Region of stable orbits in an alternating gradient synchrotron. The network of solid and dotted lines indicates the locations of resonances. Permission of Brookhaven National Laboratory

ing in a form of resonance and a catastrophic increase in oscillation amplitude. If the oscillation frequency, f, is not too large compared to the revolution frequency, f_0, it is relatively easy to keep f between resonances. If on the other hand, f/f_0 is large, slight changes in n brought about by magnetic saturation or otherwise may establish the undesired harmonic relationship. Consequently, values of f/f_0 much larger than 10 or 15 are usually not considered.

Large gradients also require extreme precision in the fabrication and alignment of the magnet sectors, since small deviations can result in large departures of the field from its intended value and consequent displacement of the equilibrium orbit. Hence, for two reasons, in any actual machine a proper balance must be struck between the theoretical advantages of large gradients in reducing oscillation amplitudes in a perfect magnet and the difficulties they can cause as a result of imperfections.

The use of alternating gradient focusing alters the conditions for phase stability as follows. A particle with energy corresponding to

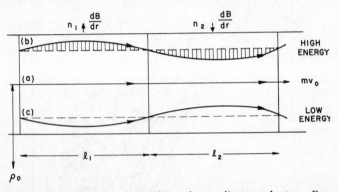

Figure 37. Stable orbits in an alternating gradient synchrotron. Permission of Brookhaven National Laboratory

the field at the center of the aperture, where the fields in alternating sectors are equal, will traverse a circular orbit. Particles of other energies will travel curved paths as indicated in Figure 37. On the average those on the outside will be in a stronger field than that corresponding to the circular path about which the orbit oscillates and vice versa. As a result, the change of orbit radius with changing momentum is not so great as in the standard synchrotron and, below some certain energy and velocity, will be less than proportional to the change in velocity. Hence the condition for phase stability will be like that of the linear accelerator, where the velocity change has the sole effect, rather than like the standard synchrotron where the change in orbit circumference is proportionally greater than the velocity change. As the energy increases and the velocity approaches that of light, the velocity changes more and more slowly with energy and, above some critical value, becomes proportionally less than the change in circumference. Hence, the phase stability changes to become like that of the synchrotron. At the critical point the phase must be changed from the *rising* to the *falling* side of the voltage wave form, and during that transition no phase stability exists. The accomplishment of this phase shift is the principal completely new element in the design of an alternating gradient synchrotron.

Plans for alternating gradient synchrotrons are in various stages of development at various laboratories. The two largest, which will greatly resemble each other, are being designed at Brookhaven and at C.E.R.N. The Brookhaven machine will have an orbital radius of 280 feet, so that, by Equation 11b', protons of 25 Bev can be contained in a magnetic field of 10,000 gauss. The 240 magnet sectors will be interspersed with a large number of straight sections in which will be placed 12 accelerating stations, injection and ejection equipment, and a large number of correcting magnets for offsetting errors in alignment, the effects of magnetic saturation, etc. The overall

Figure 38. Artist's sketch of large alternating gradient synchrotron. Permission of Brookhaven National Laboratory

circumference will be almost exactly one-half mile. The magnet will weigh approximately 3500 tons as compared to the several hundred thousand tons that would be required in a scaled-up cosmotron.

Injection will be derived from a 50-Mev Linac. This much higher injection energy than that in the Cosmotron is required in order that the magnetic field will be large enough at injection to avoid irregularities resulting from differences in residual magnetism. It will also reduce the radio-frequency change required during acceleration to a value of 3:1.

Figure 39. Magnet section for alternating gradient synchrotron. The reversed poles can just be seen part way down the gap. Permission of Brookhaven National Laboratory

The Brookhaven machine will probably be completed by 1960. Figure 38 shows an artist's concept of this accelerator. Figure 39 shows an end view of a full-scale model section of the magnet.

Summary

We have traced the development of particle accelerators from their infancy to the present and have glimpsed into the future. What has been said of their characteristics is summarized in Table 6.

The history of particle accelerators is barely 25 years old. In that time they have developed from crude beginnings to the complex, enormous, and expensive machines of today. The particle energies

TABLE 6

	Usual Particles	Orbit	Magnetic Field	Particle Velocity	Radio Frequency	Maximum Energy	Energy Limited by	Steady or Pulsed	Average Current
Direct current	Any	Straight	—	Increasing	—	~10 Mev	Breakdown	Steady	~1 ma
Electron linear accelerator	Electrons	Straight	—	Constant*	Constant	Several Bev	Cost	Pulsed	~1 μa
Proton linear accelerator	Nuclear	Straight	Constant	Increasing	Constant	< 1 Bev	Cost	Pulsed	~1 μa
Cyclotron	Nuclear	Spiral	Constant	Increasing	Constant	~25 Mev	Changing mass	Steady	~ ma
Synchrocyclotron	Protons	Spiral	Constant	Increasing	Modulated	~1 Bev	Cost	Pulsed	~ μa
Betatron	Electrons	Circle	Increasing	Constant*	—	300 Mev	Radiation loss and cost	Pulsed	~ μa
Synchrotron	Electrons	Circle	Increasing	Constant	Constant	1–2 Bev	Radiation loss and cost	Pulsed	~ μa
Proton synchrotron	{ Protons / Electrons }	Circle / Circle	Increasing / Increasing	Increasing / Constant	Increasing / Constant	~10 Bev / ~5 Bev	Cost / Radiation loss and cost	Pulsed / Pulsed	~10⁻⁹ Amp / ~10⁻⁸
A.G. synchrotron	{ Protons }	Circle	Increasing	Increasing, then constant	Increasing, then constant	~25–50 Bev	Cost	Pulsed	~10⁻⁹ Amp

* Except in early stages of acceleration.

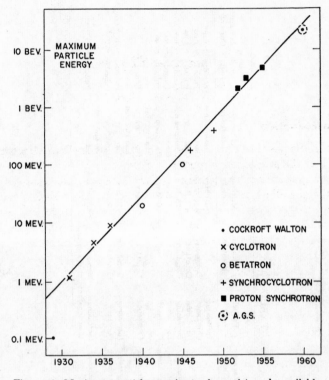

Figure 40. Maximum particle energies (on log scale) made available
since 1930.

have increased by a factor of approximately 6×10^4 over the 100
Kev available about 1930, and another factor of 5 is in prospect.
Since the cyclotron achieved one million electron volts in 1931 there
has been a steady progression by approximately a factor of 10 every
six years. Figure 40 illustrates this progress and the various machines
which have successively held the record for particle energies.

What the future will produce no one knows. Higher energy
particles than can be produced by the machines now planned would
undoubtedly be very expensive unless entirely new principles are
discovered. It is safe to say, however, that if need for still higher
energies is indicated by the research results of the next few years,
new techniques or larger budgets will be found to produce them.

Neutron Physics

NORMAN F. RAMSEY

Introduction

In the past few chapters the reader has already learned something about the properties of neutrons. Therefore, we need merely repeat here that the neutron is one of the two kinds of elementary particles of which all nuclei consist; the proton is the other kind of particle, and neutrons and protons are often called by the collective name nucleon. Neutrons and protons have about the same weight, which is about 3×10^{-27} pound; i.e., 300 million million million million neutrons make one pound. Neutrons and protons also have about the same diameter, about 10^{-13} inch or a tenth of a millionth of a millionth of an inch. Neutrons and protons differ, however, in the fact that protons are charged while neutrons have no charge at all.

Neutrons have a very special interest in nuclear physics which justifies an entire chapter in this compact volume being devoted to neutron physics. This special interest arises from several of their characteristics, of which two of the most important are: (1) neutrons are a major constituent of all nuclei save hydrogen, and (2) their absence of charge enables them to penetrate matter without interacting with it electrically so that all of the interaction is due to intrinsically nuclear forces.

Neutrons were discovered by Chadwick in 1932, who bombarded beryllium with α particles (helium nuclei) and found uncharged emergent particles which were so effective in producing recoil protons that it appeared that the two were roughly of equal mass (weight). Chadwick, therefore, proposed that these were neutral particles of approximately the same weight as the proton. He ascribed the process of neutron production to the reaction

$$_4\text{Be}^9 + {}_2\text{He}^4 \rightarrow {}_6\text{C}^{12} + {}_0n^1. \tag{1}$$

Since the discovery of the neutron they have been produced in many different ways, of which some of the most important for

197

scientific research have been the bombardment of beryllium by heavy hydrogen of mass 2 or deuterium, the bombardment of beryllium or deuterium by γ rays, and the bombardment of heavy hydrogen of mass 3 or tritium by deuterium. The fission process, which is discussed in greater detail below, has also been an important source for neutrons.

Moderation and Diffusion of Neutrons

A special property of neutrons, which results from their lack of charge and consequent penetrability through matter, is that they can be slowed down or moderated. The slowing down process is very similar to that by which the cue ball in billiards is slowed down by striking another ball of roughly the same mass. If there is a head-on collision of the two billiard balls, the originally moving ball will give up all of its kinetic energy to the struck ball, and if the collision is at a glancing angle it will give up a considerable fraction of its energy. Since protons have roughly the same mass as neutrons they are very effective in slowing them down. Therefore water (H_2O) or paraffin makes an effective neutron moderator.

Although water and paraffin are particularly effective in slowing down neutrons, they also have an important deficiency as moderators in that they capture neutrons. Therefore, in addition to slowing down the neutrons, they also diminish the number present. The capture process is as indicated by the following nuclear equation:

$$_0n^1 + {}_1H^1 \rightarrow {}_1D^2, \tag{2}$$

which shows that the number of free neutrons is diminished, while charged deuterons (deuterium nuclei) are produced. For this reason heavy water (D_2O), for which this capture process does not occur, is a more effective moderator even though more collisions on the average are required for equal amounts of slowing down of the neutrons because of the disparity in mass between the deuteron and the proton. Carbon (graphite), because of its very low capture cross section, is also an effective moderator, even though it requires many more collisions than either hydrogen or deuterium to produce the same amount of neutron moderation.

There is a limit below which the neutrons are not slowed down in the moderation process. The nuclei in water, heavy water, graphite, etc., are themselves thermally vibrating. Therefore, even if a neutron were slowed down to almost zero velocity, one of these nuclei in its vibrating motion would collide with the neutron and increase its energy. Thus, eventually the neutrons on the average reach merely the same average energy as that possessed by the atoms of the moderating medium owing to their thermal vibrations. For this reason neutrons slowed down to such average thermal velocities are called thermal neutrons. After neutrons have been slowed to thermal energies, say in a block of graphite, they diffuse through the block to emerge eventually from its surface in much the same way that heat diffuses to the surface of an internally heated block.

Fission Neutrons

Let us now turn to the consideration of an alternative neutron source—nuclear fission. In 1939 Hahn and Strassman discovered the fission process. They found that if neutrons bombarded uranium a reaction occurred with a large release of energy and with the nucleus being split into approximately equal halves. It was later discovered that neutrons were also emitted in this process. The fission process may be visualized as the capture of a neutron by the uranium nucleus, which then undergoes such violent oscillations that it, like an oversized raindrop, also splits into approximately equal halves accompanied by two or three much smaller droplets or neutrons. The splitting is a statistical process rather than one that always goes in a unique fashion; sometimes one pair of product nuclei are produced and other times another and sometimes two neutrons are produced and other times three. A typical fission reaction is

$$_{92}U^{235} + {}_0n^1 \rightarrow {}_{57}La^{147*} + {}_{35}Br^{87*} + 2{}_0n^1. \tag{3}$$

The product nuclei subsequent to the above fission process decay radioactively with emission of lighter particles until a stable nucleus is achieved. On the average about 200 Mev (million electron volts) of energy is released per fission. Also, on the average, about 2.5 neutrons are emitted. Most of these neutrons are emitted simultaneously with the fission process and are called *prompt* neutrons. Occasionally, however, some *delayed* neutrons are also produced, which come off later following the β (electron) radioactive decay of a fission product.

The interest in fission reactions is not merely that 200 Mev is much greater than the usual five Mev or so of most nuclear reactions, but of even greater significance is the fact that one neutron initiates the process while on the average 2.5 neutrons are produced by it, and these new neutrons are in turn available to initiate additional processes. Consequently a chain reaction is possible. The phenomenon is closely analogous to the chain letters that were so popular a few years ago. If one man writes to three others, each of whom writes to three others, etc., before long everyone in the United States is writing a letter.

Although the fact that more neutrons are produced in an individual fission process than are absorbed makes a self-sustained chain reaction possible, it does not make it inevitable. If it did, all uranium mines would have blown themselves up long ago. The problem of operating a successful chain reaction is closely analogous to that of operating a profitable business enterprise: not only must the items be sold for more than they cost, but they must be sold for enough more to make up for the overhead and other costs. Hence for success one must increase the sales and keep down the overhead; i.e., one must increase the probability of a neutron producing a U^{235} fission and one must decrease the effectiveness of the nonfission ways by which neutrons can be lost.

The probability of a neutron producing fission is increased by slowing the neutrons down, i.e., by moderating them as discussed in the preceding section. The cross section (effective nuclear size or cross-sectional area) for $_{92}U^{235}$ fission is much greater for slow neutrons than for fast ones, so the moderation process greatly increases the fission probability relative to the loss probability. For the operation of a controlled nuclear reactor, the use of slow neutrons is no disadvantage and in fact even eases the control problems with the reactor. On the other hand, where a sudden large release of energy is required, as for an atomic bomb, the use of slow neutrons is not satisfactory because the slower speed of the reactor in that case would lead to its melting or mildly blowing itself apart before a really large energy release had time to occur. In atomic bombs, therefore, the fission reaction relative to the loss process is enhanced instead by the use of the pure isotope $_{92}U^{235}$ or the artificially made plutonium ($_{94}Pu^{239}$).

The sources of nonfission neutron losses are (1) neutron capture by chemical impurities, (2) neutron capture by $_{92}U^{238}$ (only one part in 140 of normal uranium is $_{92}U^{235}$, which is the isotope that is effective in fission with slow neutrons), (3) neutron capture by the moderator, and (4) loss of neutrons through the surface.

A high degree of chemical purity is therefore sought for both the uranium and the moderator in a nuclear reactor. As discussed above, the harmful effects of $_{92}U^{238}$ are overcome either by the use of slow neutrons which are especially effective in producing $_{92}U^{235}$ fission or by the use of separated isotopes. The problem of neutron capture in the moderator is alleviated by the use of chemically pure moderators and by the use of a moderating substance like D_2O or C (graphite) whose neutron capture cross section is very low.

Losses through the surface are diminished by making the pile of uranium and moderator large, since the surface-to-volume ratio diminishes (the surface area varies as R^2 and the volume as R^3, whence the surface-to-volume ratio varies as $1/R$, i.e., diminishes with increasing size). Since the neutron loss through the surface is approximately proportional to the surface area while the rate of neutron generation is proportional to the volume, the relative amount of loss diminishes with increased size. This is analogous to the well-known fact that a small chip of steel heated to white heat quickly cools to room temperature while a 20-ton block of steel will take days to cool down, since the surface-to-volume ratio is small for the large block.

Therefore one need merely stack the uranium and, say, graphite blocks to a large enough pile so that the rate of neutron generation exceeds the rate of neutron loss, at which time a self-sustained reaction will continue; the pile is then said to be *supercritical*. For these reasons, such a device is normally called either a *pile* or a *reactor*.

Of course, in actual practice most piles are considerably more complicated. Provisions have to be incorporated for cooling a pile, for controlling it, and for making it safe. It is these provisions which make a pile in practice a relatively complex device. The control can be achieved, for example, by inserting a cadmium rod into the pile by an adjustable amount. Since cadmium is very effective in the capture of slow neutrons, the pile will be subcritical when the cadmium rod is fully inserted and supercritical when it is withdrawn.

A schematic view of a pile is shown in Figure 1, and an actual photograph of one face of an operating pile is shown in Figure 2.

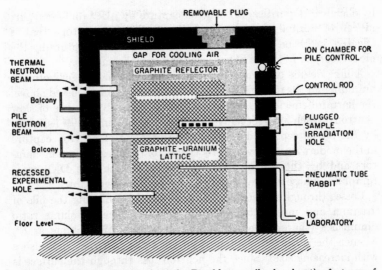

Figure 1. Diagramatic sketch of the Brookhaven pile showing the features of importance for pile neutron Research.—D. J. Hughes, *Pile Neutron Research* (Cambridge: Addison-Wesley Publishing Co., 1953)

Figure 2. View of the experimental balcony and face of the Brookhaven pile, showing typical apparatus at experimental holes.—*Pile Neutron Research*

From the point of view of the present discussion one of the principal uses of a pile is in the production of neutrons. *Fast neutrons* at energies from zero to 15 Mev are produced directly from the fission process, *resonance neutrons* at energies from one ev to one Mev can be produced by slightly moderating the fission neutrons, and *thermal neutrons* at energies of about 1/40 ev can be produced by fully moderating the neutrons. Neutron fluxes of about 10^{13} neutrons per square centimeter per second are produced in typical chain-reacting piles.

Fast and Resonance Pile Neutron Research

Typical of the research with pile neutrons are experiments on the capture cross sections (effective cross-sectional area for capturing the neutrons) of various nuclei for fast neutrons. Typical results for such measurements are shown in Figure 3 for 1-Mev neutrons as a function of the number of neutrons in the capturing nucleus.

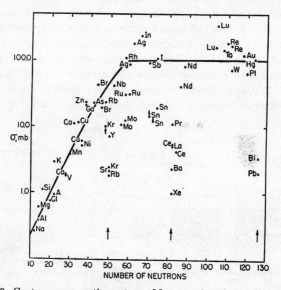

Figure 3. Capture cross sections at one Mev as a function of the number of neutrons in the capturing nucleus. The isotopes containing magic numbers 50, 82, or 126 of neutrons are marked with arrows and show extremely low cross sections.
—*Pile Neutron Research*

It is of special interest to note that nuclei of 50, 82, and 126 neutrons have especially low capture cross sections. This is but one of the many nuclear properties that have marked peculiarities at 20, 50, 82, or 126 identical nucleons, the "magic numbers." The study of the magic numbers in nuclei has shed a great deal of light on the structure of nuclei and has indicated the existence of a shell structure in nuclei.

Resonance neutron cross sections have been effectively studied with pile neutrons and a so-called crystal monochromator. Like any other particle, neutrons, according to present-day quantum mechanics, have an associated wave length λ such that if the neutron has a velocity v and a mass m

$$\lambda = \frac{h}{mv}. \qquad (4)$$

From regularly spaced layers of atoms in a single crystal only neutrons of a particular wave length are strongly reflected at a particular angle in much the same way that an optical diffraction grating separates out light of different wave lengths or colors. A typical neutron crystal monochromator is shown schematically in Figure 4.

An alternative means for monochromatizing neutrons is to emit them from a source in short bursts and then to measure their time of arrival at the detector, in which case the time of flight divided into the known distance between source and detector gives the

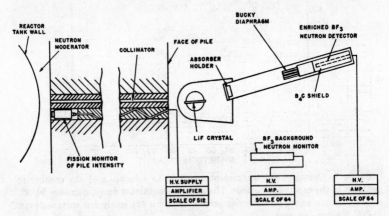

Figure 4. Typical crystal monochromator for the production of monoenergetic neutrons.—*Pile Neutron Research*

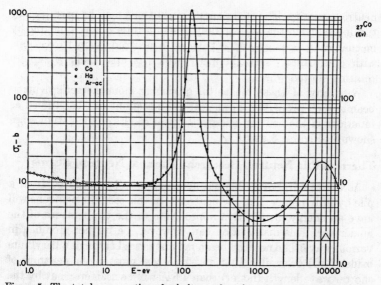

Figure 5. The total cross section of cobalt as a function of neutron energy in the resonance energy region.—*Pile Neutron Research*

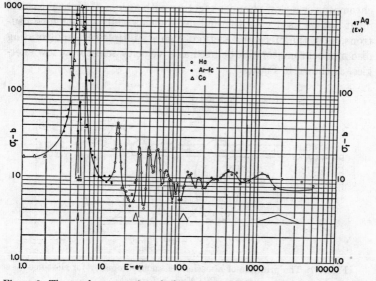

Figure 6. The total cross section of silver as a function of neutron energy in the resonance energy region.—*Pile Neutron Research*

neutron velocity. The short bursts of neutrons may be produced by turning a cyclotron on for only a short interval of time or by mechanically opening and cutting off a neutron beam from a pile with a so-called "fast chopper," which is essentially a rapidly rotating slotted wheel.

With any of these means for producing moneonergetic neutron beams, such properties as nuclear cross sections can be studied as functions of the neutron energy. Typical results of such studies are shown in Figures 5 and 6.

Thermal Pile Neutron Research; Thermal Neutron Beams

As discussed above, thermal neutrons may be produced from a pile by fully moderating the neutrons. In this case the neutrons will have an energy distribution appropriate to the temperature of the moderator. This distribution can, however, be further modified in various ways. The neutron beam may be passed through a beryllium oxide (BeO) or similar filter, in which case most of the neutrons of shorter wave length (faster) than 4.5 A will be scattered out by the BeO crystals, while most of the neutrons of longer wave length (slower) will be retained in the beam. Alternatively, a crystal monochromator or a slow chopper together with a time-of-flight measurement can be used with thermal neutrons as well as resonance neutrons, as in the preceding section. Also a multiple sectored rotating disc monochromator can be used as a velocity selector at low energies, as shown in Figure 7.

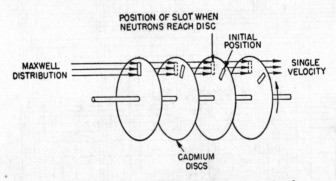

Figure 7. The principle of a mechanical monochromator for slow neutrons.—*Pile Neutron Research*

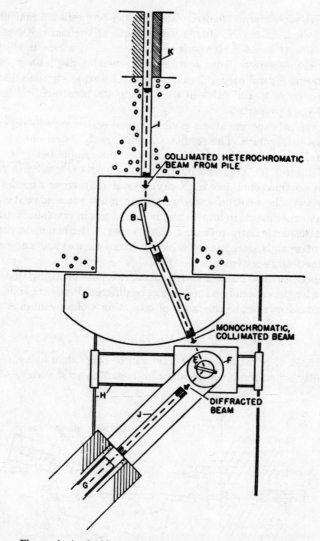

COLLIMATED HETEROCHROMATIC
BEAM FROM PILE

MONOCHROMATIC,
COLLIMATED BEAM

DIFFRACTED
BEAM

Figure 8. A double crystal neutron diffraction apparatus
the monochromatizing crystal is at B and the powder sample
being studied is at E.—*Pile Neutron Research*

With such thermal neutron beams many properties of matter can be studied. Since the neutron wave length at thermal energies is of the same order of dimensions as the spacing of atoms in crystals, interference effects from scattering by neighboring atoms in the scattering crystal play a dominant role. Consequently such neutron beams are of special value in studying crystal structure and similar solid-state properties.

A typical experiment is a double crystal scattering experiment as shown in Figure 8. The results are dominantly determined by the crystalline and solid-state properties of the sample being studied. The information obtained in these experiments is similar in many ways to that obtained in X-ray crystal diffraction experiments. However, the neutron experiments are much more effective than X-ray experiments in locating hydrogen atoms in crystals. Neutrons are also particularly revealing about some of the magnetic properties of crystals since neutrons have a magnetic moment and can be magnetically scattered.

Since neutrons intereact with solids, it is not surprising that their wave length λ should on the average be different inside the solid than outside. However, as the index of refraction n of a medium is given by

$$n = \lambda_{air}/\lambda_{medium}, \tag{5}$$

the index of refraction of the solid will be other than unity. Consequently a neutron beam incident on a smooth solid surface will be

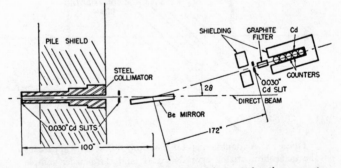

Figure 9. Neutron mirror reflection equipment for the accurate measurement of the critical angle of beryllium.—*Pile Neutron Research*

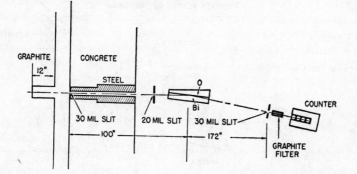

Figure 10. Apparatus for the measurement of the neutron-electron interaction by neutron reflection from a bismuth-liquid oxygen interface.

both refracted and reflected by the medium. At a sufficiently small glancing angle with the surface, total reflection can be achieved just as in optics with total reflecting prisms. The critical angle at which total reflection just begins can be measured accurately. From measurement of this critical angle important nuclear information (the coherent neutron scattering cross section) can be inferred. An apparatus for measurement of critical angles is shown in Figure 9.

In this way the small interaction between a neutron and an electron has been determined. The critical angle at the interface between

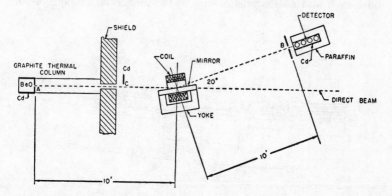

Figure 11. Plan view of apparatus for the study of neutron reflection from magnetized mirrors.—*Pile Neutron Research*

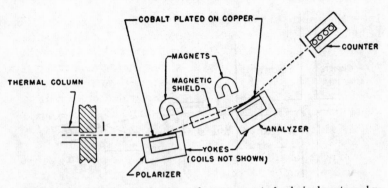

Figure 12. Equipment for production and measurement of polarized neutrons by mirror reflection.—*Pile Neutron Research*

bismuth and liquid oxygen has been accurately measured. From nuclear scattering alone the index of refraction at this interface should be approximately unity so the departure corresponding to the observed critical angle is due chiefly to the neutron-electron interaction and to the fact that the electron density in bismuth is much greater than in oxygen. A diagram of the apparatus used in this experiment is shown in Figure 10.

If an iron neutron mirror is strongly magnetized the index of refraction will be different for neutrons whose magnetic moments (compass needle property) are oriented parallel to the magnetic induction B and antiparallel, owing to the magnetic interaction be-

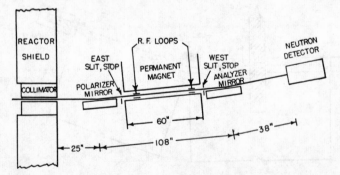

Figure 13. Apparatus for the precision measurement of the neutron magnetic moment.—*Pile Neutron Research*

tween the neutron and B. Consequently, the index of refraction will be different for the two neutron orientations, and the critical angles for total reflection will differ. Therefore, an incident angle can be selected such that the neutrons of one orientation are totally reflected while those of the opposite orientation are not. In such a case the reflected beam will consist dominantly of neutrons with the same orientation of their magnetic moments; such beams are ordinarily called polarized beams. Figure 11 shows an apparatus for the production of polarized neutron beams and for the study of neutron reflection from magnetized mirrors. The degree of polarization achieved can be measured by two successive polarizing reflections, as in Figure 12. These polarized neutron beams can then be studied by methods closely analogous to the molecular and atomic beam magnetic resonance methods. In this way the neutron magnetic moment has been measured with high precision with the apparatus shown schematically in Figure 13.

In conclusion, it should be emphasized that the foregoing material presents only briefly and qualitatively the many interesting developments in the very new and rapidly growing field of neutron physics. For further study in this field this writer would recommend especially the recent book on *Pile Neutron Research* by D. J. Hughes

Transistor Physics*

W. Shockley

Introduction

The development of the transistor has made potentially possible
many new advances in technology. This discussion, however, is
concerned with the science of semiconductors, upon which transistor
electronics is based. The semiconductors of chief interest, germanium
and silicon, can best be understood in terms of insulators. A potentially insulating crystal becomes a semiconductor when it contains
either of two electronic imperfections: *excess electrons* over and above
those necessary to complete the valence bonds, and *holes*, or electron
shortages, in the valence bonds. Both the excess electron and the
hole are mobile and can carry electric current. In addition to these
two electronic imperfections, three other classes of imperfections,
atomic in nature, must be considered. These are *donors, acceptors,*
and *deathnium.* Donors are chemical impurities that induce excess
electrons, whereas acceptors induce holes. An excess electron can
combine with a hole, the result being a normal valence bond and
thus annihilation of both imperfections; deathnium is a chemical
imperfection that catalyzes the recombination. The ways in which
the five imperfections interact and lead to useful processes are
described. New experiments based on transistor techniques have
demonstrated the properties of excess electrons and holes.

The transistor made its first appearance on the public scene in
June of 1948 and is now approximately eight years old. During these
years the transistor has developed from a state of feasibility in the
laboratory to a useful article of commerce. In the fall of 1952, no
commercial application of the transistor was available for use by the
general public, but by the spring of 1953 several competing companies were offering hearing aids incorporating transistors.

We are not concerned primarily with the applications of the
transistor, however, but with the relationship of the transistor to the

* Reprinted from the *American Scientist,* 42 (1954), 41–72.

physics of semiconductors. In the case of the transistor, the relationship between progress in fundamental science and progress in useful devices has been unusually close. It has occurred several times that the achievement of experimental control over the physical and chemical processes has led at once to the realization of a useful, practical device. At the same time, improvements brought about in order to produce useful devices have put in the hands of scientists tools which have enabled them to carry out basic research better than before.

Semiconductors and the Language of Imperfections

Transistor physics and transistor electronics are based upon the properties of semiconductors. Semiconductors are so termed because of their electrical properties, which are intermediate between those of metals, which conduct electricity very well, and insulators, which conduct electricity hardly at all. Semiconductors are more easily understood, however, in terms of insulators than in terms of metals. In fact, they are in a sense imperfect insulators, and their semiconducting properties result from the features possessed by their imperfections. For this reason, the key words that are used in discussing semiconductors are the names of imperfections in crystals that would otherwise be perfect insulators.

In order to describe semiconductors, we shall, therefore, start by

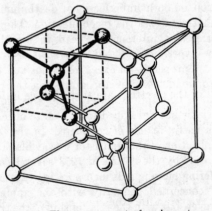

Figure 1. The arrangement of carbon atoms
in the diamond structure

considering the nature of an ideal insulating crystal. The crystal selected for this purpose, shown in Figure 1, is perhaps the most famous of all crystals. The diamond structure gives each carbon atom an ideal opportunity to form chemical bonds with its neighbors. In this figure, one carbon atom is singled out for attention. It is represented as being connected to its four nearest neighbors by heavy lines. These heavy lines represent the electron-pair bonds well known in chemistry. Each bond is formed by the cooperative action of a valence electron from each of the two carbon atoms. Since the

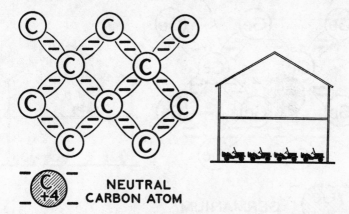

NEUTRAL CARBON ATOM

Figure 2. Diamond structure. Symbolic representation of the insulating properties of the valence bonds

carbon atom has four valence electrons, the diamond structure permits each atom to employ all of the valence electrons in forming covalent bonds.

In a perfect diamond crystal, there will be no electronic conductivity, since all of the electrons are tied in place in forming the covalent or electron-pair bonds. As Figure 2 indicates, no electronic traffic is possible in this crystal, and the situation is somewhat analogous to that in a parking garage in which the lower floor spaces are completely filled with vehicles.

Excess Electrons and Holes as Imperfections

If the electronic structure is made imperfect, however, electronic conduction can take place. We shall illustrate this condition in germanium. Two of the most important semiconductors from the point of view of transistor electronics are silicon and germanium. These two elements come in the fourth column of the periodic table, as does the diamond, and also have four valence electrons per atom. Silicon and germanium crystallize in the diamond crystal structure, and their valence electrons are used to form electron-pair bonds in the same way.

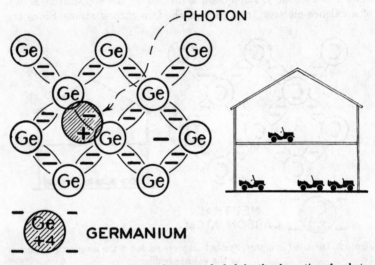

Figure 3. Production of an excess electron and a hole by the absorption of a photon in germanium

Figure 3 illustrates one way in which conduction may be produced in a germanium crystal. A quantum of light is represented as being absorbed in a germanium crystal. It has long been established that light energy comes in units, or quanta. Each quantum of light has an energy that depends on the wave length or color of the light. This relationship is given by the well-known equation of Planck:

$$\text{Energy} = h\nu = hc/\lambda, \tag{1}$$

where h is Planck's constant, c is the speed of light, and $\nu = c/\lambda$ is the frequency of light. This relationship between energy and frequency applies throughout quantum mechanics. In order to distinguish quanta of light from other quanta, light quanta are generally called *photons*.

It has been shown by experiments that photons are absorbed in germanium crystals by a very simple mechanism.[1] If a photon of sufficient energy falls upon the crystal, it will be annihilated, and all of its energy will be imparted to one of the valence electrons. This electron is ejected from the electron-pair bond, leaving an incomplete bond behind. Both of these imperfections, the *excess electron* which has been ejected and the incomplete bond, or *hole*, can contribute to the electrical conductivity of the crystal. The excess electron and the hole are the first two of the five imperfections listed in Table 1 which must be considered in discussing transistor electronics. As the parenthesis in Table 1 implies, an excess electron is frequently referred to simply as an electron.

TABLE 1

1.	$-$ (excess) electron
2.	$+$ hole
3.	deathnium
4.	$\oplus$ donor
5.	$\ominus$ acceptor

As shown in the table, the excess electron is a negative imperfection; that is, the part of the crystal in which it is located was neutral before the electron appeared there and, therefore, must have a negative charge equal to the charge on the electron by virtue of the presence of one excess electron. The hole, on the contrary, represents a positive charge of the same magnitude, since the part of the crystal from which the electron was removed was neutral before the electron was removed and must, therefore, have one net positive charge.

We must next consider the behavior of an excess electron. Since the covalent bond is a very stable electron configuration, one might think that the extra electron would slip into one of the covalent bonds and thus contribute to the binding of the crystal at that point. There is, however, a sort of quantum mechanical zoning ordinance which requires that two, and only two, electrons may cooperate to form a covalent bond. This zoning ordinance, technically known as the *Pauli exclusion principle*, thus prevents the excess electron from fitting into any of the covalent bonds. As a result, it cannot become bound in place but is free to move in the crystal.

If the excess electron is placed at some point at rest in a germanium crystal at room temperature, it will not remain at rest, because the atoms of the germanium crystal have heat energy of motion. As a result, they are vibrating about equilibrium positions and jostle the excess electron. This sets the excess electron in motion so that it moves through the crystal.

Once set in motion, an excess electron may move for the surprisingly long distance of 10^{-5} cm in a straight line before being deflected. This distance is referred to as "surprisingly long" because it is about 1000 times the distance between germanium atoms. As the electron moves through the crystal, it is vigorously repelled by the negative charges of the electrons in the electron-pair bonds and strongly attracted by the positive charges at the core of the germanium atoms. The excess electron is thus subjected to large forces, and it is remarkable that the electron is not violently deflected from its course in traveling one interatomic distance.

There is no simple way to explain how the electron can move 1000 interatomic distances without being deflected. The explanation is not that the electron is moving down the rows of atoms, like a man walking through an orchard parallel to the lines of trees. In fact, the excess electron can move for this distance in any direction in the crystal. The reason for the long *mean free path* is found in terms of the wave equation which describes the motion of the electron. In general it is a property of wave motion that waves can proceed unattenuated in periodic structures. This is true of acoustical waves in a gas, of mechanical waves in a solid, or of electromagnetic waves moving through electrical filters or periodic metallic structures in space. In all of these cases if the structure is perfectly periodic, the wave will proceed indefinitely without attenuation. (The structures must be loss-less to be analogues of the wave equation for electrons.) The same condition is true for the waves which describe the motion of an electron. Although it is now generally known and accepted that an electron has a dual nature, behaving in some ways like a particle and in other ways like a wave, a true understanding of this behavior cannot be given in simple terms. It can best be acquired by the tedious process of taking a course in quantum mechanics for a semester or two.

On the basis of wave mechanics, we can understand how the electron may proceed indefinitely through a perfectly periodic structure, like a perfect crystal, without being deflected. This leads us to change our question from "Why is the mean free path so long?" to "Why is the mean free path as short as 1000 interatomic distances?" Why does not the electron proceed all the way through the crystal in a single straight line? The answer is that the same thermal agitation which set the electron into motion causes the crystal to be not quite periodic. The atoms are vibrating about their average positions, and, as a result, one unit cell of the crystal is not quite like the next. It is this thermal agitation that causes the electron to be deflected after it travels about 1000 interatomic distances. If the thermal agitation were increased, for example, by doubling the absolute temperature of the crystal, that is, by raising it to 300°C., then the vibration of the atoms would be increased, and the mean free path of the electron would be about 500 lattice constants instead of 1000.

Diffusion and Drift

The resultant behavior of an electron is shown in Figure 4. The electron follows a random or Brownian motion, proceeding in steps of about 10^{-5} cm. The average length l of these steps is called the

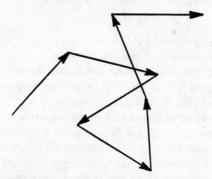

Figure 4. An electron at room temperature moves with an average speed of 10^7 cm/per second (thermal velocity) in straight line steps of about 10^{-5} cm average length (mean free path). It thus proceeds for about 10^{-12} second (mean free time) between changes of direction

mean free path. The electron has its proper share of thermal energy, and from this it can be concluded by methods of statistical mechanics that its average speed, or thermal velocity v, is about 10^7 cm per second. As a result, the electron changes its direction of motion about 10^{12} times per second. If a group of electrons were placed at some point in the crystal, the Brownian motion would cause them to spread out in a process known as *diffusion*, as illustrated in Figure 5.

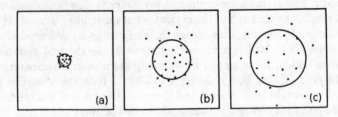

Figure 5. A small group of electrons spreads out progressively as a result of diffusion

The diffusion process is described by a *diffusion constant* denoted by D From statistical mechanical theories, one can express D in terms of the microscopic behavior of the electron and one finds approximately that for the values of Figure 4:

$$D \cong \tfrac{1}{3}\, vl \cong 30 \text{ cm}^2/\text{sec}. \tag{2}$$

For this example, it would follow that a group of electrons would spread out to a radius of about one centimeter in $1/30$ second.

If an electric field is applied to the crystal from left to right, as indicated in Figure 6, then the electron will be subjected to a steady force toward the left, since it has a negative charge. This force will be superimposed upon the random or Brownian motion of the electron with the result that it will drift steadily toward the left. Statistical mechanical reasoning may be applied to the microscopic situation of Figure 4 in order to calculate the *drift velocity* to the left. The mobility, μ, is defined as the ratio of drift velocity to electric field. The equation for mobility is

$$\mu = eD/kT \cong evl/3kT. \tag{3}$$

The first equality is exact in this equation and is known commonly as the *Einstein relationship*. The second equality is based on the approximate formula for the diffusion constant given in Equation 2. The value of mobility corresponding to the values given in Figure 4 is 1200 cm² per volt second. This means that an electron in a field of one volt per centimeter will drift with a speed of 1200 cm per second. If the field strength is doubled, the drift velocity will also be doubled.

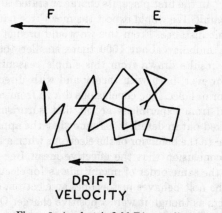

Figure 6. An electric field E in one direction exerts on an electron a force F in the opposite direction, and this superimposes a drift velocity on a random diffusion motion

Thus we see that the two quantities are deduced from the microscopic picture of Figure 4. One of these is diffusion and the other is mobility. A later section of this discussion describes how new experiments based on transistor developments permit us to observe the diffusion and drift of electrons far more directly than was formerly possible.

The Behavior of a Hole

The word hole is used to describe the electronic imperfection produced by removing one electron from a valence bond. Such a disturbance obviously represents one positive charge equal to the electronic charge. Like the excess electron, this charge will be shielded by the dielectric constant of the material. When the perfection of the crystal is disturbed by the presence of a hole, electronic conduction takes place by a replacement process. An electron in an adjacent bond can jump into the hole in the incomplete bond, thus producing an electronic motion and a reciprocal motion of the hole. If an electronic field is applied such as to move electrons to the left, the hole will move toward the right as a result.

On the basis of this picture, what would we expect the attributes of a hole to be? In the first place, its charge as stated above would be $+1$ electronic unit. We would expect the mean free path to be about one interatomic distance. From this we would predict that the hole would have a mobility about 1000 times smaller than that of an electron. The results drawn from this simple reasoning are in disagreement, however, both with theory and with direct observation of the behavior of holes. The conclusions drawn from more complete reasoning and from experiment are at first surprising. When the theory is worked out in detail, it is found that the application of the wave equation to the behavior of the electrons when a hole is present leads to the conclusion that the effective mean free path for hole motions is of the same order of magnitude as for electrons. Qualitatively then, the hole behaves just as does an electron, except for the fact that it acts as though it were a positive charge. Quantitatively, D and μ are somewhat less for a hole than for an electron.

There is no simple way of showing how the electron replacement process can lead to these long mean free paths for holes; the analytical reasoning required to reach this conclusion inevitably seems to be complicated. But from the experimental point of view, the behavior of the hole may be regarded as an established fact. The mobility and diffusion constants for holes in germanium have been directly measured, as have those for electrons. It is found that the hole is approximately one-half as mobile as an electron in this case. (If the mean free path were really as short as one interatomic distance, the ratio would have to be 1:1000 instead of 1:2.) Thus, the important attributes of a hole may be regarded as determined by direct experimental observations. So we are justified in using these attributes of the behavior of holes in design theory and in the explanation of the way in which transistor devices function.

Although the hole has acquired a very substantial reality as a result of new experiments in transistor physics, its true nature should not be forgotten. The hole concept is, after all, simply a convenient way of describing the behavior of an incomplete assemblage of electrons. Attributing to the hole a positive mass, a positive charge, and a mean path of about 10^{-5} cm leads to a correct description of the way in which this imperfection in the incomplete assemblage diffuses and drifts under the influence of electric and magnetic fields. Since these processes are of prime importance in transistor electronics, no error will be made for them if we consider the hole to be a real particle. There are pitfalls, however, in the blind acceptance of this concept, and there are circumstances in which the true electronic nature of hole currents may become apparent.[2] For example, adding a hole to a specimen will not increase its mass. Adding a hole is really removing an electron, and the mass of the specimen will be decreased by the mass of an electron. The linear momentum of a current of holes in a specimen will be in the opposite direction from the motion of the holes, since the momentum really arises from the motion of the assemblage of electrons, and this motion is in the opposite direction from the hole motion. These considerations are presented chiefly to prevent possible confusion which may arise if the concept of the hole is taken too literally.

Photoconductivity and Recombination

If light shines on an otherwise perfect germanium crystal, then the pairs of excess electrons and holes that are formed will impart a conductivity to the crystal. This conductivity is known as *photoconductivity*. If the source of light is removed, the photoconductivity will die away, owing to the recombination of the holes and the electrons. Thus, if an electron falls into an incomplete bond, one hole-electron pair will be eliminated.

The photoconductivity dies away with a characteristic time known as the *lifetime*. Thus, after the light is turned off, the photoconductivity will drop to approximately one-half its value in one lifetime. This process continues with a reduction of approximately one-half in each subsequent period of one lifetime.

If the process of recombination of holes and electrons were a direct one, the lifetime would be the same in all germanium crystals. It is found experimentally, however, that two otherwise very similar germanium crystals will have lifetimes that differ by as much as a thousandfold. In one crystal, the lifetime may be a millisecond, whereas in another it may be a microsecond. This variation in lifetime requires the presence of some sort of imperfection which catalyzes the recombination of the holes and the electrons.

As listed in Table 1, the generic name given to this imperfection is *deathnium*; this name is one of its best-known attributes. Actually, there are several forms of deathnium. For example, if electrons having an energy of several million electron volts fall upon a germanium crystal, the lifetime is subsequently reduced.[3] From the investigation at Purdue University, it is known that such bombardment produces disorder of the germanium atoms.[4] A high-energy electron can eject a germanium atom bodily from its normal position in the crystal structure, thus leaving a vacancy behind, where there should be an atom, and causing the ejected atom to become either an extra atom or an interstitial atom fitting into a place in the structure which would

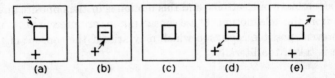

Figure 7. A recombination center (deathnium) captures alternately an electron and a hole and thus catalyzes their recombination, as shown in (a), (b), and (c). The thermally activated generation process is shown in (d) and (e)

normally be empty. It has been found at Bell Telephone Laboratories that these disordering effects function as deathnium. It has also been found that copper and nickel chemical impurities in the germanium produce marked reductions in lifetime.[5]

The way in which deathnium catalyzes the recombination process is indicated in Figure 7. In (b) of this figure, an electron is captured by a deathnium center. The deathnium center thus becomes a baited trap which is ready to capture a hole. If a hole comes near to the deathnium center, the electron can drop into it, thus forming a normal covalent bond, and the deathnium center is then uncharged and ready to repeat the process.

It is a characteristic of all microscopic processes that they may go backward as well as forward. Thus, the deathnium center may generate hole-electron pairs as well as eliminate them. The generation process is indicated in (d) and (e) of Figure 7. In (d) the deathnium center captures an electron from an adjoining normal electron-pair bond. This produces a hole which wanders off. Somewhat later, the deathnium center ejects the electron and thus reverts to its empty state, in which it is ready either to recombine or to generate another hole-electron pair.

Under conditions of thermal equilibrium, both the recombination process and the generation process proceed continuously. The energy required to generate the hole-electron pair is furnished by the thermal energy of vibration of the atoms in the germanium crystal. The condition of thermal equilibrium is achieved when the two processes balance. For germanium at room temperature, this leads to a conductivity of about 0.02 ohm^{-1} cm^{-1}. The concentration of holes and electrons under equilibrium conditions is governed by a sort of mass action law which requires that the product of hole density multiplied by electron density is a constant, independent of the concentration of deathnium. For example, if the concentration of deathnium is doubled, both the rate of generation and the rate of recombination are doubled, but the equilibrium concentrations of holes and electrons are unaltered.

Evidence that the deathnium mechanism shown in Figure 7 is correct has been obtained by studying the dependence of the rate of recombination upon hole and electron densities.[6] These studies are found to be in general agreement with the predictions based on the statistical model of Figure 7.

n-Type Germanium

The specimens of semiconductors of principal interest in transistor physics and most frequently used in transistor electronics are those which derive their conductivity not from light or from the generation of hole-electron pairs by the deathnium process but from the presence of chemical impurities. Figure 8 illustrates a specimen of germanium which has a permanent or built-in conductivity due to the presence of arsenic atoms. An arsenic atom has five valence electrons, which surround an inner core having a charge of $+5$ units. If a germanium crystal is grown from molten germanium containing arsenic as an impurity, then some of the arsenic atoms crystallize in place of germanium atoms. The arsenic atoms use four of their valence electrons to complete the bond surrounding them, but the Pauli exclusion principle prevents the fifth electron from fitting into this structure. As a result, the extra electron becomes free and wanders through the crystal as an excess electron.

The negative charge of the excess electron is neutralized by an unbalanced positive charge on the arsenic atom. It is apparent that the arsenic atom represents a positive charge, since its share of the four surrounding valence bonds is only four electrons, whereas the charge on the core of the arsenic atom is +5.

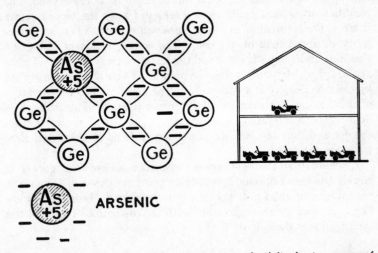

Figure 8. *n*-Type germanium, with a permanent conductivity due to presence of arsenic atoms

In Table 1 the arsenic atom is classified as a *donor* and given the symbol of a plus sign surrounded by a circle. This symbol, which is used in some of the subsequent drawings, indicates that the arsenic atom represents a positive imperfection in the crystal, and the circle indicates that it is immobile. Although an electric field will exert a force on an arsenic atom, the covalent bonds hold it so tightly in position that it cannot move, and thus the atom remains fixed permanently in place and does not contribute to the electrical conductivity.

Other elements from the fifth column of the periodic table, which have five valence electrons as does arsenic, also act as donors and give conduction electrons to the germanium. A specimen of germanium containing donors is known as *n*-type, since its conductivity is produced by *negative* carriers of current.

p-Type Germanium

Conductivity in which the current carriers are holes is known as *p*-type conductivity and is produced by chemical impurities from the third column of the periodic table. An example of this type of conductivity is shown in Figure 9. In this figure a gallium atom is

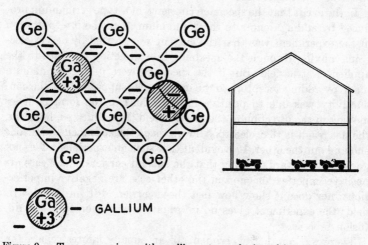

Figure 9. *p*-Type germanium, with a gallium atom substituted for one germanium atom

represented as being substituted for one of the germanium atoms. The gallium atom does not have enough valence electrons to complete the three bonds and steals an electron from somewhere else. As a result, a hole is set free to contribute to the conductivity, and the gallium atom acquires a negative charge. Because of its thieving nature, a gallium atom is known as an *acceptor*, and is shown in Table 1 by a minus sign surrounded by a circle.

Pre-transistor Experiments

Holes, electrons, donors, acceptors, and even, to a lesser extent, deathnium were well-developed concepts prior to the invention of

the transistor. The experimental foundation for these concepts, however, was of a very indirect character before the development of transistor physics. A typical pre-transistor experiment consisted of taking
a specimen of semiconductor and making a resistor out of it. If voltage is applied to the semiconductor, it is found that Ohm's law is
obeyed, and the flow of current through it is proportional to the
applied voltage. The reason that this proportionality holds is that
the drift velocity of the carriers is directly proportional to the electric field—that is, the mobility is independent of the electric field.

In the event that the specimen consisted of n-type germanium produced by adding donors to the germanium, then the interpretation
of the experiment was that the current was carried by excess electrons moving through the specimen in a direction opposite to the
applied electric field. But if the specimen were p-type germanium
made by adding acceptors to the melt, it was supposed that the conductivity was due to positive imperfections in the form of holes
moving in the direction of the electric field. In both cases, however,
the net result is that electrons flow *through* the specimen—in at one
end and out the other. It is evident that such an experiment does not
go very far toward showing that the current carriers in one case are
positive imperfections and in the other case are negative imperfections, nor does it show how fast these carriers drift in the electric
field; the experiment gives no information whatever upon the diffusion process.

There was another experiment, of an equally indirect character,
known as the Hall effect. If a magnetic field is applied to the specimen with the field direction perpendicular to the direction of current
flow, a transverse electric field develops in the specimen. This transverse electric field is found to be of opposite sign for n-type and for
p-type germanium, which is in accordance with theory. The magnitude of the transverse field can thus be used to estimate the concentrations of carriers and also their drift velocities. The Hall effect
suffers, however, from being a thoroughly macroscopic measurement, as does the measurement of Ohm's law, so that no really
direct evidence was provided by these experiments for such
attributes as the diffusion and drift of holes and electrons discussed
in connection with Figure 4. As will be described below, this situation
has been drastically changed by the development of transistor
physics.

Amplifiers, Transformers, and the Point Contact Transistor

Before considering the new experiments of transistor physics we shall discuss the relationship of the transistor to electronic amplifiers. In order to exhibit the essential characteristics of an electronic amplifier, we shall start by describing the difference between transformers and amplifiers.

Figure 10 illustrates the simplest and earliest form of transformer, which consists of a lever. As everyone knows, a crowbar transforms a

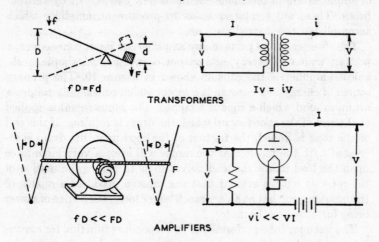

Figure 10. Some examples of mechanical transformers and amplifiers

small force applied on the handle to a large force applied at the point. However, this amplification of force is accomplished at the expense of a reduction in distance of motion. As a result the power or work available at the output end of a crowbar is never larger than that received at the input end. The same is true of an electrical transformer. An electrical transformer can be used to amplify a voltage, but it does so at the expense of a reduction in current, with the result that the output power of a transformer is always slightly smaller than the input power.

An electrical transformer performs many useful functions. However, it does not possess the essential function needed for long distance electrical communication, namely, the production of an enlarged replica of an input signal. This may be illustrated in terms of the telephone problem. Thus when a telephone conversation is carried over telephone wires, it gradually attenuates, and after traveling a distance of 30 to 50 miles the telephone conversation becomes so weak as to be almost inaudible. The use of a transformer at this point accomplishes no useful purpose, since it cannot increase the energy available for hearing in the earphone. What is required is the production of an enlarged copy of the weak signal that can either be heard or transmitted further over the telephone lines. The function of amplification in telephone circuits is now carried out by vacuum tubes. These are combined so as to produce an amplifier which accomplishes the desired purpose.

The three essential parts of any amplifier are input connections, a primary source of energy, and output connections. A simple mechanical amplifier is the capstan shown in Figure 10. The primary source of energy in a capstan is a motor which continually rotates a drum, around which a rope is wrapped. The input signal is applied to the end of the rope toward which the drum is rotating. If this end of the rope is pulled, the friction of the rope upon the drum is increased with the result that the motor will exert a very large force upon the load unless the load moves so as to reduce the tension of the rope. It is thus evident that the capstan produces a replica of the input motion but at a very much larger force, the source of power being furnished by the motor.

The vacuum tube performs the corresponding function for electrical signals. A small current and voltage applied to the grid of a vacuum tube produce a larger current and voltage in the output circuit and thus result in the amplification of power. The primary source of power in this case is the B battery, which supplies the plate voltage to the vacuum tube. For purposes of this discussion we shall not consider the mechanism and functioning of the vacuum tube but instead will see how the existence of the vacuum tube served as a stimulus for the invention of the transistor.

Prior to the invention of the transistor, some workers in this field had forseen such a device as a possibility by following a line of reasoning suggested in Figure 11. This figure represents a modern form of the cat's whisker or crystal detector. In this example the crystal is of n-type germanium, rather than of galena, which was used in the early days of radio. On one side of the crystal, contact is made with a small sharp point and on the other side a passive, large-area contact is made. It is then found that when positive voltages are applied to the point, large currents flow through the crystal but when negative voltages are applied to the point, small currents flow. Devices having this sort of current voltage characteristic are known as rectifiers and serve useful electronic purposes. However, they do not have separate input and output circuits nor a primary source of power and so cannot perform the essential function of amplification.

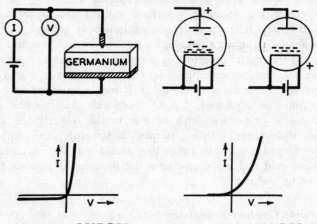

GERMANIUM RECTIFIER   VACUUM TUBE RECTIFIER

Figure 11. Comparison of a semiconductor diode rectifier (*left*) and a vacuum tube diode rectifier (*right*)

Figure 11 also shows a vacuum tube rectifier. Such a rectifier has a hot filament out of which electrons boil into the surrounding vacuum. Also within the vacuum there is a cold plate. If this plate is made positive, electrons flow across the vacuum to the plate and a large current flows through the device. If the plate is negative, it repels electrons and drives them back into the filament, and no current flows. Thus the current voltage characteristic of this device is similar to that of the germanium diode.

The invention which ushered in the electronic age was made in the second decade of this century by Lee DeForest, who introduced a grid or screen between the filament and plate of the vacuum tube. He then found that input signals, applied between the grid and the filament, could produce enlarged replicas in the circuit between the

filament and the plate, so long as a suitable source of primary power
in the form of a battery or rectifier was available. This electronic
amplification underlies all modern forms of electrical communication. It is used in amplifying telephone signals so that they may be
carried across the continent. Without this amplification the signals
transmitted by radio and television transmitters would be unable
to operate loud speakers or television tubes. This same form of
electronic amplification is responsible for the functioning of electronic computing machines, electronic control circuits for use in
production, and military electronic equipment in general.

The similarity between the rectification curves of the vacuum tube
diode and the crystal detector suggested that it might be possible to
make a semiconductor amplifier by the introduction of a grid into
the germanium or the semiconductor. If such a semiconductor amplifier could be developed, it seemed probable that it would have
many useful properties. Such devices would evidently be much
smaller than vacuum tubes, simpler in structure, and probably
cheaper to produce. Furthermore they would have the advantage of
operating cold and not requiring a hot filament or cathode to be
warmed beforehand.

The Point Contact Transistor

The attainment of such an electronic amplifier was announced in
June of 1948. This is the point contact transistor illustrated in
Figure 12. The germanium crystal is mounted on a plug in a metal
tube which constitutes one of the terminals of the device. The other
two terminals are brought out through an insulating plug at the
top. These latter two terminals are formed into pointed cat's whiskers which touch the germanium. One can appreciate at a glance
the great stride forward made by Bardeen and Brattain,[7] who in-
vented the point contact transistor, for, whereas the old crystal
detector had only a one-point contact, the point contact transistor
has two point contacts. There are, however, a number of additional
features incorporated in the point contact transistor. One of these
is that the semiconductor employed must not be too high in deathnium concentration.

In this discussion how the point contact transistor works will not
be described in detail. Instead transistor action, in terms of a some-

what simpler type of transistor known as the *junction transistor*, will be illustrated. One of the chief differences between the two types of transistors is that the point contact transistor depends in its functioning upon the nature of the contact between the metal wire and the germanium. This intimately involves the nature of germanium surfaces about which we still know considerably less than about the interior of the germanium. However, the study of the input or emitter terminal of the point contact transistor has led

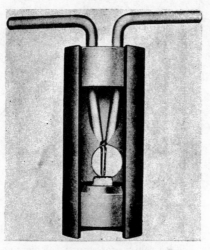

Figure 12. Structure of a point contact
transistor

to a much better understanding of the functioning and behavior of carriers in semiconductors. Before leaving the point contact transistor, it should be remarked that when an input signal is applied between one of the point contacts and the shell or base of the semiconductor, then an enlarged replica is obtained between the other terminal and the base, so long as a suitable primary power source in the form of a battery or rectifier is provided.

Hole Injection

Under operating conditions, the emitter point of a point contact transistor is biased in the forward or easy-flow direction. If the germanium is n-type, this means that the emitter point is biased positive and tends to withdraw electrons from the semiconductor. Figure 13 represents this situation and indicates that two possible processes for electron removal must be considered.

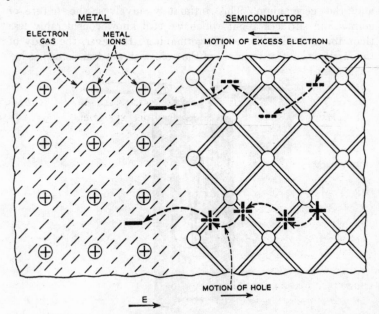

Figure 13. Two possible mechanisms for current flow near an emitter point as described in text

In Figure 13, the metal is represented in a highly pictorial fashion. The valence electrons in a metal are thought of as forming an electron gas, which permeates the entire structure. Thus, the electrons are not held in position in valence bonds as they are in an insulator. The electron gas can flow freely through the structure of the metal, and this fact accounts for the high conductivity of metals. In the upper part of Figure 13 one of the processes for removing electrons from the semiconductor is represented. Since the semiconductor is n-type, it contains excess electrons; these excess electrons may be drawn to the metal by its positive charge and thus enter the metal to produce a current of electrons flowing out of the emitter point through the connecting lead.

Another possible mechanism for electron transfer from semiconductor to metal is shown in the lower part of Figure 13. In this case, an electron is withdrawn from one of the valence bonds adjacent to the metal. This process also transfers an electron from the semiconductor to the metal, but when the transfer occurs a hole is left behind. The hole is repelled by the positive charge on the emitter contact and moves deeper into the semiconductor.

Both of the processes discussed above have the same effect so far as the metal emitter point and conducting leads to the emitter point are concerned. Both produce a net flow of electrons from semiconductor to the emitter point and through the leads to the emitter terminal. It is thus evident that some more subtle experiment than simply measuring the current to the emitter point is necessary to show that both processes of electron removal from the semiconductor occur. Suitable experiments have been planned and performed, with the result that it is possible to show that both of the processes of Figure 13 occur, and also to determine the fraction of current carried by each. In fact, in a good emitter point it can be shown that more than 90 per cent of the current is carried by the process which injects holes into the semiconductor, and less than 10 per cent by the process which removes electrons.

In an ideal emitter point, all of the current would be carried by the hole injection process. The reason for this result is that the electron removal process does not disturb the state of affairs within the semiconductor. If electrons are removed from the semiconductor in the neighborhood of the emitter point, they are promptly replaced by electrons flowing from more distant parts of the semiconductor, and these electrons in turn are replaced by other electrons flowing in from whatever contact to the semiconductor completes the electrical current path or circuit. In the hole injection process the situation is quite different. Normally, the number of holes in the n-type semiconductor is negligible. However, when electrons are removed from the valence bonds and holes are injected, relatively large numbers of holes will be introduced. The conductivity of the semiconductor will be increased in the neighborhood of the emitter point in much the same fashion that it would be if light were to shine on the semiconductor and produce hole-electron pairs. This disturbance in the electronic structure can be used to produce amplifying action in the transistor.

Instead of discussing the quantitative experiment which is used to distinguish between the two processes shown in Figure 13, a qualitative experiment which shows that hole injection does occur at an emitter point will be described. This experiment permits quantitative studies to be made of the behavior of holes and provides a method for the direct measurement of diffusion and drift.

The experimental arrangement which was first carried out in this form by J. R. Haynes is illustrated diagrammatically in Figure 14.

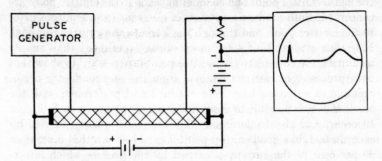

Figure 14. Schematic representation of experiment to observe the drift and diffusion of injected holes in n-type germanium

The germanium specimen is in the form of an elongated point contact transistor. There is, however, an extra contact on the base. The germanium is present as a rod, about $\frac{1}{32}$ of an inch in cross section and approximately one inch long. A "sweeping field" is applied from end to end of the rod by a battery. This field acts in such a direction as to draw electrons from right to left through the rod. If any holes were introduced in the rod, they would drift from left to right.

When the pulse generator at the left-hand point contact, or emitter point, operates, the emitter point is biased positive and thus in the forward direction. According to the ideas presented in Figure 13, this condition causes holes to be injected into the rod. These holes are then drawn down the rod by the sweeping field. After a time they arrive in the neighborhood of the collector point, which, as the figure shows, is biased negative. It thus tends to attract holes, and some of the holes flow to the collector point and thus contribute to the current flowing in the collector circuit. This current flows through a resistor, and the voltage across the resistor is applied to the vertical plates of a cathode-ray oscilloscope.

Under operating conditions, the operation of the pulse generator is accomplished electronically and is synchronized with the functioning of the oscilloscope, so that just before the switch is closed, the electron beam in the oscilloscope starts to move across the tube face from left to right. At time t_1 the switch to the emitter point is closed for a brief moment; the time of closing is indicated by a "pick up" signal on the face of the oscilloscope. After this nothing happens until time t_2 when some of the holes arrive at the collector point; the concentration of holes builds up for a moment and then decays as the group of holes injected at time t_1 pass by the collector point. The arrival pulse at the collector point is not so sharp as the "pick up" pulse because the holes, which were injected approximately at one point and at the same time, spread out by diffusion so that by the time the group of holes reaches the collector point it is relatively large in extent along the rod.

It is evident that this experiment permits observation and measurement of both diffusion and drift. It is possible to measure the distance between the points and the electric field between the points; by calibrating the oscilloscope, the time of travel may be measured. Thus the drift velocity may be measured directly, verifying the fact that the disturbance occurring at the emitter point behaves precisely as would be expected if the emitter point injected small numbers of positive carriers into the rod. For example, if the distance between points is doubled the time lag between pick-up at t_1 and the arrival of the pulse is also doubled. This result shows that the carriers drift at a constant drift speed in the rod. But if the sweeping field is doubled, the time lag is cut in half. This fact shows that the speed of the carriers is proportional to the electric field. If the polarity of the sweeping field is reversed, we would expect the injected carriers to be drawn to the left in the filament so that none arrive at the collector point, and it is found experimentally that this is true.

As was indicated above, the spread of the time of arrival of holes is a measure of the diffusion constant. From studies of the dependence of this spread upon the transit time from emitter to collector, it can be verified that the holes spread out in accordance with the laws expected for diffusion phenomena. The value of the diffusion constant D can also be measured.

J. R. Haynes and his colleagues have performed various experiments of this sort. They have also experimented with the case of electron injection into p-type germanium and have dealt with the two corresponding cases for silicon. The values of mobility and diffusion constant which they obtain in this way are tabulated in Table 2.[8]

It should be noted from Table 2 that in each case the ratio of diffusion constant to mobility is approximately $1/40$, and the dimensions of this quantity are in volts. In other words the ratio of D to μ is 25 mv. This value has a fundamental significance, and the relationship between D and μ is commonly known as the Einstein relationship. This relationship has recently been investigated in detail, by the means described above, for germanium.[9] The significance of this value of 25 mv is that an electron moving with random thermal energy will, on the average, be just capable of surmounting a poten-

TABLE 2. Mobilities in cm²/Volt sec and Diffusion Constants in cm²/sec

	Electrons		Holes	
	μ	D	μ	D
Silicon	1200	30	250	6.5
Germanium	3600	93	1700	43

tial hill of 25 mv. In other words, 25 mv is the electrostatic potential corresponding to thermal energy for one electron. Put in another way it can be stated that if any electron was set in motion with thermal energy in free space against any electric field, the electron would be slowed down by the electric field and by the time it had moved 25 mv against the field its velocity would be brought to zero and it would start to move in the opposite direction. The fact that a value of 25 mv is obtained shows that the charge of the carriers which are drifting and diffusing in the Haynes experiment is the electronic charge. If it were half or twice this value, for example, the ration of D to μ would be 12.5 or 50 mv, respectively.

Figure 15 is a photograph of a typical experimental setup used for carrying out the experiments just described. The scale may be judged from the microscope objective at the top of the figure, which is about one inch in diameter. The germanium rod is near the center of the figure supported on a lucite block. It is surrounded by four micromanipulators, which are controlled by the screws having knurled heads. The micromanipulators move relatively massive copper wires.

Figure 15. Photograph of experimental apparatus for studying the drift and diffusion of injected carriers

Attached to the ends of the wires are sharpened tungsten points, or cat's whiskers. Two of the points are placed on the rod to supply the sweeping field, and the other two (not clearly visible) used as emitter and collector points.

The description given above shows clearly that, as a result of transistor techniques, it is now possible to measure directly the attributes of the behavior of holes and electrons, characteristics which were only very indirectly observed in the past. However, both the diffusion constant and the mobility are, in a sense, microscopic quantities which are certain combinations of the more fundamental quantities represented in Figure 4.

Future Experiments

Recently a new line of experimentation has commenced by means of which it is hoped that an even more intimate insight will be obtained of the basic microscopic quantities themselves. The first experiment is essentially a measurement of the collision frequency of electrons. This measurement has been completed at reduced temperatures at which the frequency of collision is somewhat lower than usual, being about 10^{11} collisions per second, rather than 10^{12} collisions per second. Under this condition the frequency of collision of the electrons is comparable to the frequency of microwaves, such as those used in radar. If the conductivity of a germanium specimen is measured at microwave frequencies, it is found that inertial effects of the electrons affect conductivity. The electrons do not have time to build up their full drift velocity before the electric field is reversed. As a result the conductivity and dielectric constant show "dispersion" and have values which depend upon the applied frequency. From this effect, it is possible to compare the collision frequency with the known frequency of the applied electromagnetic waves. T. S. Benedict,[10] who has performed these experiments, has been able to show that the collision frequencies have the orders of magnitude as discussed in connection with Figure 4.

Still more enlightening experiments are being planned which will make use of even lower temperatures, at which the collision frequency is small compared to the frequency of the wave. Under these conditions the application of magnetic fields will cause the electrons to "resonate." Perhaps experiments of this sort will permit direct observations of some of the properties associated with the way in which the electron waves travel through the crystal. These properties are fundamental in the theory of the interaction of electron waves with crystals.

The p-n Junction

In the previous section, experiments have been described which show the properties of holes and electrons with a high degree of directness. These are only a few of a large variety of experiments which have been undertaken to exhibit the behavior of the imperfections listed in Table 1. We shall now consider how the imperfections already discussed may be combined in ways so that useful and interesting functions may be performed.

Basic to a large amount of the development of transistor physics and electronics is the so-called *p-n* junction. Such a junction is represented in Figure 16. This junction is to be regarded as grown from a single crystal of germanium. Such a crystal may be grown by taking a pot of molten germanium and dipping into it a small seed crystal that has previously been prepared. If the temperature is gradually reduced and at the same time the seed is gradually withdrawn, then the melt solidifies upon the seed crystal. The pattern of atoms is determined by the pattern within the seed so that all of the rows of atoms are lined up throughout the crystal. For the experiment shown in Figure 16 the melt was doped initially with donors. As the crystal grew, however, acceptors were suddenly added to the melt so that beyond a certain point an excess of acceptors was found in the crystal. After the crystal is grown and cooled, a small section is cut out containing the junction between the donor-rich and acceptor-rich regions.

Figure 16 illustrates this small section of a crystal, one part of which contains donors, and the other part both donors and acceptors with the acceptors present in greater abundance. In the second part

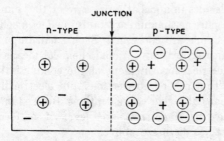

Figure 16. A *p-n* junction comprising a *p*-type region produced by overcompensation

of the crystal a phenomenon known as *compensation* takes place. One might at first think that both holes and electrons would be present in this region. However, if they were both present, recombination would occur and finally only holes would be left. The number of holes is just sufficient to cause this part of the crystal to be electrically neutral.

The phenomenon of compensation has very significant industrial implications; it is not necessary to remove imperfections of one chemical type in order to obtain material of the opposite conductivity type, but only to add enough acceptors to a sample of n-type material to neutralize the *chemical charge*. Under these conditions the material acts substantially as though it were chemically pure. The addition of either acceptors or donors to this compensated material results in specimens whose properties are much the same as if only the excess concentration of donors or acceptors were present.

Thus the crystal consists of an n-type region and a p-type region. The junction between the two regions is not observable mechanically. Actually the level of impurities is such that if in a typical example one were to traverse a row of atoms within the crystal from one end to the other only one or two donors or acceptors would be encountered. This means that the chemical purity is of the order of one impurity atom in 100 million germanium atoms.

It is probable, in fact, that the germanium used in transistor electronics is the purest of all chemical substances prepared in solid form. Specimens have been obtained in which the density of impurities is only one part in 10 billion. This corresponds to a density of impurities of 10^{12} per cubic centimeter, a density comparable to the density of molecules in a gas at a pressure of 10^{-5} mm of mercury. In this sense a pure germanium crystal is in effect a solid vacuum so far as imperfections are concerned. Such small impurity densities cannot be measured by conventional chemical means but must be inferred by electrical measurement of the conductivity. It is thus quite possible that other imperfections, not electrically active, are present in somewhat higher concentrations. But so far as the important impurities are concerned, the level of perfection has the phenomenal values discussed above.

One of the striking features about p-n junctions is that they are excellent rectifiers of electricity. In Figure· 17 the mechanism for rectification is illustrated in qualitative terms. Only the holes and the electrons are shown, the chemical imperfections being omitted for the sake of simplicity. Part *a* of this figure represents the distribution of holes and electrons under conditions of thermal equilibrium with no voltages applied externally to the junction. There are a few holes

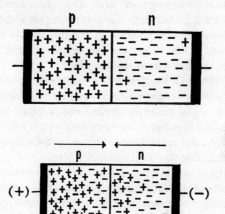

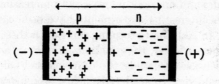

Figure 17. Distribution of current carriers in a
p-n junction for (a) thermal equilibrium, (b)
forward bias, and (c) reverse bias

in the *n*-type region and a few electrons in the *p*-type region. These minority carriers are formed by the generation process carried out by deathnium. Such minority carriers quickly recombine, also by the deathnium process, but, under conditions of thermal equilibrium, a few will be continuously present.

If the *n*-type region is connected to the negative terminal of a battery as is shown in part *b* of Figure 17, the region tends to become more attractive for holes and less attractive for electrons. As a result, electrons and holes cross the junction in both directions flowing toward the attractive terminals of the battery. They do not, however, penetrate very far into either region owing to the presence of deathnium. Deathnium catalyzes the recombination of electrons injected into the p-type region with the holes which are present there; and holes injected into the n-type region similarly combine with other electrons. The polarity shown in part b is the forward or easy-flow polarity—the larger the voltage the greater the degree of injection to both sides across the junction.

Part c of Figure 17 illustrates the situation for reverse bias. In this case, the polarity of the battery tends to withdraw electrons and holes away from the junction toward the positive terminal of the battery. Thus no injection of carriers tends to occur. Although one might think that the current would be zero, there is actually a small reverse current due to the thermally generated carriers. These minority carriers sometimes diffuse to the junction before they recombine through the deathnium process. As a result a small current of thermally generated minority carriers flows across the junction. This current is substantially independent of the reverse voltage applied across the junction, provided this voltage exceeds the thermal voltage of 25 mv by a factor of two or more. Thus the reverse current *saturates* and does not increase with increasing reverse bias.

A number of interesting experiments have been carried out with p-n junctions. In addition to forming some of the best rectifiers that have ever been produced, the junctions are active as photo cells.[11] They have been used to study the diffusion and behavior of holes and electrons in very high electric fields, which occur under the conditions of large reverse voltages. Time and space do not permit further consideration of these effects, and we shall turn instead to one of the most interesting and significant applications of p-n junctions.

Junction Transistors

Figure 18 shows three regions separated by two p-n junctions. Such a structure may be formed in a single crystal of germanium. For purposes of illustration the charges of the donors and acceptors are separated in the figure from the charges of holes and electrons. Actually, of course, the electronic and chemical imperfections occupy the same regions in space and produce a condition of electrical neutrality. Such an *n-p-n* sandwich as that shown in Figure 18 may be made into a transistor by connecting electrical conductors in the form of wires to the three regions.[12]

Under conditions of thermal equilibrium, electrons are attracted to the *n*-type regions because of the chemical charge of the donors,

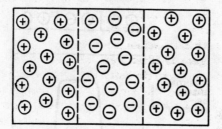

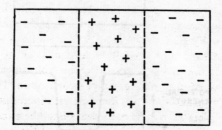

Figure 18. Distribution of donors and acceptors and of holes and electrons in an *n-p-n* structure. *Above*, distribution of charge due to chemical impurities. *Below*, distribution of charge due to holes and electrons

and the distributions of holes and electrons adjust themselves so that the *n*-type regions are regions of low potential energy for electrons. As a result the potential energy of an electron is as shown in Figure 19. The potential energy of a hole is just the reverse, since its charge is opposite to that of the excess electron.

The structure illustrated in Figures 18 and 19 may be made into a transistor by making electrical connections to the three regions of the *n-p-n* sandwich. Such a transistor is shown in Figure 20. The germanium in the junction transistor is embedded in a small block of plastic and is actually only about ⅛ inch long and about ¹⁄₃₂ inch on an edge in cross section. The three leads are seen coming out of the plastic block.

Although its physical size is noteworthy, it is not in its mechanical dimensions that the junction transistor is most remarkable—point contact transistors can also be made with equally small dimensions.

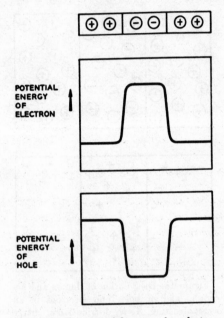

Figure 19. The potential energy of an electron and of a hole in the *n-p-n* structure

The tiny junction transistor is particularly remarkable from an electrical point of view for it can be made to operate at power levels as small as one millionth of a watt, or one microwatt. The basis for this phenomenally low power requirement is threefold: first, the cross section of the transistor is physically small so that for any value of current density the total current will also be small; second, under operating conditions one of the junctions is biased in the reverse direction. Under these conditions the current which flows is that generated by the deathnium process. The germanium used is relatively free of deathnium, and this is the reason why the currents may be very small; they may in fact be less than a microampere. The third reason that the device will operate at such small power levels is that the currents are controlled by the input electrical signals whenever the thermal voltage value of 25 mv is exceeded. In other words, the junction transistor can be brought fully into the operating range with voltages of a few times 25 mv, say 0.1 volt.

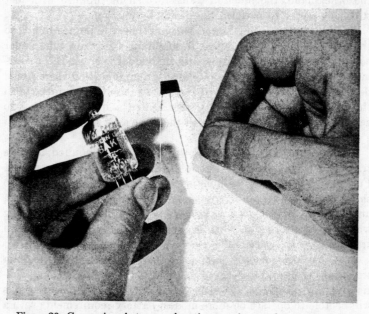

Figure 20. Comparison between a junction transistor and a vacuum tube

The development of an electronic amplifier capable of operating at these extremely low power levels has had a profoundly stimulating effect upon the thoughts of people in the communications field and has particular relevance in respect to telephony. A telephone signal, as it arrives in the earphone, is carried at a power level that can be measured in microwatts; its value may be in the neighborhood of 10 to 100 microwatts. Previously it has not been practical to think about putting amplification in the telephone of an individual subscriber, except in very special circumstances, because vacuum tubes require too large a power level; even the miniature tube shown in Figure 20 requires several watts to put it into operating condition, and it is capable of handling signal powers of this same order of magnitude. To use such a vacuum tube to carry telephone signals is like using a freight train to deliver a pound of butter. Even using a subminiature vacuum tube, which operates on a power of about 100 milliwatts, is like using a two-ton truck for the same purpose. On the other hand, the junction transistor can be supplied with just sufficient power to perform the desirable function.

In addition to wasting power, vacuum tubes are limited in life, so that it would not be practical to maintain a vacuum tube under conditions of steady operation with individual telephones. Furthermore, if vacuum tubes were provided for amplification there would be a time lag when the subscriber wished to use the telephone until the filaments in the amplifiers were heated and ready to go into action. This delay would be about the same as is encountered when a radio set is turned on.

With a transistor, however, no warm-up time is required, and the transistor is ready to go into action as soon as the power is applied. Furthermore, in using the junction transistor, the power level is so small that it can be left on continuously with negligible power costs, and the heat developed is so insignificant that no increase in aging would be apt to occur. This flexibility in the use of the junction transistor opens a new era in the future of telephone service.

It is this low power requirement that has caused the junction transistor to appear in hearing aids as the first commercial application before the public. By using junction transistors, hearing aids will be able to operate on more modest battery requirements with a consequent saving to the user of from two- to tenfold, depending upon the particular arrangement and the hearing loss that must be overcome.

The means by which the junction transistor carries out its amplification is indicated in Figure 21. The upper part of the figure represents the situation under a condition of thermal equilibrium. When voltages are applied the collector junction, shown at the right, is biased in the reverse direction, and the potential energy diagram from the point of view of electrons is as shown in the lower part of the figure. This energy potential is such that large numbers of electrons tend to be drawn from the emitter region at the left toward the collector region. However, in order to travel from one region to the other they must travel over the potential barrier of the *p*-type region. The situation is similar to that which occurs when there is a water reservoir behind a dam. If unchecked, water will flow from a reservoir at high altitude to a lower level; but if the sluice gates in the dam are opened and closed, the flow of water through a power-

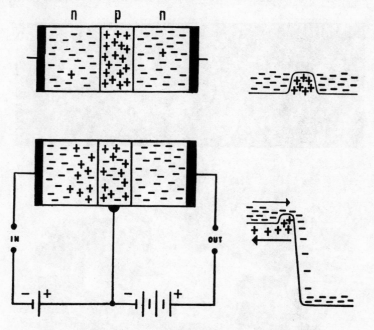

Figure 21. Principle of amplification by a junction transistor

house may be varied. The operation in a junction transistor, corresponding to opening the sluice gates, consists of applying a potential between the emitter and the base layer. If the emitter junction is biased forward, then electrons will be injected into the base layer. The base layer in the junction transistor is thin and contains very little deathnium, so that it is very unlikely that an electron injected into the base layer will there combine with a hole. As a result, very small currents flowing to the base layer can control large currents flowing between the emitter and collector. Furthermore, large voltage variations at the collector terminal do not affect the current flowing to the collector, so long as the voltage across the collector junction exceeds the critical thermal value of 25 mv by a factor of two or three.

As a result of these features the junction transistor has a large gain of both current and voltage, and may have a power gain as high as 100,000-fold or 50 db. Also the junction transistors are quiet in the

Figure 22. Four forms of transistors (*above*) and several transistor-circuit packages (*below*)

electrical sense and produce little noise; types have now been made which compete quite favorably with vacuum tubes from the point of view of noise.[13]

It should be emphasized that the junction transistor has certain limits which make it inferior to point contact transistors for some applications, such as those involved in electrical computing machines. Figure 22 illustrates some recent developments in the transistor field. Four point contact transistors are shown above mounted in ways different from that of the early point contact type. Some packaged circuits are shown below which contain transistors, germanium diodes, resistors, and condensers so as to make amplifiers or memory units. A memory unit may consist, for example, of a scale-of-two counter, which operates on pulses in an electronic brain or computing machine. Such a scale-of-two counter will give out one pulse after it has received two and is capable of remembering one pulse indefinitely while waiting for the second pulse of a pair to arrive.

Conclusion

This discussion has been concerned with certain selected and limited phases of transistor physics and transistor electronics. The emphasis has been placed chiefly on the most basic underlying physical phenomena; some phenomena which may occur and which have practical value have not been considered. Other principles of amplification exist; the point contact and junction transistors do not exhaust the field by any means. Furthermore, in addition to silicon and germanium, other substances are known which give transistor action. In particular, it has been found at the University of Reading in England that both lead sulfide, the old galena of crystal radio days, and lead telluride can be used to make transistors.[14] The conclusion reached from these facts is that transistor electronics is still a young field, in which much remains to be done in fundamental physics and also in development, to say nothing of practical applications in the world of industry and commerce. It seems likely that the field will grow for many years and that interesting and satisfying work will continue along these lines for a long time to come.

References

1. F. S. Goucher and others, *Phys. Rev.*, **78** (1950), 816; *ibid.*, **81** (1951), 637.
2. Confusion has recently occurred in connection with metals that conduct by

the hole process. For such conduction it was found that the ratio of momentum to current was that expected for electrons and not for positive particles. See S. Brown and J. S. Barnett, *Phys. Rev.*, **87** (1952), 601. This result is not surprising, as Brown and Barnett imply; it is just what should be expected on the basis of the reasoning presented above and is entirely consistent with the theory of the hole presented in this article and elsewhere in connection with the semiconductors and the anomalous Hall effect. See also W. Shockley, *Phys. Rev.*, **88** (1952), 953, and N. Rostoker, *Phys. Rev.*, **88** (1952), 952.

3. W. Shockley, *Electrons and Holes in Semiconductors* (New York: D. Van Nostrand & Co., Inc., 1950), chap. 12.

4. K. Lark-Horovitz, *Semi-Conducting Materials* (London: Butterworth Scientific Publications, 1951), pp. 47–48.

5. J. A. Burton, G. W. Hull, F. J. Morin, and J. C. Severiens, "Effect of Nickel and Copper Impurities on the Recombination of Holes and Electrons in Germanium," at Symposium on Impurity Phenomena, Schenectady, N. Y., 1953, *Jour. Phys. Chem.*, **57** (1953), 853.

6. The theory of this process has been developed by W. Shockley and W. T. Read, Jr., in *Phys. Rev.* **87** (1952), 835–42. Experimental findings in agreement with the theory have been obtained by Burton, Hull, Morin, and Severiens (see 5 above) and by R. N. Hall, *Phys. Rev.*, **83** (1951), 228; *ibid.*, **87** (1952), 387.

7. J. Bardeen and W. H. Brattain, *Phys. Rev.*, **74** (1948), 230; *ibid.*, **75** (1949), 1208–25.

8. J. R. Haynes and W. Shockley, *Phys. Rev.*, **81** (1951), 835–43. J. R. Haynes and W. Westphal, *Phys. Rev.*, **85** (1952), 680.

9. J. R. Haynes, ed., "Transistor Teachers Summer School," *Phys. Rev.*, **88** (1952), 1368–69.

10. T. S. Benedict and W. Shockley, *Phys. Rev.*, **89** (1953), 1152.

11. J. N. Shive, *Proc. Inst. Radio Engrs.*, **40** (1952), 1410; *Jour. Opt. Soc. America*, **43** (1953), 239.

12. W. Shockley, *Bell System Tech Jl.*, **28** (1949), 435–89. W. Shockley, M. Sparks and G. K. Teal, *Phys. Rev.*, **83** (1951), 151–62. W. Shockley, *Proc. Inst. Radio Engrs.*, **40** (1952), 1289–1313. For a method of contacting the center layers, see W. Shockley, U. S. Patent 2,654,059.

13. H. C. Montgomery, and M. A. Clark, "Shot Noise in Junction Transistors." *Journal of Applied Physics*, **24** (1953), 1337–8.

14. H. A. Gebbie, P. C. Banbury, and C. A. Hogarth, *Proc. Phys. Soc.* (London), **B63x** (1951), 371. A. F. Gibson, *Proc. Phys. Soc.* (London), **65B** (1952), 378. P. C. Banbury, *Proc. Phys. Soc.* (London), **65B** (1952), 236.

Ferromagnetism

R. M. BOZORTH

Introduction

We are all familiar with the fact that magnetic bodies attract each other. A more quantitative measure of magnetic quality is described by the magnetization curve of Figure 1, in which the magnetic moment per unit volume, I, is plotted against the magnetizing field strength, H. Alternative ordinates are B and $4\pi I$. (Here cgs units are used.)

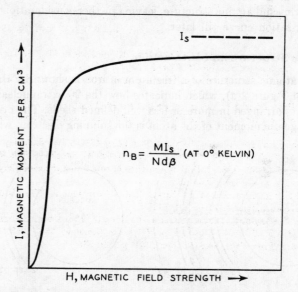

$$n_B = \frac{MI_s}{Nd\beta} \text{ (AT 0° KELVIN)}$$

Figure 1. Typical magnetization curve showing asymptotic approach to saturation, I_s. Bohr magneton number is derived from I_s at low temperature

The I vs. H curves approach asymptotically the saturation magnetization, $I = I_s$. From this quantity we can readily calculate the magnetic moment per atom or molecule of the substance:

$$m = \frac{I_s M}{N d},$$

M being the atomic or molecular weight, N Avogadro's number, and d the density. The value of I_s varies with temperature and usually approaches a constant value at $0°K$; from this we can find the magnetic moment m_0 per atom when the atoms are not disturbed by heat motions. Since we know the magnetic moment of a spinning electron (the Bohr magneton, β), we can determine the number of Bohr magnetons per atom in a material, for example, iron:

$$n_B = \frac{m_0}{\beta}$$

We will now look at the relation between the Bohr magneton number n_B and atomic structure, leaving further consideration of the magnetization curve till later.

Atomic Structure and Interaction

The atomic structure of a free atom of iron is shown by the diagram of Figure 2(a), which indicates how the 26 extranuclear electrons are arranged in more or less well-defined shells. The origin of the magnetic moment of the atom is the spinning electron, which is

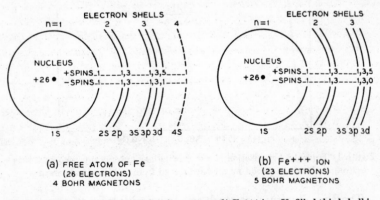

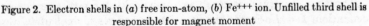

Figure 2. Electron shells in (a) free iron-atom, (b) Fe^{+++} ion. Unfilled third shell is responsible for magnet moment

known to have a moment of 0.927×10^{-20} in cgs units or one Bohr magneton. Although some magnetic moment results from the orbital motion of the electrons, this is not of prime importance in ferromagnetism.

The arrangement of electrons in the two inner shells is such that the spins cancel each other, leaving a net moment of zero. However, the third part of the third shell is not completely filled, and the spins are here oriented so that they only partially neutralize each other. The atomic moment of atoms and ions of iron, cobalt, and nickel can be attributed to the unbalanced spins of their 3d electrons.

In a free atom of iron the atomic moment should be the difference between the five $3d+$ spins and one $3d-$ spin or four Bohr magnetons. In metallic iron the electron distribution is changed by the close proximity of neighboring atoms and as a result the net atomic moment is reduced to 2.2 Bohr magnetons.

In the ferrites, which will be mentioned in more detail later, the iron is present mainly as the ferric ion, Fe^{+++}. The electronic structure of this ion is shown in Figure 2(b), and from this we can see that its magnetic moment is five Bohr magnetons.

In ions such as Fe^{+++}, Fe^{++}, Ni^{++}, and Mn^{++}, which occur in nonmetallic compounds, the experimentally determined moment is usually close to that which can be deduced from the number of electrons in the ion. In the metals, however, the atomic moments are not so simply determined because of the uncertainties resulting from the conduction electrons. The average moment of the atoms in a pure metal or in an alloy can readily be determined by dividing the measured moment of a specimen by the number of atoms in it. If we plot this average moment against the number of extranuclear electrons, we obtain Figure 3.[1] According to simple theory one expects that the average moment will depend only on the number of electrons, and this expectation is reasonably well fulfilled when the alloying elements differ by only one or two electrons, as in the series Ni-Cu and Fe-Ni. Different trends are noticed when, for example, Cr (24 electrons) is added to Co (27 electrons); it is believed that in these instances the moments of the two kinds of atoms are mutually opposed.

If a material is to be ferromagnetic not only must its atoms have magnetic moments but also there must be interatomic forces that maintain neighboring atoms parallel. The kinds of magnetism that

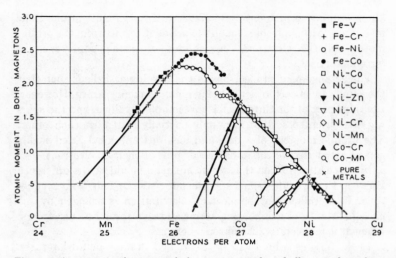

Figure 3. Average atomic moment in iron group metals and alloys, as dependent on electron concentration

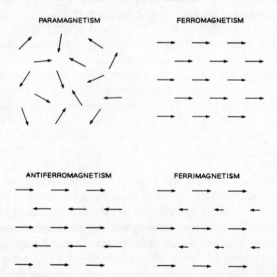

Figure 4. Kinds of magnetism associated with various kinds of interatomic interaction: paramagnetism, weak interaction; ferromagnetism, "positive" interaction; antiferromagnetism, negative interaction; ferrimagnetism, negative interaction between unequal moments

are associated with different kinds of interaction are illustrated in Figure 4: no interaction leads to *paramagnetism*, "positive" interaction to *ferromagnetism*, "negative" interaction between nearest neighbors to *antiferromagnetism* when the atomic moments are equal and by definition to *ferrimagnetism* when they are unequal. Antiferromagnetic materials have only small permeabilities, of the same order of magnitude as paramagnetic materials. Ferrimagnetic materials have the high permeabilities of ferromagnetism.

We have not discussed diamagnetic substances, which are composed of atoms having no permanent magnetic moments but do have small moments induced by the applied field and opposed to it in direction. In fact the atoms of all substances have small moments of this kind, but if they have permanent moments the induced moment is relatively small and unimportant.

The interaction that exists between neighboring atoms and orients their magnetic moments is quantum mechanical in origin. So far its magnitude cannot be calculated precisely enough to be useful. It is believed, however, on the basis of accurate calculations for simple atoms, that the sign of the interaction changes in somewhat the manner shown in Figure 5: if atoms are too close together their moments will tend to be held antiparallel, if far enough apart they will be parallel. Slater[2] has shown that the ferromagnetic elements

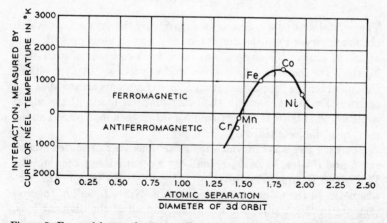

Figure 5. Form of interaction curve. Interaction measured as Curie (or Néel) point, θ, in °K. Interaction energy is $k\theta$

are those which have an unusually large ratio of interatomic distance to the diameter of the electron shell in which the magnetic moment (unbalanced spin) resides, the critical ratio between ferromagnetism and antiferromagnetism being at about 1.5. Our best measure of the energy of interaction is the Curie point on the Kelvin scale; this, when multiplied by the Boltzmann constant k, is a measure of the disordering energy of thermal agitation which is necessary to counteract the ordering of ferromagnetism and is about 1000°C in iron. In antiferromagnetic materials the antiparallel ordering is destroyed at a definite temperature called the Néel point, which is a measure of the antiparallel interaction.

Ferrites

The relation of the atomic moments and interaction to atomic structure and interatomic distance are well illustrated by the properties of the ferrites. These are refractory materials composed of the oxides of iron and other metals, usually Mn, Co, Ni, Cu, Zn, or Mg. They are pressed in powder form to the required shape and fired. Chemical reaction then occurs, and when they are cooled to room temperature they are hard, strong, and brittle.

Nickel ferrite, for example, has the chemical composition represented by

$$NiO \cdot Fe_2O_3 \text{ or } Ni^{++}Fe_2^{+++}O_4^{--}.$$

The crystal structure is determined mainly by the oxygen ions, which are much larger than the metal ions and form a close-packed cubic array. In among the oxygen ions there are two kinds of interstices in which the metal ions lie. In one kind of position (the A position) the metal ions is equidistant from four oxygen ions arranged at the corners of a tetrahedron, in the other kind (B position) the metal is placed so that there are six equidistant oxygen ions placed at the corners of an octahedron.

There are two ways in which the metal ions are distributed among the A and B sites. In $ZnFe_2O_4$ the Zn^{++}'s occupy the A sites and the Fe^{+++} the B sites. Ferrites that have this distribution are nonmagnetic. In the magnetic ferrites, such as $NiFe_2O_4$, half of the iron ions are in the A sites, the other half and all of the divalent ions, such as Ni^{++}, are in the B sites. The former structure is generally designated a *normal* spinel structure, the latter an *inverted* spinel.

TABLE 1. Atomic structure and magnetic moments of some iron-group ions

	1st Shell	2nd Shell		3rd Shell	4th Shell	Net Moment
+Spin	1	1,3	26 Fe	1,3,5	1	4(2.2)*
−Spin	1	1,3		1,3,1	1	
	1	1,3	23 Fe^{+++}	1,3,5	0	5
	1	1,3		1,3,0	0	
	1	1,3	23 Mn^{++}	1,3,5	0	5
	1	1,3		1,3,0	0	
	1	1,3	24 Fe^{++}	1,3,5	0	4
	1	1,3		1,3,1	0	
	1	1,3	25 Co^{++}	1,3,5	0	3
	1	1,3		1,3,2	0	
	1	1,3	26 Ni^{++}	1,3,5	0	2
	1	1,3		1,3,3	0	
	1	1,3	27 Cu^{++}	1,3,5	0	1
	1	1,3		1,3,4	0	
	1	1,3	28 Zn^{++}	1,3,5	0	0
	1	1,3		1,3,5	0	

* Net moment is four in a free atom, 2.2 in the compact metal.

The magnetic moments of the metal ions can be deduced from the diagrams of the kind shown in Figure 2. The moments of the ions that occur most frequently in the ferrites are given in Table 1.

Néel[3] showed that in the magnetic ferrites the interactions between the ions in the A and B sites are antiferromagnetic, so that the moments of A ions are antiparallel to those of B ions. In magnetic $NiFe_2O_4$ and nonmagnetic $ZnFe_2O_4$ we can represent the situation as shown in Figure 6. The net moment of $NiFe_2O_4$ is then expected to be two Bohr magnetons. Experimentally Gorter found 2.3. At room temperature $ZnFe_2O_4$ has random directions of the Fe^{+++}

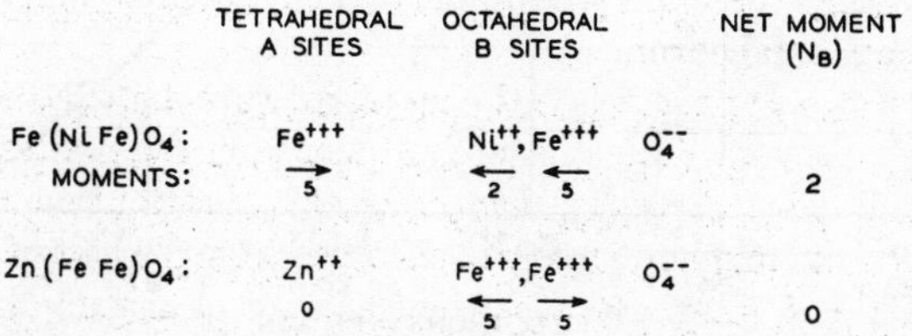

	TETRAHEDRAL A SITES	OCTAHEDRAL B SITES		NET MOMENT (N_B)
Fe (Ni Fe)O$_4$:	Fe^{+++}	Ni^{++}, Fe^{+++}	O$_4^{--}$	
MOMENTS:	$\rightarrow$ 5	$\leftarrow$ 2 $\leftarrow$ 5		2
Zn (Fe Fe)O$_4$:	Zn^{++}	Fe^{+++}, Fe^{+++}	O$_4^{--}$	
	0	$\leftarrow$ 5 $\rightarrow$ 5		0

Figure 6. Distribution of ions on A and B sites in inverse spinel (Ni ferrite) and normal spinel (Zn ferrite) structures, and corresponding magnetic moments

moments, but below 10°K the Fe^{+++}'s go into an antiparallel arrangement and so show a weak antiparallel or negative interaction.[4]

Similarly one can estimate the moments for the other ferrites in the series Mn, Fe, Co, Ni, Cu, Zn with increasing atomic number. In the inverse ferrites one expects the molecular moment to be just that of the divalent ions of these elements, because the two Fe^{+++} in the A and B positions cancel each other. Using the moments of the divalent ions as given in Table 1 and plotting the molecular moments for the corresponding ferrites, we obtain the straight line of Figure 7. The observed moments, derived from the saturation magnetization at 0°K, are shown as points. The small discrepancy between calculated and observed moments has been attributed to the moments resulting from the orbital motions of the electrons.

The agreement between theory and observation shows that we have a good understanding of the atomic structure and interatomic interactions in simple ferrites.

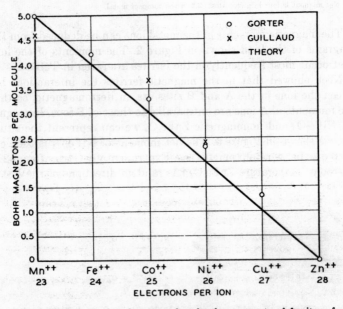

Figure 7. Theoretical and measured molecular moments of ferrites of iron-group elements

An interesting and useful material is made by combining a small amount of nonmagnetic zinc ferrite with magnetic manganese ferrite. Let us calculate the magnetic moment of a mixture of 90 per cent $MnFe_2O_4$ and 10 per cent $ZnFe_2O_4$. We can easily do this with the aid of the moments given in Table 1. As indicated in Figure 8, pure $MnFe_2O_4$ has the inverse structure and the Mn^{++} and Fe^{+++} each have a moment of five magnetons. The Fe^{+++} in the A position maintains the Mn^{++} and Fe^{+++} moments antiparallel to it as shown by the arrows. In pure $ZnFe_2O_4$ the Zn^{++} is in the A position and has zero moment, the Fe^{+++}'s are in the B positions and have five Bohr magnetons each. Since the Zn^{++} has zero moment there will be no

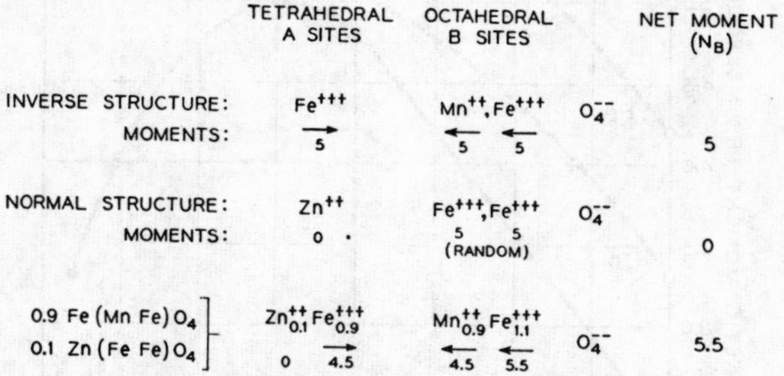

	TETRAHEDRAL A SITES	OCTAHEDRAL B SITES		NET MOMENT (N_B)
INVERSE STRUCTURE:	Fe^{+++}	Mn^{++}, Fe^{+++}	O_4^{--}	
MOMENTS:	→ 5	← ← 5 5		5
NORMAL STRUCTURE:	Zn^{++}	Fe^{+++}, Fe^{+++}	O_4^{--}	
MOMENTS:	0 ·	5 5 (RANDOM)		0
0.9 Fe (Mn Fe) O_4	$Zn_{0.1}^{++} Fe_{0.9}^{+++}$	$Mn_{0.9}^{++} Fe_{1.1}^{+++}$	O_4^{--}	
0.1 Zn (Fe Fe) O_4	0 → 4.5	← ← 4.5 5.5		5.5

Figure 8. Increase in molecular moment of manganese ferrite by addition of nonmagnetic zinc ferrite

force of interaction between it and the two Fe^{+++}'s, so the latter will be directed at random and the net moment will be zero. In $MnFe_2O_4$, on the contrary, the net moment is five, as already pointed out.

If now some $ZnFe_2O_4$ is added to $MnFe_2O_4$, the Zn^{++} ions will go in the A positions and the Mn^{++} will remain in the B positions. The net moment of the chemical mixture is readily calculated and is found to be 5.5, an increase of 0.5 over that for $MnFe_2O_4$. As long as added Zn^{++} ions go into the A positions we should expect the moment to rise as indicated by the upper broken line of Figure 9 ("ideal slope"), which has this same increase of 0.5 Bohr magneton for each addition of ten per cent of $ZnFe_2O_4$. Actually the experiments of Gorter[5] give the data of Figure 9 for additions of $ZnFe_2O_4$ to several of the simple ferrites. The first additions give curves starting with the ideal slope. Eventually the moments of ions in the A positions are too weak to influence the moments of ions in the B positions and the mixture becomes nonmagnetic like pure $ZnFe_2O_4$.

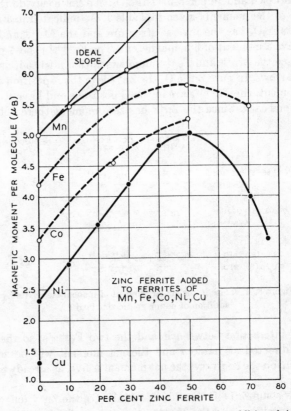

Figure 9. Observed change in moment of several ferrites by addition of zinc ferrite. Ideal theoretical increase is approached for small additions

The technical value of the ferrites depends not only on their magnetic properties but also on their electrical resistivities. These are one million to one billion times the resistivities of the common magnetic alloys like silicon-iron and Permalloy. The significance of these high values is the reduction of eddy-current losses in a transformer core or other similar structure that is subjected to alternating magnetic fields. At high frequencies these losses are especially important and practically determine the quality of the material. As a measure of quality, we have $Q = 2\pi f L/\Delta R$, L being the inductance at the frequency f of a coil of wire containing the material, and ΔR the effective resistance of the coil caused by the presence of the material.

The factor of merit of a material of this kind is μQ, μ being the permeability. In Figure 10, μ and μQ are plotted against frequency

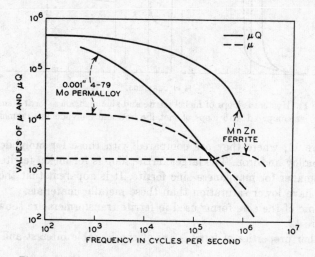

Figure 10. Effective low-field permeability μ and product with quality factor Q (reciprocal of energy loss) as dependent on frequency.—*Am. Jl. Physics*, **21** (1953), 260

for zinc manganese ferrite and are compared there with a high-quality iron-nickel alloy, molybdenum Permalloy. Because of the high resistivity of the ferrite its μQ declines less with increasing frequency, and at one megacycle per second the μQ is 50 to 100 times as great as for the alloy. This is in spite of the facts that (1) the permeability of the alloy at low frequencies is about ten times as great as the ferrite, and (2) the alloy is severely laminated so as to reduce the eddy-current loss, whereas the ferrite is a solid piece of material.

The hysteresis loops of two of the common ferrites are shown in

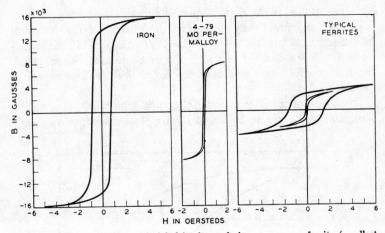

Figure 11. Hysteresis loops of nickel ferrite and zinc manganese ferrite (smallest loop) as compared with loops of metallic iron and molybdenum Permalloy

Figure 11, where they are compared with those for molybdenum Permalloy and iron. The larger ferrite loop is for nickel ferrite and the smaller for manganese zinc ferrite. It is apparent that the ferrites have lower saturation than these metallic materials.

Some of the core forms used in ferrite transformers are shown in Figure 12.

Other properties of ferrites are of considerable interest and pos-

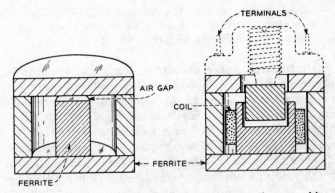

Figure 12. Some ferrite core forms, showing construction as used in transformers. Diameters are about 1.5 inches

sible engineering value. One is the magnetostriction of cobalt ferrite. Figure 13 shows the expansion measured[6] in a single crystal of cobalt ferrite upon application of a field, after the specimen was cooled in a magnetic field. In the direction of the crystal axis the expansion is over 800 parts per million, a dimensional change much larger than that reported for any other material. The materials commonly used as magnetostrictive elements are nickel and alfer (an Fe-Al alloy),

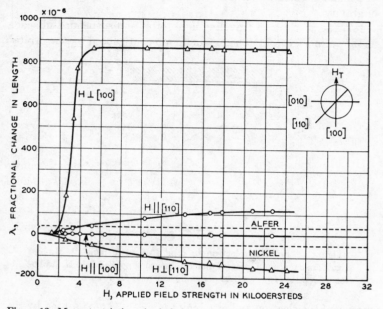

Figure 13. Magnetostriction of cobalt ferrite crystal as compared with nickel and alfer

which have contraction and expansion, respectively, of about 50 parts per million.

Another application is in high-speed switching and in storage of information. When a pulse is put through a coil the eddy-current delay in the core is usually the important factor in limiting the high-speed response. In ferrites the high resistivity is thus an important element in attaining higher speeds in the microsecond range. Hysteresis loops that are rectangular in shape are also of special value in the storage of information.

High-Frequency Phenomena

Other new properties of the ferrites have been observed at high frequencies and give promise of important industrial applications as well as further insight into the behavior of magnetic materials. These properties come about mainly because the uncompensated electron spins of ferromagnetic materials precess under the influence of a magnetic field just as a gyroscope precesses under the influence of gravity.

Imagine an electron traveling in an orbit and suspended in space as shown in Figure 14. The magnetic moment caused by the orbital

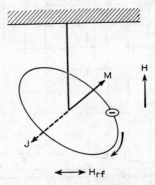

Figure 14. Spinning electron in orbit. Magnetic moment M, and angular momentum J, precess under influence of applied field H. Radio-frequency field H_{rf} is applied perpendicular to H for resonance

motion of the electron and also by its spin can be represented by the vector M. Antiparallel to M is the vector J, which represents the angular momentum of the electron. If a magnetic field, H, is applied as indicated, the vectors M and J will precess with the frequency $MH/(2\pi J)$.

Now let us apply a small-amplitude alternating field, H_{rf}, having a direction perpendicular to H and a frequency equal to or near the precession frequency. The amplitude of the precessing magnetic moment will become larger and larger, because it is continually pulled by the alternating field, until a final amplitude is reached which depends on the internal damping or energy loss associated with the precession. Measurement of the amplitude of the magnetic moment obtained with a given alternating field enables one to calculate an effective permeability. By varying the frequency of H_{rf} until the permeability is a maximum (at resonance) we can determine the natural frequency of precession.

In an actual material, one way of observing resonance at microwave frequencies is indicated in Figure 15. A wave guide is termin-

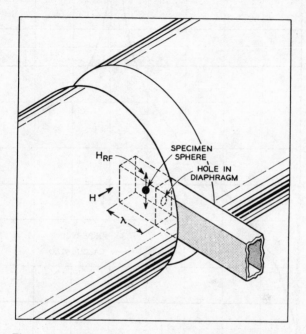

Figure 15. Electromagnet with section of wave guide showing cavity used for ferromagnetic resonance

ated at one end by a cavity one wave length long, and a small spherical specimen is supported at the center of the cavity by a polystyrene rod, as shown. Under these conditions the alternating field, obtained by excitation of the wave guide, is perpendicular to the constant field H of some thousands of oersteds, which is supplied by an electromagnet. The results of an experiment[7] in which the material Supermalloy was excited at 24,000 megacycles per second is shown in Figure 16. The position and sharpness of the

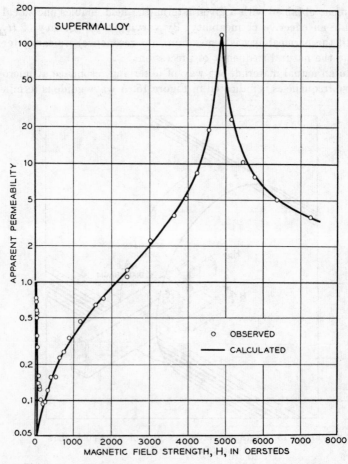

Figure 16. Peak in permeability at resonance. Material, Supermalloy

peak give basic information about the gyromagnetic properties of the atoms and the interaction between them.

Hogan[8] observed that if manganese ferrite is placed in a wave guide as shown in Figure 17, the plane of polarization of the electromagnetic wave is rotated through large angles. On entering at the left the polarization is perpendicular to the short dimension of the wave guide. The wave may be considered as made of two circularly polarized waves rotating in opposite directions. In one of these waves the direction of rotation is the same as that of the precession of the spinning electrons; consequently, the effective permeability of this component will be high and the wave velocity small[9] as compared with the other wave, which will have only a small reaction with the electron spins. Consequently, one wave component will fall behind the other and there will be a rotation of the resultant plane-polarized wave, as in the Faraday effect for light.

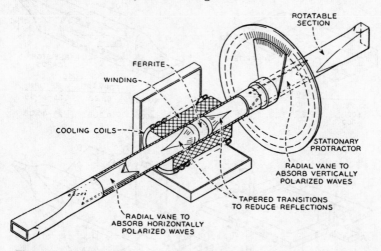

Figure 17. Rotation of plane of polarization in wave guide resulting from transmission through magnetized ferrite (Faraday effect).—Hogan, *Bell System Tech. Jl.*, **31** (1952), 1

A specimen of manganese ferrite a few centimeters long, or preferably of magnesium manganese ferrite, will rotate the plane of polarization in a 3-cm wave by 90° or more. The amount of rotation can be adjusted by changing the field applied to the ferrite. Since the material is transparent to these waves as long as the frequency is not too near resonance, the transmission loss is slight.

There are many possible applications of this device. If the material and field are adjusted for a 45° rotation and the rectangular wave guides properly oriented, a signal will pass in the forward direction with only a small loss. A signal going in the opposite direction, however, will be turned so that it will not be transmitted back beyond the ferrite into the rectangular wave guide. Thus waves reflected backward in a transmission line will be reduced practically to zero.

The Faraday rotation with 45° or 90° rotation permits construction of the "circulator" which has many possible uses in ultra-high-frequency circuits. As shown schematically in Figure 18, a signal enters at A and leaves only at C, or one may enter at C and leave at

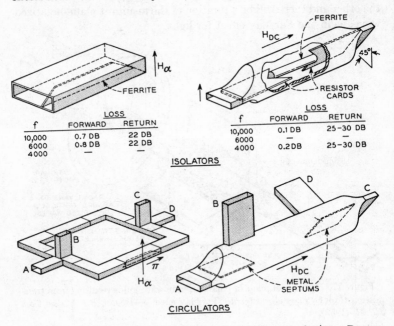

Figure 18. Wave guide circuits using Faraday effect; f in megacycles/sec.—Rowen, *Bell System Tech. Jl.*, **32** (1953), 1533

B, and so on. Some designs of circulators and other circuit combinations are outlined in this figure. These and other uses are given in papers by Hogan,[10] Fox and Weiss,[11] Kales, Chait, and Sakiotis,[12] and Rowen.[13] The theoretical aspects are discussed also by Suhl and Walker.[14]

Domains and the Processes of Magnetization

In discussing ferrites we have been concerned with the atomic moments and interatomic forces that are necessary for the existence of ferromagnetism. What goes on inside of a magnetic material when a magnetic field is applied to it is more appropriately discussed in connection with the metallic materials. It was during the study

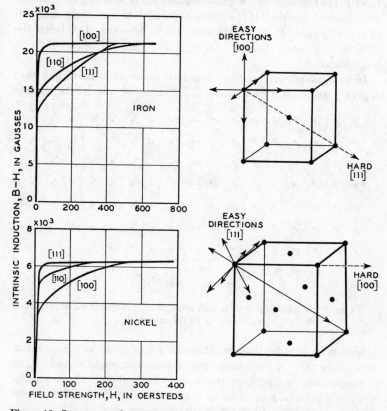

Figure 19. Structure and magnetization curves of iron and nickel crystals. Note that directions of easy magnetization are [100] in iron, [111] in nickel

of these materials that we saw under the microscope the changes that take place during magnetization.

As a background for discussing the mechanism of change of magnetization let us first consider some of the properties of single crystals. Figure 19 shows the magnetization curves measured with the magnetic field applied in turn along each of the three principal direc-

tions. In iron and iron-silicon alloys, which have a body-centered
crystal structure, the crystal is most easily magnetized along a
crystal axis, a [100] direction. Only a relatively weak field is required
to saturate the material in this direction whereas about 400 oersteds
are required for the [111] direction parallel to the body diagonal
of the unit cube. In nickel the situation is reversed, [111] being the
direction of easy magnetization, [100] that of most difficult
magnetization.

In an unmagnetized piece of magnetic material we now know that
separate regions or domains exist, inside of which the atomic

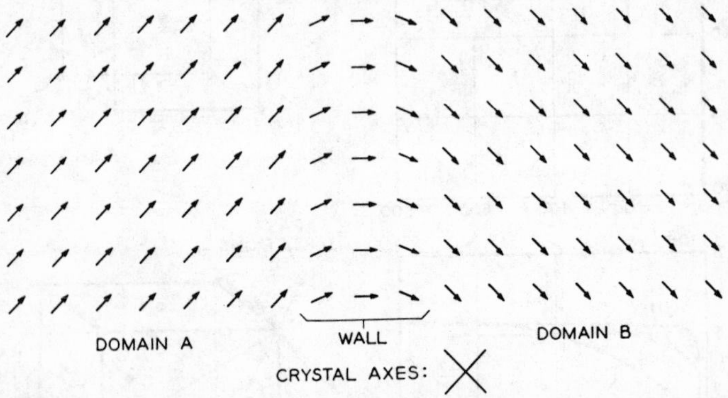

Figure 20. Schematic of domain wall as transition between domains. Actual
walls may be 1000 atoms thick

moments lie parallel to each other along an axis of easy magnetization. Since there are six such directions in iron (eight in nickel), an
unmagnetized or demagnetized iron crystal will normally have one-
sixth of its domains oriented in each of the six directions, the average magnetization of the whole crystal being zero.

Portions of two domains are shown in Figure 20. The boundary
between domains is not sharp on an atomic scale; as indicated in
Figure 20, the orientation of the atoms is changed progressively
across the "wall." In iron the wall is in fact about 1000 atoms thick
instead of four as shown in the schematic drawing. The domains
themselves are normally a few tenths of a millimeter on a side or
about 1000 times the wall thickness.

When a field is applied the magnetization is normally changed by
motion of the domain wall, as shown in Figure 21 (a) to (b). This

mechanism accounts for the changes occurring below the knee of the magnetization curve. When this process is complete (c) and the direction of magnetization is parallel to the axis nearest to the direction of the applied field, an increase in the strength of the field causes the magnetization to turn toward parallelism with the field, as shown at (d). This occurs above the knee of the magnetization curve and is called *domain rotation*. Under certain circumstances, for example,

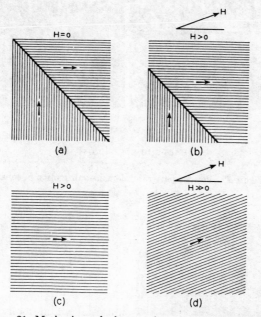

Figure 21. Mechanism of change of magnetization. Domain wall motion in weak fields, domain rotation in strong fields

in very fine particles when no domain walls exist, the rotation process is the only one that occurs. In this case a higher field is usually necessary to produce a change in magnetization, that is, the permeability is lower than when domain-wall motion can play a part.

The motion of the domain boundaries has now been observed under the microscope by the use of a colloidal suspension of fine magnetic particles. Domain walls are made visible[15] with this in much the same way that cracks in iron and steel are made visible with iron filings. Two of the patterns obtained with the colloid are

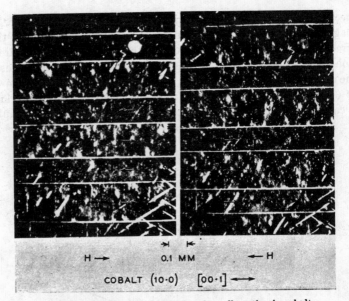

Figure 22. Powder pattern of domain-wall motion in cobalt

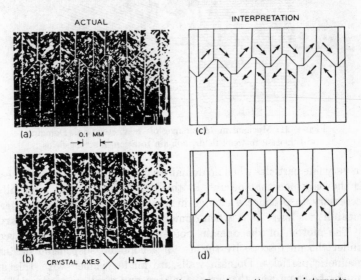

Figure 23. Domain-wall motion in iron. Powder pattern and interpretation.—*Electr. Engg.*, **68** (1949), 471

shown in Figures 22 and 23. They are best observed in a moving picture film *Action Pictures of Magnetic Domains*, prepared by H. J. Williams, C. Kittel, and F. M. Tylee.[16]

The stability of domains and the geometrical forms that they assume under various conditions have been discussed a number of times and will not be repeated in detail here. When a specimen is

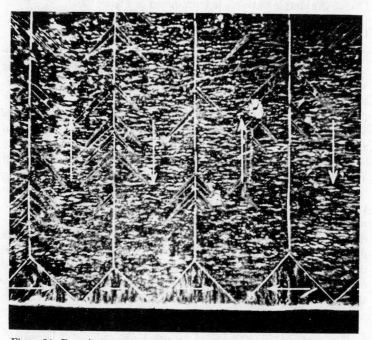

Figure 24. Domain structure in (100) plane of iron, showing triangular domains of closure at edge of crystal.—*Ferromagnetism* (New York, D. Van Nostrand Co., 1953), p. 536

cut from a single crystal so that it has a simple geometry and its surfaces are simply related to the atomic planes, the pattern can usually be understood in terms of three kinds of magnetic energy. It is believed that the following energies, associated with well-known phenomena, will explain the complicated patterns as well as the simple ones:

1. Magnetostatic energy associated with magnetic poles situated on the surface of the material or on domain walls.

2. Energy associated with the walls themselves (equal to 1 or 2 ergs per square centimeter in iron).

3. Energy associated with mechanical stress, generally proportional to the amount of stress and to the magnetostrictive strain associated with magnetization at saturation. The pattern which is formed is that for which the sum of these energies is a minimum. One of the simple patterns is reproduced in Figure 24.

Fine Particles and Permanent Magnets

Domain theory not only enables us to understand many of the essential facts about magnetic materials in general but also gives us a lead that may result in the development of greatly improved magnet materials for permanent magnets. If we could put together particles of iron of just the right size and shape and orientation, we are convinced that we would have a better magnet than any now in existence.

The theory underlying this is as follows. Imagine two cubes of single crystals of iron, as shown in Figure 25, one without domain walls and one with. The first is magnetized so that it has poles on two of its surfaces, and as a result it has a large external field and a magnetostatic energy associated with it. The second cube has no energy of this kind, but it does have energy associated with its domain walls. The magnetostatic energy varies as the cube of the cube edge, the wall energy as the square; consequently the second cube will have the lesser energy when the particle is small. In iron the critical size is about 300 A. Since the normal wall thickness is

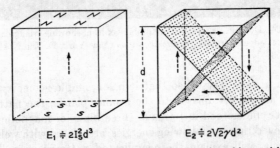

$$E_1 \doteq 2I_s^2 d^3 \qquad\qquad E_2 \doteq 2\sqrt{2}\gamma d^2$$

Figure 25. Two possible domain structures in cubic particle: (a) stable in small particles, (b) in large. γ is energy of wall per cm². —*Electr. Engg.*, **68** (1949), 471

larger than this, one can readily believe that there will be no wall in a particle of this size. Such small particles are then single domains; however, if they are too small they are disturbed by thermal fluctuations, therefore there is an optimum size.

In these small particles the mechanism of magnetization must be quite different from that in larger particles. Absence of domain boundary movement means that the only way for the magnetization to change is for the atomic magnets to rotate. This requires a greater force to be supplied by the field, because the magnetization must be turned through the direction of hard magnetization. In Figure 26

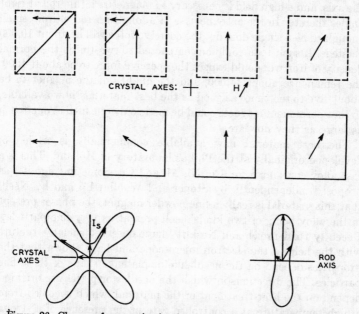

Figure 26. Change of magnetization by domain-wall movement in large particles, and by domain rotation in small particles. Rotation controlled by crystal anisotropy (clover) or by anisotropy resulting from shape (dumbbell)

the upper row shows the boundary movement that occurs in large particles, the second row the rotation in small particles. The cloverleaf pattern shows the energy that must be supplied by the field to magnetize a crystal in various directions. When the particles are small the field necessary to pull the magnetization over the energy maximum and reverse it is the coercive force of the particle. It can be calculated from the known properties of the crystal, and the data for iron check the calculation. Coercive forces of over 1000 oersteds have been measured in fine iron powder, whereas the coercive force of large pieces of iron is normally about one oersted. This material is not at present commercially important in this country, however, because it loses its high coercive force when it is compacted.

If the fine particles are not cubes or spheres but are elongated— for example, if they are rods—an even higher coercive force may be expected. The direction of easy magnetization of a rod is parallel to the axis, and a high field is necessary to magnetize a thin rod at right angles thereto In the extreme case of a long thin rod of iron, small enough to be a single domain, the coercive force will be about 10,000 oersteds. If such rods could be compacted to two-thirds the normal density of iron we should expect the coercive force to be about 4000, the remanence about 14,000, and the quality of the magnet to be about five to ten times as good as the best materials now available, so that permanent magnets could be made only one fifth to one-tenth as large as they now are.

The best material now available commercially is Alnico 5, developed originally at the Philips laboratory in Holland. This is a cast alloy containing Fe, Co, Ni, Al, and Cu. Sometime ago it was proposed independently by Stoner and Wohlfarth[17] and by Néel[18] that this material is really a fine powder magnet, the phases present in the alloy being of two kinds, each present as very fine particles. Recently Heidenreich and Nesbitt[19] have observed such a structure with the help of the electron microscope and have shown that the properties depend on the needlelike or platelike shape of these fine particles. The directions in which the needles or plates are oriented depend on the heat-treatment of the material, which is cooled from a high temperature at a controlled rate in the presence of a strong magnetic field. Figure 27 shows how the structure of the precipitate, formed in a single crystal, is influenced by the direction of the magnetic field used in cooling.

Finally, Figure 28 shows some curves that describe the magnetic properties of the more important permanent magnets. These are the portions of the hysteresis loops of these materials that lie in the second quadrant. High values of B and of (negative) H are desirable. The best single criterion of the usefulness of the material,

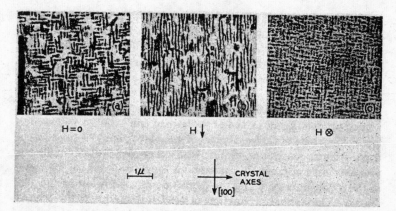

H=0 H↓ H⊗

1μ CRYSTAL AXES
↓[100]

Figure 27. Electron micrographs showing particle shape in Alnico 5 as influenced by magnetic field present during heat-treatment. Magnetic fields: (a) none, (b) vertical, (c) normal to plane.—Heidenreich & Nesbitt, *J. App. Phys.*, **23** (1952), 352

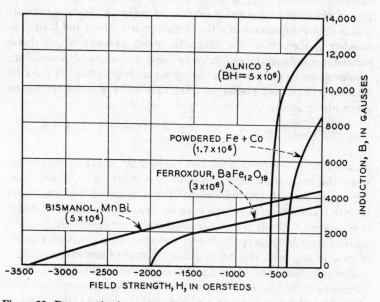

Figure 28. Demagnetization curves of some important materials for permanent magnets. Factor of merit ("energy product") in parentheses

apart from the cost, is the maximum value of the product of B and H at a point on the curve, and this is given in the figure for each material. The highest value, 5×10^6, is well below the theoretical 40×10^6 for compacted parallel small needles of iron.

Iron-Silicon Alloys

These alloys are still the big business of magnetic materials, the annual product being valued at more than one hundred million dollars.[20] The value of the yearly loss of magnetic energy in the cores of transformers, generators, motors, and other electrical equipment is probably several times this amount. A rough estimate can be made in the following way, using the figures designated below as (a), (b), (c), etc. The annual production of electrical energy in the United States in 1953 was (a) over 400 billion kwhr, from which a revenue of almost seven billion dollars was derived. The installed capacity in this country for generating and distributing power is (b) almost twice of that used. The loss of an excited transformer, when it is carrying no load, is (c) about one-half of one per cent of its rated power; this is almost entirely due to the magnetic losses in the core and is about the same when the transformer is under full load. The number of steps involving magnetic losses, through which power normally goes from the generator to the consumer, is (d) about four. The average cost of power to the consumer is (e) 1.8 cents per kilowatt hour. Then as a preliminary estimate we have, using the figures given above as (a), (b), etc.,

$$400 \times 10^9 \times 2 \times 0.005 \times 4 \times \$0.018 = \$300 \times 10^6.$$
$$\quad (a) \qquad\quad (b) \quad\ (c) \quad\ (d) \qquad (e)$$

This is too low for one reason and too high for another; too low because the magnetic losses in motors and other kinds of consumer equipment must be added and the losses in generators are higher than in transformers; too high because some of the industrial power is consumed without passing through so many stages. It must be right as to order of magnitude and is probably right within a factor of two. In any case, it is an important source of lost revenue

The importance of the magnetic losses has naturally led to attempts to reduce them. The progress that has been made has been plotted by Houdremont[21] up to 1940, and the losses in 1955 can be added to his curve, with the result given in Figure 29.

Before 1900 the material was ordinary iron containing substantial amounts of impurities but no added silicon. The first big improvement came about 1900 as a result of the work of Barrett, Brown, and Hadfield. The silicon that they added had several merits: (1) the resistivity was increased and caused a reduction in eddy-current losses, (2) the hysteresis loss was reduced, (3) the permeability was

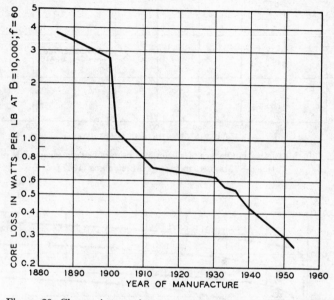

Figure 29. Change in core loss of commercial transformer material with year of manufacture

increased so that smaller exciting currents were required, and (4) the deterioration with time was almost eliminated.

The second big improvement started in the 1930's largely as the result of the work of Goss.[22] His contribution was to so fabricate and heat-treat the material that the individual crystals were oriented in the sheet with their directions of easy magnetization parallel to the length of the sheet, the direction in which it was to be magnetized in use. Measurements of single crystals of silicon-iron[23] show (Figure 30) that to magnetize them to $B = 15,000$ in the [100] direction of easy magnetization requires a field of only 0.1 oersted, while in the

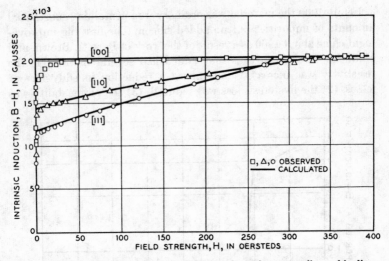

Figure 30. Magnetization curves of silicon-iron in various crystallographic directions.—"Magnetism," *Encycl. Britannica* (1947)

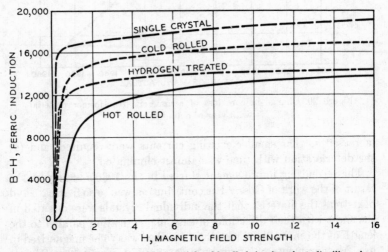

Figure 31. Comparison of commercial cold-rolled (grain-oriented) silicon-iron with hot-rolled (nonoriented) material. Purification of nonoriented material by hydrogen treatment is beneficial in low fields

[111] direction of hard magnetization this requires 100 oersteds, 1000 times as much.

The method of fabrication and heat-treatment used by Goss has been adapted to commercial production by several large steel companies. A product is now readily available which approaches the properties of a single crystal, as shown in Figure 31. The alignment of crystals can now be so controlled that most of the crystals have a direction of easy magnetization within 10° of the rolling direction of the sheet. The orientation[24] taken by the unit cube of the crystals is depicted in Figure 32. At 55° to the rolling direction lies the

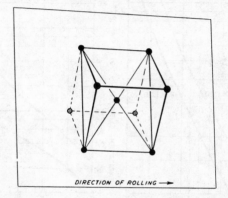

DIRECTION OF ROLLING ➝

Figure 32. Orientation of crystals in grain-oriented silicon-iron strip

"hard" [111] direction, while the cross direction, perpendicular to the direction of rolling, is the intermediate [110] direction.

The quality of the present-day silicon-iron is influenced markedly by another factor, the impurity content. In the transformer core material produced in 1890 it is reported that about one per cent carbon was present as an impurity. In 1905 the first silicon-iron sheet contained about 0.1 per cent carbon. In the hot-rolled product of a decade ago the content was about 0.03 per cent; in present-day cold-rolled material it is probably less than 0.01 per cent. The carbon present in this material as it comes from the rolling mills is reduced by treating in moist hydrogen at about 800°C and further reduced during the final high-temperature treatment of the strip at 1100 to 1200°C in dry hydrogen. Important work on the removal of various impurities from iron by hydrogen was carried out over a period of years by Yensen,[25] Cioffi,[26] and others.[27]

The difference in power loss of hot-rolled and grain-oriented (cold-rolled) material, produced commercially, is shown[28] by the curves of Figure 33. This difference shows the almost twofold improvement in losses resulting from the development of grain orientation alone.

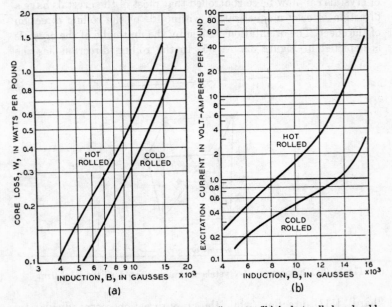

Figure 33. Core losses and exciting current (in watts/lb) in hot-rolled and cold-rolled material

It has been known for many years that fabrication and annealing effect a nonrandom orientation of the crystals composing metallic materials. Although something is known of the nature of slip on certain crystal planes, and the growth during annealing of crystals in certain preferred directions, a real understanding of the mechanism of grain orientation in silicon-iron and other metals is still lacking. The early stages in the development of the grain-oriented transformer sheet were actually carried out without the knowledge that the crystal grains were oriented in a special way by the processing. The understanding of the results in terms of crystal orientation, however, enabled the development to proceed more rapidly and to a further extent. This understanding was provided by solid-state physics.

Iron-Nickel Alloys

In contrast to the iron-silicon alloys, which are used to transmit large amounts of power, the iron-nickel alloys are used mainly to detect and transmit the small signals used in communication. The small signal currents produce small magnetic fields inside transformers and other equipment, and it is therefore desirable to make the flux (voltage) response as high as possible. The material should then have a high permeability in low fields. Whereas in power transformers the induction may have an amplitude of 15,000 gausses, in communication transformers it may be much less than 100. The first

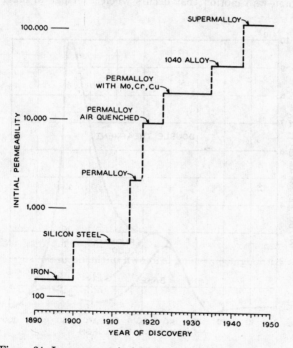

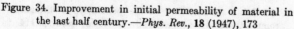

Figure 34. Improvement in initial permeability of material in the last half century.—*Phys. Rev.*, **18** (1947), 173

criterion of a material for this use is the initial permeability, μ_0, the limiting ratio of B/H which is approached as H becomes indefinitely small.

The outstanding qualities of the iron-nickel alloys (Permalloys) were reported by Elmen[29] in 1916. For the first time a search was then being made for a material with a higher initial permeability than silicon-iron. Progress in the last half century is shown in Figure 34.

Figure 35 shows two of the characteristics of the Permalloys: a peak in the initial permeability at about 79 per cent nickel and a large variation of permeability with the rate at which the alloy is cooled through the temperature range 600° to 400°C. These are two of the several properties that physicists set out to understand

In trying to understand these phenomena, let us consider again the domain-wall motion that occurs when a change in magnetiza-

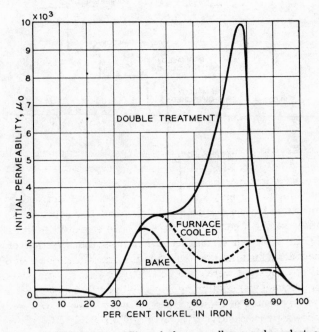

Figure 35. Initial permeability of the permalloys as dependent on composition and heat-treatment.—*Ferromagnetism*, p. 114

tion takes place. Figure 36 shows a wall moving from (*a*) to (*b*) under the influence of an applied field directed from right to left. In 79 Permalloy (79 per cent Ni, 21 per cent Fe), the alloy having the highest initial permeability, the directions of easy magnetization are parallel to the cube diagonals [111]. Movement of the boundary therefore takes place between domains oriented in two such directions.

When the boundary moves from (*a*) to (*b*) the volume of material swept over by the wall is distorted by magnetostriction, the change in dimension that accompanies a change in magnetization. This distortion requires expenditure of force, and so a higher field is required

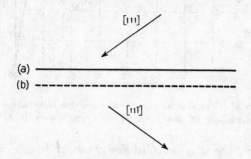

Figure 36. Movement of domain wall in iron-nickel alloy having easy direction [111].—*Revs. Mod. Phys.*, **25** (1953), 42

to cause wall movement. One therefore expects the permeability of the material to be high when the magnetostriction *in the direction of easy magnetization* is small.

The direction of easy magnetization, and the "degree" of ease, are measured by the magnetic crystal anisotropy constant K. This constant specifies the energy, or force (field strength), necessary to rotate the direction of magnetization from the direction of easy magnetization into another given direction. Measurements of the anisotropy constant were made[30] in single crystals of the iron-nickel alloys (Permalloys) containing 35 to 100 per cent nickel, after they were slowly cooled or rapidly cooled. Results (Figure 37) show that the anisotropy is sensitive to cooling rate, probably because there is a tendency for a regular arrangement of the Fe and Ni atoms to take place in alloys near 75 atomic per cent nickel. This atomic ordering

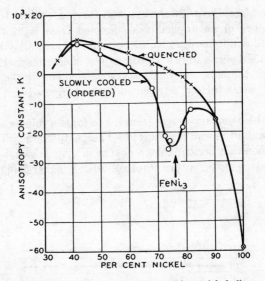

Figure 37. Crystal anisotropy constants of iron-nickel alloys after quenching or slowly cooling.—*Ferromagnetism*, p. 571

occurs only if the alloy is cooled slowly enough to give time for diffusion to take place, and the direction of easy magnetization is then [111] (this corresponds to a negative value K). When the high permeability 79 per cent alloy is quenched the anisotropy is very weak.

The magnetostriction of these crystals is shown in Figure 38, where λ represents the expansion ($\lambda > 0$) or contraction ($\lambda < 0$) in the directions indicated ([111] or [100]) when magnetized parallel to these directions in turn.

These two properties, the crystal anisotropy and the magnetostriction, provide a good qualitative explanation[31] of the important properties of Permalloy: movement of the domain wall between two domains, magnetized in the easy [111] directions, is subject to a minimum of resistance when $\lambda_{111} = 0$, as already shown in Figure 36. The composition at which $\lambda_{111} = 0$ is very close to that for highest permeability in quenched alloys.

A further test of the basic correction of this explanation is the existence of another peak in the permeability vs. composition curve at 45 per cent nickel, because here the direction of easy magnetiza-

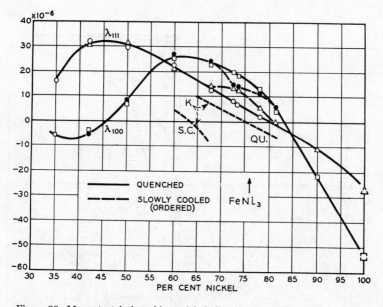

Figure 38. Magnetostriction of iron-nickel alloys in directions of easy and hard magnetization. Effect of heat-treatment is small but definite.—*Revs. Mod. Phys.*, **25** (1953), 42

tion is [100] $(K > 0)$, and $\lambda_{100} = 0$. This peak is observed (see Figure 35).

To repeat, the principal characteristics of Permalloy can be understood in terms of the magnetostriction and magnetic anisotropy. We should like to be able to calculate these quantities from our knowledge of atomic and crystal structure, but we are by no means able to do that yet. It is currently believed that both anisotropy and magnetostriction result from the mutual forces between electron spin and orbital motion of electrons, when they are influenced by an applied field.

Another part of the Permalloy problem is the effect of annealing the material in a magnetic field. Kelsall[32] noted a fivefold increase in maximum permeability of 79 Permalloy when it was cooled from 600°C in the presence of a magnetic field of a few oersteds. In 65 Permalloy an increase of almost a hundredfold has been observed. At the same time the form of the hysteresis loop is observed[33] to become "square," as shown in Figure 39.

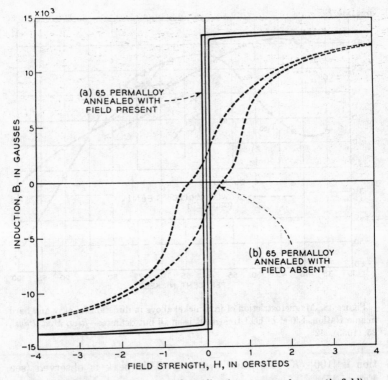

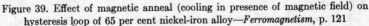

Figure 39. Effect of magnetic anneal (cooling in presence of magnetic field) on hysteresis loop of 65 per cent nickel-iron alloy—*Ferromagnetism*, p. 121

We know from several kinds of experiments that the domains in this material are aligned parallel to the field present during cooling, with all domain walls also parallel to the same direction. Thus each domain has about the same stability of orientation, and when one is reversed by an applied field the others follow quickly by a "chain reaction" and produce a vertical section of the hysteresis loop. The material is composed of many crystals oriented at random, and the domain walls cut across crystal boundaries. This is in agreement with the fact that the crystal anisotropy of this series of alloys is very small, so that small forces, magnetic or mechanical, can readily affect the orientation of the domains.

What we do not understand is why the domains, when pulled out of their original orientation by a strong magnetic field at right angles, return always to their original orientations when the field is removed. Possibly the atomic ordering fixes the stable position of the domains to the crystal lattice in some way not now known.

References

1. R. M. Bozorth, *Phys. Rev.*, **79** (1950), 887; see also *Ferromagnetism* (New York, D. Van Nostrand Co., 1951), for a fuller account of this and other material of this paper.

2. J. C. Slater, *Phys. Rev.*, **36** (1930), 57. Values of shell diameters are now believed to be somewhat smaller.

3. L. Néel, *Ann. Physique*, **3** (1948), 137.

4. Private communication from S. A. Friedberg and J. E. Goldman.

5. E. W. Gorter, *Comp. rend.*, **230** (1950), 194.

6. R. M. Bozorth and J. G. Walker, *Phys. Rev.*, 88 (1952), 1209.

7. W. A. Yager, *Phys. Rev.*, **75** (1949), 316.

8. C. L. Hogan, *Bell System Tech. Jl.*, **31** (1952), 1.

9. The wave velocity is proportional to $(\mu\epsilon)^{-\frac{1}{2}}$, where μ is the permeability and ϵ the dielectric constant of the medium.

10. Hogan; *ibid.*

11. A. G. Fox and M. T. Weiss, *Rev. Mod. Phys.*, **25** (1953), 262.

12. M. L. Kales, H. N. Chait, and N. G. Sakiotis, *J. App. Phys.*, **24** (1953), 816.

13. J. H. Rowen, *Bell System Tech. Jl.*, **32** (1953), 1333.

14. H. Suhl and L. R. Walker, *Bell System Tech. Jl.*, **33** (1954), 579 and 939.

15. H. J. Williams, R. M. Bozorth, and W. Shockley, *Phys. Rev.*, **75** (1949), 155.

16. The 16-mm film, without sound, can be made available on loan for educational purposes by writing to Publication Department, Bell Telephone Laboratories, Inc., 463 West Street, New York 14, N.Y. It takes about 30 minutes to run.

17. E. C. Stoner and E. P. Wohlfarth, *Trans. Roy. Soc.* (London), **240** (1948), 599.

18. L. Néel, *Comp. rend.*, **225** (1947), 109.

19. E. A. Nesbitt and R. D. Heidenreich, *Electr. Engg.*, **71** (1952), 530.

20. W. Jones, *Metal Progress*, **65**, No. 2 (1954), p. 70.

21. E. Houdremont, *Stahl u. Eisen*, **59** (1939), 33.

22. N. P. Goss, *Trans. Am. Soc. Metals*, **23** (1935), 515.

23. H. J. Williams, *Phys. Rev.*, **52** (1937), 747.

24. R. M. Bozorth, *Trans. Am. Soc. Metals*, **23** (1935), 1107.

25. T. D. Yensen, *Trans. Am. Inst. Elec. Engrs.*, **43** (1924), 145.

26. P. P. Cioffi, *Phys. Rev.*, **45** (1934), 742.

27. G. H. Cole, *Electr. Engg.*, **72** (1953), 411.

28. *Ibid.*

29. See ref. 1, p. 109.

30. R. M. Bozorth and J. G. Walker, *Phys. Rev.*, **89** (1953), 624.

31. R. M. Bozorth, *Rev. Mod. Phys.*, **25** (1953), 42.

32. G. A. Kelsall, *Physics*, **5** (1934), 169.

33. J. F. Dillinger and R. M. Bozorth, *Physics*, **6** (1935), 279.

Cryogenics: Very-Low Temperature Physics and Engineering

F. G. BRICKWEDDE

1. Historical

The word *cryogenics* is derived from an ancient Greek word *cryos*, meaning cold. Cryogenics is the science and technology of low temperatures—generally restricted to very low temperatures.

Cryogenic physics and engineering are not of recent origin, for helium (the most difficult of all gases to condense) was liquefied in 1908, and electrical superconductivity was discovered in 1911. The separation of oxygen from the atmosphere and the purification of oxygen, by distillation of liquid air for the cylinder-gas industry, were established before World War I. Whereas there was only one place (Leiden, Holland) where helium was being liquefied before World War I, there were twelve laboratories liquefying helium and experimenting with it by World War II. By this time temperatures within 0.01°K of the absolute zero of temperature were being reached by a new method: that of magnetizing and then demagnetizing adiabatically paramagnetic salts. Important cryogenic engineering developments between the two World Wars were: the dry ice industry; the separations of helium from natural gas, and of argon, neon, and krypton from the atmosphere on an industrial scale; and the transport of liquid oxygen in large truck and railway-car Dewars. Spectacular developments since World War II are: the large-scale production of gaseous oxygen (not of high purity) at low cost for chemical and metallurgical processes; efficient, low-temperature turbine expanders for generating low-temperature refrigeration by the adiabatic expansion of compressed air in air-liquefaction processes; and switch generators for the purification of gases by refrigeration.

Two recent important developments are the Collins-Helium-Cryostat developed by Professor S. C. Collins of the Massachusetts Institute of Technology and fabricated for sale in large numbers by

Arthur D. Little, Inc., and the large-scale production of liquid para-hydrogen, a variety of liquid hydrogen having much better storing properties than liquid normal hydrogen (25 per cent *para* and 75 per cent *ortho*), developed by Dr. Edward F. Grilly of the Los Alamos Scientific Laboratory. More than 80 Collins-Cryostats have been sold by Arthur D. Little, Inc., a few of them in Europe, thus greatly increasing the number of laboratories where cryogenic research may be carried on.

A large, National Bureau of Standards, cryogenic engineering laboratory, at which hydrogen can be liquefied at a rate of 350 liters per hour, and helium at a rate of 150 liters per hour, was established at Boulder, Colorado, for the development of equipment and techniques to make the handling of large quantities of low-temperature refrigerants, like liquid hydrogen and helium, more convenient and less hazardous.

2. Cryogenic Physics: A General Discussion

Cryogenic physics is the physics of matter at low temperatures. Until 20 years ago its principal concern was with the temperature variation of physical phenomena and properties, and with the finding and explaining of limiting values of properties of matter at the absolute zero of temperature. Today, cryogenic physics has a concern that is fundamentally more significant from the standpoint of physical theory. Today cryogenic physics may be said to be the quantum physics of condensed states of matter, that is, of systems of interacting particles. Ordinarily, quantum mechanics is thought of in connection with elementary particles or *micro*scopic systems of particles like atoms and molecules. Cryogenic physics, however, is concerned with *macro*scopic systems measured in cubic centimeters or even in liters. In the microscopic domain of atoms and molecules there are certain phenomena (line spectra instead of the continuous spectra predicted by classical physics, and discrete values of allowed energy, angular momentum, and spatial orientation, instead of the continuous variations characteristic of classical physics) that are contrary to the concepts of classical physics and show the controlling influence of a different kind of physics, namely, quantum mechanics. In a parallel way, there are phenomena of macroscopic systems that are contrary to classical physics and show the influence of quantum principles. Among these are: the *frictionless* flow of electrons in superconductors and of liquid helium through capillaries ($<1\mu$ diameter), an extraordinarily high rate of heat transfer in liquid helium (10^3 times the best solid conductor), and the perfect diamagnetism of superconductors. These phenomena have not been explained satisfactorily and are a continuing challenge to some of our best experimental and theoretical physicists. Their discussion constitutes the major portion of this chapter, but first we discuss some simpler quantum mechanical effects longer known and better understood.

The decrease of specific heats of all substances as $0°K$ is approached (see Figure 1) was the first quantum effect of a condensed state to be recognized and understood. Classical physics says (law of Dulong and Petit) that the specific heat of a monatomic solid is $3R$, independent of temperature, even at $0°K$. In 1907 Einstein proposed a new theory for specific heats of monatomic solids at low temperatures based on the Planck quantum hypothesis and

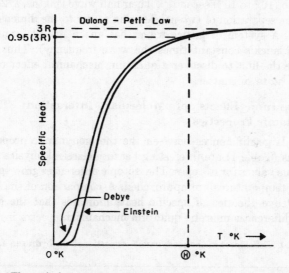

Figure 1. Theoretical curves for the specific heat of a monatomic solid. The ordinates are in units of R (energy/deg mole), the universal gas constant. $\theta = h\nu_{max}/k$ is a parameter of the Debye theory, where ν_{max} is the limiting frequency of elastic waves in the solid. θ is also a characteristic property of a crystal. Experimental data are in better agreement with the Debye theory than the Einstein theory, especially near $0°K$, where Einstein values are too small

on the assumption that atoms vibrate about their equilibrium positions in the crystal lattices like simple harmonic oscillators, *each atom vibrating independently of its neighbors and without any interaction with them.* Hence, all atoms of a monatomic crystal were assumed to vibrate with the same frequency. Einstein obtained a result (see curve in Figure 1) which did not agree with the experimental data near 0°K; that is, the observed specific heats were considerably larger than the calculated ones. Later (1912), Debye obtained good agreement here by introducing the interactions of neighboring atoms as an essential feature of the problem. As a consequence of the interaction, the motions of neighboring atoms are related like the phases at neighboring points of a space traversed by waves. Accordingly, Debye made a Fourier analysis of the seemingly irregular motions of the atoms resolving the motions into a large number ($3N_0$ per mole of atoms) of systems of standing waves in the lattice, with frequencies covering a whole range of values from $\nu = 0$ to (10^{12} to 10^{13}) second $^{-1}$. Their half wave lengths, $\lambda/2$, extend from the separation of two neighboring atoms to the dimension of a crystal. A system of lattice waves has an energy $nh\nu$ (an integer times Planck's constant times the wave frequency). Thus, Debye became the first to discover a quantum mechanical effect of a condensed state of matter.

3. Quantum Effects of Molecular Interaction: Thermodynamic Properties

The large differences between the thermodynamic properties of isotopes (Table 1) are interesting because classical physics predicts the same values for isotopes. The isotopic differences grow smaller as higher temperatures are approached. A comparison of the classical and Debye theories of specific heats indicates that the origin of these differences must be quantum mechanical.

TABLE 1. Differences in thermodynamic properties of the hydrogen and helium isotopes

Isotope	H_2	HD	D_2	He^3	He^4
Boiling point ($T°$, K)	20.38	22.12	23.56	3.20	4.20
Triple point temperature (°K)	13.95	16.59	18.71		
Triple point pressure (atm)	0.071	0.122	0.169		

It is interesting that as early as 1919 Professor Lindemann (now Lord Cherwell) reasoned from Debye's theory of specific heats that heavier isotopes should have higher vapor pressures than lighter ones and that the vapor pressure differences at low temperatures should increase with rising temperatures; this differs from Table 1 and from our experience with other isotopes at low temperatures. Professor Lindemann reasoned as follows: According to Debye's theory the heavier isotope at low temperatures has a greater crystalline heat capacity because the frequencies of its lattice vibrations are smaller ($\nu \ \alpha \ [\text{mass}]^{-1/2}$). At the lowest temperatures,

$$C = 464 \ (kT/h\nu_{\text{max}})^3 \text{ cal (mole deg)}^{-1}, \qquad (1)$$

where ν_{max} is the maximum frequency of the lattice vibrations of a crystal. The term $(h\nu_{\text{max}}/k)$ is called the Debye temperature and is usually represented by Θ. It is a characteristic property of a crystal and is smaller for heavier than for lighter isotopes. A greater heat capacity makes the heat content (enthalpy) greater, at high temperatures, and the heat of vaporization smaller, since the heat content of a vapor (monatomic) is independent of its atomic weight.[1] On this basis, therefore, the heavier isotope with the higher heat capacity and smaller heat of vaporization would be expected to have the higher vapor pressure. Professor Lindemann put his ideas to test by making many fractional distillations of Pb, but he was not able to make any detectable change in the concentration of the Pb isotopes. He was obliged to conclude there are no differences between the vapor pressures of the Pb isotopes at high temperatures. Since the vapor pressures are the same the heats of vaporization must be the same also. From this Lindemann reasoned that there must be at 0°K a difference in the energies of vibration of isotopic lattices and that this difference must equal the difference in the heat contents $\left(\int_0^T C dT \right)$ of the isotopes at high temperatures and be of opposite

---

[1] The *heat content* H is a thermodynamic property: $H = E + pV$.

$$H(T_2, p_0) = H(T_1, p_0) + \int_{T_1}^{T_2} C_{p_0} \, dT.$$

The heat of vaporization equals the difference between the H's of the vapor and the condensed state.

sign. This meant that the lattice is in vibration at 0°K (a new idea in 1919) and has an energy $(h\nu/2)$ for each standing-wave vibration of the lattice or

$$\int_0^{\nu_{max}} [\mathrm{n}(\nu)h\nu/2]\,d\nu = (9R\Theta/8) \qquad (2)$$

for all the standing-wave vibrations of a crystal. This 0°K vibrational energy, which Lindemann postulated in advance of any explanation for it, explains not only why the vapor pressures of the lead isotopes are equal at high temperatures but also why at low temperatures the heavier isotopes have the lower vapor pressures, as shown by Table 1.

Tables 2 and 3 reveal quantum effects in the molecular interactions of compressed gases.

An expanded form of the van der Waals equation of state of a gas is

$$pV = RT\left[1 + \left(b - \frac{a}{RT}\right)\frac{1}{V}\cdots\right]. \qquad (3)$$

TABLE 2. Differences in critical point properties of the hydrogen and helium isotopes

Isotope	H_2	HD	D_2	He^3	He^4
T_c (°K)	33.2	35.9	38.3	3.34	5.30
P_c (atm)	12.8	14.6	16.4	1.15	2.26
V_c (cm³/mole)	67.0	62.8	60.3	72	58.8

TABLE 3. Second virial coefficients B(cm³/mole) of the isotopes of helium for the equation of state:

$$PV = RT\,[1 + (B/V)]$$

T, °K	He^3 Calc.*	He^4 Calc.*	Obs.†
2.154	−125	−172	−176
2.324	−116	−157	−158
2.862	−92	−123	−124
3.348	−77	−102	−103
3.961	−62	−83	−84
4.245	−58	−76	−78

* J. E. Kilpatrick, W. E. Keller, and E. F. Hammel, *Phys. Rev.*, 97 (1955), 9.
† W. E. Keller, *Phys. Rev.*, 97 (1955), 1.

It is especially convenient for this discussion because it shows the influence of the molecular interactions: a results from the attractive forces between molecules and b from the repulsive forces which are very great when there is a close approach of the molecules. For molecules that are impenetrable spheres, b is four times the volume of the molecules. Equation 3 is in the form of the virial equation of state:

$$pV = RT \left[1 + \frac{B(T)}{V} + \frac{C(T)}{V^2} + \cdots \right]. \qquad (4)$$

Isotopes have the same electronic structures; consequently, their sizes and force fields are the same. On this basis the a's and the b's in Equation 3 should be the same, and no difference would be expected in the data of state of isotopes. This is true at higher temperatures, but Tables 2 and 3 show that differences appear at lower temperatures and increase as $0°K$ is approached. A difference that is zero or very small at high temperatures and grows large as $0°K$ is approached was characteristic of the differences in crystalline specific heats and vapor pressures of isotopes discussed above. It is an indication that the explanation of the differences in the equations of state of isotopes is quantum mechanical also.

In quantum mechanics the interaction of molecules is considered on the basis of the scattering of their de Broglie matter waves. The wave length of these waves that surround the molecules and move with them is

$$\lambda = h/mv. \qquad (5)$$

The average wave length for a gas whose molecules move with different speeds is

$$\bar{\lambda} = h/\sqrt{8\pi mkT/3}. \qquad (6)$$

When λ is small compared with the diameter d of a molecule, that is, $T \gg 3h^2/8\pi mkd^2$, the de Broglie waves are *reflected* by molecules in collision in accordance with the laws of geometrical optics (classical physics). But at lower temperatures where $\lambda > d$, the de Broglie waves are *diffracted* and wave theory (wave mechanics) is required for the explanation of the scattering of molecules in collision. The result is an apparent increase in the cross section or size of molecules that grows as the temperature is reduced and λ increases. Equation 6 shows that for a given T, $\bar{\lambda}$ is greater the smaller the mass m of an isotope and, therefore, the increase in collision cross section of molecules is greater for the lighter isotope. This makes the parameter b in the van der Waals equation 3 greater for the lighter isotope, He³, and the virial coefficients $B(T)$ in Equation 4 and Table 3 also greater (algebraically) for He³.

At quite low temperatures—less than 2°K for He—the average de Broglie wave length $\bar{\lambda}$ is comparable with the distance between the molecules. In this situation there are deviations from the classical Maxwell-Boltzmann law for the distribution of velocities of gas molecules. For He³ there are fewer molecules with low velocities than predicted by the Maxwell-Boltzmann statistics and more with higher velocities. For He⁴, it is contrariwise; that is, there are more molecules with lower velocities and fewer with higher velocities. Since molecules with greater velocities and momenta exert more pressure on the wall of a container, it is understandable how gas pressures in He³ can exceed those in He⁴ for the same temperature and molecular density. This is shown by the difference in virial coefficient $B(T)$ for He³ and He⁴ in Equation 4 and Table 3.

It is interesting to see why the deviations from Maxwell-Boltzmann statistics of the velocity distributions for He³ and He⁴ molecules, introduced above, are of opposite sign. He⁴ atoms consist of an even number of fundamental particles (2 nuclear protons, 2 nuclear neutrons, and 2 extranuclear electrons), whereas He³ atoms consist of an odd number of particles, since their nuclei hold only a single neutron. Because of this difference, these isotopes are governed by different kinds of quantum statistics—He⁴ by Bose-Einstein (even) and He³ by Fermi-Dirac (odd). The distribution law for energies ($\epsilon = mv^2/2$) is

$$dN(\epsilon) = \frac{4\pi m}{h^3} \frac{(\sqrt{2m\epsilon})\, d\epsilon}{c + e^{-\gamma} e^{\epsilon/kT}}\, V, \qquad (7)$$

where $dN(\epsilon)$ is the number of molecules in volume V having energies between ϵ and $(\epsilon + d\epsilon)$ and the constant c takes the values 0, +1, and −1 for the classical Maxwell-Boltzmann and the quantum Fermi-Dirac and Bose-Einstein statistics respectively. The value of the parameter γ is adjusted to satisfy the following equation for the total number of gas molecules, N, in volume V:

$$\int_0^\infty dN(\epsilon) = N. \qquad (8)$$

When the deviations from classical statistics are not large,

$$e^{+\gamma} \doteq \frac{h^3 N}{V(2\pi mkT)^{3/2}} \left[1 + c \frac{h^3 N}{2^{3/2} V(2\pi mkT)^{3/2}} \right]. \tag{9}$$

When this is substituted in Equation 7 and c is given the appropriate value, the earlier stated result follows, that is, He^3 has a greater fraction of its molecules in higher energy (velocity) states and He^4 a greater fraction in lower energy (velocity) states than is predicted by the classical Maxwell-Boltzmann statistics.

The difference in quantum statistics is a consequence of the Pauli exclusion principle, which excludes the possibility of two equivalent interacting molecules being in the same quantum state if these particles contain an *odd* number of fundamental particles, as He^3 does. A cell with volume h^3 in the six-dimensional phase space (coordinate-momentum space) constitutes one quantum state of a gas. The Pauli principle permits only one He^3 molecule to occupy a cell in phase space at a time. (This becomes two for He^3 and conduction electrons in metals, if we introduce the spins of He^3 nuclei and electrons which make two states out of each cell in phase space.) Since the number of low-momentum (low-energy) cells is limited, the exclusion principle limits the number of molecules that can have a low energy, and this results in a greater fraction of high-velocity, high-energy molecules than there would be classically. When the molecules contain an even number of fundamental particles, as He^4 does, occupancy of a cell by one molecule increases the probability that a second molecule will enter and share it. Double occupancy of a cell makes it even more probable that a third molecule will enter, and so on. At low temperatures where the probability of filling low-energy (momentum) cells is increased by the limited availability of thermal energy, the Bose-Einstein statistics make this probability even greater. This is just opposite to the effect of the Fermi-Dirac statistics in reducing the probability of the low-velocity states.

4. The Quantum Liquid: Helium II

The quantum effects in molecular interactions discussed in Sections 2 and 3 are interesting departures from classical physics and ordinary experience, but no strikingly new phenomenon appeared—only unanticipated differences in properties. Liquid helium below 2.183°K, however, is so very different from any other liquid that it has been said to constitute a new or fourth state of matter unlike any solid, liquid, or gas.

Figure 2 is a diagram of the specific heat of liquid helium showing an anomaly at 2.183°K. The transition in liquid helium at 2.183°K was named the λ transition because of the similarity of the specific heat curve and the Greek letter lambda (λ). There is no latent heat of transition and no change in density of liquid helium at $T_\lambda = 2.183°K$. Moreover, there are no changes in the patterns of

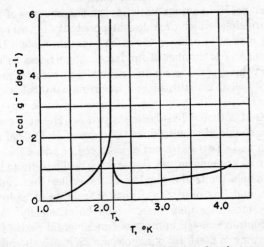

Figure 2. The specific heat of liquid He⁴ showing the anomaly at 2.183°K called the λ-transition. Liquid helium above the transition is called He I and below it is called He II

diffracted X-rays and neutrons from liquid He when passing through T_λ, showing that there is no change in the geometrical arrangement of He atoms in the liquid at T_λ. There are phenomenal changes in other properties, however. The higher temperature form, named liquid He I, has properties approximating those anticipated for a normal liquid at very low temperatures. It is the lower temperature form, liquid He II, that has the remarkable properties of super-fluidity, the creeping film, a new kind of reversible heat transfer, and second sound.

Figure 3 is a phase diagram of helium, schematically drawn. Helium is unique for a chemically stable substance in that there is no condition of temperature and pressure at which the three phases, solid, liquid, and vapor, can coexist in equilibrium. Liquid He alone may not be solidified by simply lowering the temperature of the liquid in contact with its vapor. To solidify He, it is necessary to compress it—25 atm (at 0°K) is the minimum freezing pressure. For solidification at higher temperatures, higher pressures are required.

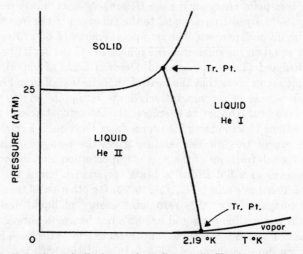

Figure 3. A schematically drawn phase diagram for He⁴ showing a lower limiting pressure of 25 atmospheres for the existence of solid He. There is no ordinary solid-liquid-vapor triple point. Helium has two triple points in which two of the three phases in equilibrium are liquid He I and liquid He II. There is an equilibrium line for He I and II connecting these triple points

Helium has two triple points (states of coexistence of three phases); the line connecting them separates the He I and He II regions of the phase diagram in Figure 3.

Liquid He has an unusually large molecular volume—32 cm³ per mole at 4.2°K and 28 cm³ per mole at 0°K, which may be compared with 8 cm³ for a close packing of He atoms (hard spheres) 2.7 × 10⁻⁸ cm in diameter. The heat of vaporization of liquid helium at its boiling point, 4.2°K, is only 20 cal per mole, whereas 85 cal per mole is calculated from Trouton's rule.

The unusual properties of liquid He—large molecular volume, low heat of vaporization, and no solid-liquid-vapor triple point—are related and explainable on the basis of the 0°K motions of atoms and molecules found essential in Section 3 for the explanation of the differences in vapor pressures of isotopes.

The zero-point energy of liquid He calculated from the specific heat of liquid He below 1°K using the Debye theory of lattice specific heats is ~ 73 cal per mole. A value of ~ 60 cal per mole is obtained for the zero-point energy using the Heisenberg uncertainty relation, $(\Delta x \cdot \Delta p_x \sim h)$, by setting Δx equal to the cube root of the free volume of the liquid per He atom. The zero-point energy of 60 to 70 cal per mole is equal to the difference (85 minus 20 cal per mole) between the calculated (Trouton rule) and observed heats of vaporization. Hence, it seems clear that the heat of vaporization of liquid helium is small because of a comparatively large zero-point energy which reduces the heat required to overcome the attractive forces of neighboring atoms in vaporizing He atoms from the liquid. For all substances except the low temperature gases the zero-point energies are very small fractions of the heat of vaporization, and hence zero-point energies are not added to heats of vaporization in the statement of Trouton's rule $(\Delta H_{\text{vap}}/T_B \doteq 20)$ for other substances.

The comparatively large zero-point energy of liquid and solid helium is responsible for liquid helium's not having a normal freezing point. There is a one cubic centimeter per mole decrease in volume when liquid helium is solidified. In solid He, with the smaller free volume for the motions of the atoms, the zero-point kinetic energy exceeds that in the liquid—a consequence of the Heisenberg uncertainty relation. The greater kinetic energy of the solid is partially—but only partially—offset by a decrease in the lattice potential energy that results when the atoms are packed together more closely. Hence, solid He, with a one cubic centimeter per mole smaller volume than liquid He at vapor pressure, has a greater energy (negative heat of fusion) than liquid helium and is therefore unstable.

When the liquid is compressed to 25 atm at 0°K (135 atm at 4.2°K) and He atoms are packed more closely, the decrease in lattice potential energy is greater than at lower densities for the same differential change in volume. At 0°K and 25 atm the decrease in potential energy and the increase in kinetic energy on solidification just balance, so that liquid and solid helium have the same energy and the heat of fusion is zero. Because the heat of fusion is zero, the slope

dp/dT of the solid-liquid equilibrium line in Figure 3 at 0°K is zero. At 4.2°K, the heat of fusion is 1.8 cal per mole, because of a difference between the heat capacities of solid and liquid He along the solid-liquid line, in Figure 3, from 0° to 4.2°K.

The unusual properties we have just been discussing are consequences of quantum effects in molecular interactions—a phenomenon seen in Sections 2 and 3 to be of general occurrence at low temperatures. But there are properties of liquid He II that are not just unusual—they are unique. The more important of these are:

1. Superfluidity (frictionless flow of liquid at 20 to 30 cm per second through capillaries 0.1μ in diameter).

2. The creeping film (frictionless flow of liquid against gravity over the surfaces of containers at speeds of 20 to 30 cm per second independent of the driving pressure).

3. Phenomenal rates of heat transfer (hundreds of times that in our best conductors, Ag and Cu).

4. Second sound (temperature or thermal waves propagated through the liquid He undamped like ordinary sound).

These phenomena are so different from ordinary experience that a description of their details is bewildering without a correlating theory in mind. Hence, a theory for liquid He II is discussed first.

We start with Equations 7 and 9 for Bose-Einstein statistics ($c = -1$). The denominator of Equation 7, giving the number of He⁴ atoms in the energy range $d\epsilon$, is zero and $dN(\epsilon)$ is infinite for $\epsilon = 0$ at very low temperatures. This mathematical catastrophe is averted by an accumulation of He⁴ atoms in the state $\epsilon = 0$ ($p = 0$), which sets in at the temperature called the Bose-Einstein *condensation temperature*. This accumulation of atoms in the state $\epsilon = 0$ ($p = 0$) progresses as the temperature falls so that at 0°K all atoms are in the $\epsilon = 0$ ($p = 0$) state. It has already been pointed out that in Bose-Einstein statistics the occupancy of a quantum state (cell in phase space) by one molecule increases the probability that other molecules will enter it. The accumulation (condensation) of molecules in the $\epsilon = 0$ ($p = 0$) cell is a culmination of this. Equation 9 for e^γ shows that the Bose-Einstein condensation temperature depends on the volume V. For a gas of noninteracting He⁴ atoms having the density of liquid He, the calculated condensation temperature is about 3.3°K. In liquid He, condensation begins at the λ transition, 2.183°K. As the temperature falls below the λ transition, the fraction of the atoms in the Bose-Einstein condensed state increases while the fraction of normally excited atoms ($p \neq 0$) decreases. Because, as will be seen later, the $p = 0$ component is responsible for the superfluid properties of He II, it is called the *superfluid* component and the other component the *normal fluid*. The λ point is the temperature of appearance or disappearance of the *superfluid*. There is no latent heat of transition at T_λ since the fraction of superfluid is zero at the λ point and increases at a finite rate as the temperature falls. The excess heat capacity of liquid He above an anticipated low-lying curve in Figure 2 can be attributed to the energy of excitation (or transition) of superfluid to normal fluid.

In the phase diagram of He (Figure 3) it is seen that the slope dp/dT of the solid-liquid equilibrium line, which is zero at 0°K, is *practically* zero up to 1°K, where it begins gradually to increase. If dp/dT is inserted in the Clapeyron equation

$$\frac{dp}{dT} = \frac{L}{T(V_{11q} - V_{sol})} = \frac{S_{11q} - S_{sol}}{(V_{11q} - V_{sol})} \tag{10}$$

it is seen that the entropies, S, of solid and liquid He are practically equal from 0° to 1°K. Since the entropy of solid He is zero at 0°K (third law of thermodynamics), the entropy of liquid He II is zero also. The entropies of supercooled liquids (glasses) at 0°K are greater than zero. A zero entropy is a consequence of a perfect ordering (a single quantum state). In crystals at 0°K, atoms are ordered in geometric space on lattice sites and vibrate randomly in momentum space with the zero-point motions. In liquid He II the ordering is in momentum space, and the distribution of atoms in geometric space is random, as required by the Heisenberg uncertainty principle.

This model for liquid He II consists of two components: a superfluid component with zero entropy and a normal component carrying all the thermal energy and the entropy of He II. Landau in Russia proposed that liquid He II supports two different kinds of motion which are thermally excited. He named these two motions phonons and rotons. Phonons are quantized packets ($\epsilon = h\nu$) of Debye waves similar to those in crystal lattices. The rotons are rotational or vortex motions with quantized angular momentum, i.e., with integral multiples of the quantum element of angular momentum, $h/2\pi$. Each of the quantized states of these motions involves a large number of He atoms with coordinated phase relations. The roton motions have considerably greater energy than the phonon motions and hence are excited only at higher temperatures. The phonon motions with very small frequencies are excited even at the lowest temperatures. Experimentally, it has been found that the roton motions are not appreciably excited below 0.5°K. The He atoms carrying the phonon and roton motions constitute the normal component of liquid He, and the atoms with zero thermal energy and zero entropy constitute the superfluid.

Isotopic liquid He³ is a test for this theory since He³ is governed by the Fermi-Dirac statistics, which does not allow accumulation of atoms in any cell of phase space because of the Pauli exclusion principle. As would be expected on this basis, liquid He³ does not possess the very unusual properties that characterize He⁴ II such as superfluidity, creep, phenomenal heat transfer, and second sound. Liquid He³ does exhibit the more ordinary quantum effects of molecular interaction at low temperatures, such as an unusually large molecular volume (at 0°K, 39 cm³ per mole for He³ and 28 cm³ per mole for He⁴); an unusually low heat of vaporization (at 0°K, 5 cal per mole for He³ and 15 cal per mole for He⁴); no solid-liquid-vapor triple point; and a minimum freezing pressure of 27 atm (25 for He⁴). Larger quantum effects are to be expected for He³ than He⁴ because of its smaller mass.

We discuss now the viscosity and flow properties of liquid helium with this theory for He⁴ II in mind. There are two commonly used methods for the measurement of viscosities, η. One involves a measurement of the volume rate of flow, $\dot{V}$, through a capillary tube of length L and radius r and makes use of the Poiseuille equation:

$$\dot{V} = \frac{1}{\eta} \frac{\pi r^4}{8} \frac{\Delta p}{L}. \tag{11}$$

The other method makes use of the rate of damping (the logarithmic decrement) of the rotational oscillations of a disc (or cylinder) immersed in the liquid under investigation, the rotations of the disc taking place in its own plane. Damping results from the viscous drag of the liquid on the oscillating disc.

Figure 4 is a diagram of the viscosity of bulk liquid and gaseous He determined with the oscillating disc. A spectacular feature of this diagram is the rapid falling off of the viscosity of liquid He II below

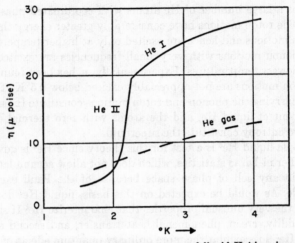

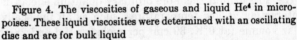

Figure 4. The viscosities of gaseous and liquid He⁴ in micro-poises. These liquid viscosities were determined with an oscillating disc and are for bulk liquid

the λ transition and the low value to which the viscosity falls, becoming less than that of its vapor, which is unique. This is explainable if it is assumed that the viscosity of the superfluid component of He II is zero and that the viscous drag on an oscillating disc is due to the normal (thermally excited) component whose concentration also falls off rapidly below the λ transition, like the viscosity of He II in Figure 4.

Another interesting feature of Figure 4 is the sign of the temperature coefficient of viscosity of liquid He I. Viscosities of liquids normally decrease with rising temperature, whereas the viscosities of gases increase. In this respect gaseous He is normal but He I behaves like gas and not like a liquid. This may result from: (1) the relatively large separations of He atoms in its liquid phase, which has an unusually large molecular volume, and (2) from the rather small van der Waals forces in He, which might make molecular interactions in liquid He more like those in normal gases than in normal liquids.

The low viscosity of liquid helium may be compared with a viscosity of 10^4 micropoises for water and 180 micropoises for air at 20°C.

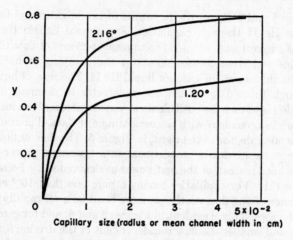

Figure 5. A plot of the index y in the equation: $\dot{V} = \text{const.}\,(\Delta p)^y$. Here $\dot{V}$ is the volume rate of flow of liquid He through capillaries and through channels in tubes packed with powders. The pressure head is Δp. For normal (Poiseuille) flow, the index y is one. The two curves are for 2.16°K and 1.20°K

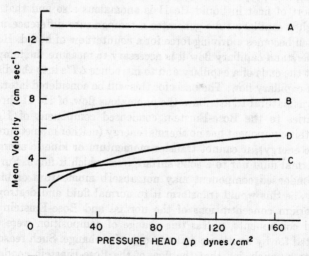

Figure 6. The mean velocity of flow of liquid He at 1.20°K through capillary channels. The channel widths are: A(1×10^{-5} cm), B(8×10^{-5} cm), C(4×10^{-4} cm), and D(5×10^{-3} cm). For normal (Poiseuille) flow, the mean velocity is proportional to the pressure head Δp

Figures 5 and 6 represent the results of investigations of the flow of liquid He II through capillaries. For normal liquids the same values of viscosity are obtained from measurements of flow through capillaries and from measurements of the damping of oscillating discs, but this is not the case for liquid He II. The flow of liquid He II through tubes larger than one millimeter in diameter follows Poiseuille's law, and the coefficients of viscosity from these measurements are in agreement with the oscillating disc data. Tubes of these sizes are off-scale, far to the right, in Figure 5. The flow of liquid He II through capillaries is proportional to a fractional power of the pressure head instead of the first power as demanded by Poiseuille's equation (11). For capillaries having a bore less than 10^{-2} cm, the dependence of the flow on the pressure head falls off rapidly as the bore decreases. This is evident in Figures 5 and 6, and for capillaries 10^{-4} cm and smaller the flow is independent of the driving force Δp. A flow that is independent of the pressure difference Δp and increases its linear speed when the capillary is made finer is just contrary to all other hydrodynamic experience. It is clear that viscosity has no meaning as a property for liquid He II. Later we shall see that the transport of heat in liquid He II is anomalous also and that flow through a capillary tube generates a temperature difference in He II which becomes a driving force for a counterflow of liquid. Hence, to understand capillary flow it is necessary to measure the temperature at the ends of a capillary and to introduce ΔT's into the discussion of capillary flow. The basis for this will be considered later.

It was natural to attribute the anomalous flow of He II through capillaries to the Bose-Einstein condensed component of He II. Since this component has no thermal energy (neither momentum nor kinetic energy), it cannot transfer momentum or kinetic energy to the normal fluid nor to a solid surface over which it flows. Further, this condensed component may not absorb momentum or kinetic energy, as this would transform it to normal fluid and destroy the equilibrium concentrations of the normal and Bose-Einstein condensed components, unless this change of composition were compensated for by another equal and opposite change. Such reasoning leads to a conclusion that the flow of the Bose-Einstein condensed component is frictionless since friction would involve transfers of energy and momentum. The Bose-Einstein condensed component was, therefore, named the superfluid component. The drag on oscillating discs in liquid He II is, therefore, attributed to the normal component.

Making use of these ideas, Andronikashvili, in Russia, built an ingenious apparatus to determine the proportion of normal fluid and superfluid in He II (see Figure 7). The apparatus consisted of a stack of 50 thin discs (2.5 cm diameter) with a separation of 0.02 cm between faces of adjacent discs, suspended from a torsion fiber.

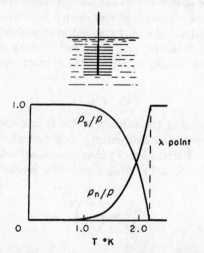

Figure 7. A schematic diagram of the stack (1.2 cm high) of 50 thin discs (2.5 cm diameter) with 0.02 cm separations, used by Andronikashvili in his determination of the mole fractions of the superfluid (ρ_s) and normal fluid (ρ_n) components of He II shown in the graph. The bulk density of He II is: $\rho = \rho_n + \rho_s$

The height of this assembled pile was only 1.2 cm, and its moment of inertia *in vacuo* only 6.7 gram cm². The period of the rotational oscillations of the discs was greater in liquid He II than *in vacuo*, showing that there was an increase in the moment of inertia of the disc assembly. This increase was due to the normal-fluid component between the discs which was dragged by the discs as they oscillated. From the change in the moment of inertia, Andronikashvili calculated the mass of normal fluid dragged by the discs and from this derived the density of the normal component. This leads to the ρ_n/ρ curve in Figure 7, where ρ_n and ρ_s are the densities (grams per cubic

centimeter) of normal fluid and superfluid components, and ρ is
the observed density of liquid helium, equal to $(\rho_n + \rho_s)$. An empirical equation that fits the experimental data *approximately* is

$$\frac{\rho_n}{\rho} = \left(\frac{T}{T_\lambda}\right)^6. \tag{12}$$

If these assumptions are made: (1) the superfluid has zero heat
capacity and the observed heat capacity of liquid He II (Figure 20)
is principally heat of transition (per degree Kelvin) of superfluid to
normal fluid, and (2) the entropy of the superfluid is zero at all
temperatures, the following relations result. These relations can have
only approximate validity because of the approximate nature of the
assumptions.

$$S/S_\lambda \doteq \rho_n/\rho, \tag{13}$$

since practically all of the entropy of He II is associated with the
normal component, and this entropy is practically all entropy of
transition (heat of transition/T) from the superfluid to the normal
fluid. At T_λ, $S = S_\lambda$ and $\rho = \rho_n$. Combining Equations 12 and 13,
we have

$$\frac{S}{S_\lambda} \doteq \left(\frac{T}{T_\lambda}\right)^6 \tag{14}$$

and

$$C = T\frac{dS}{dT} \doteq 6S_\lambda\left(\frac{T}{T_\lambda}\right)^6. \tag{15}$$

Equation 15 fits approximately the observed specific heats (Figure
2) from $1.0°$K to T_λ.

Below $0.5°$K, the heat capacity of liquid He II is proportional to
T^3, which is normal for the specific heat of lattice vibrations (see
equation 1). Hence, it is believed that below $0.5°$K, the thermal
energy of He II is in the phonons, the quantized packets ($\epsilon = h\nu$) of
lattice waves. There can be below $0.5°$K only a very little (insignificant fraction) of the thermal energy in high-energy ($\sim kT_\lambda$) roton
excitations. Equations 12 to 15 were based on the assumption
that the thermal energy of liquid He II was practically all roton
energy, which is valid above $1.5°$K but not below $0.5°$K. Hence, the
Equations 12 to 15 cannot be expected to be valid below $0.5°$K.

The first superfluid property of He II discovered (1935) was the *Rollin creeping film*—a phenomenon that does not occur with He I or any other liquid. Figures 8 (*a*) and 8 (*b*) illustrate an essential characteristic of the film: it covers and creeps over cold surfaces that dip into bulk liquid He II. The creeping film evaporates at places where the temperature of the cold surface reaches T_λ. There is a flow of liquid He through a film that continues until the surfaces of liquid helium inside and outside a vessel stand at the same horizon-

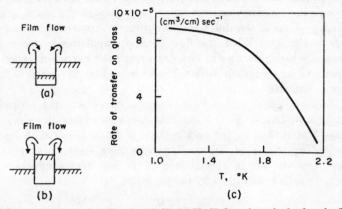

Figure 8. The creeping film. In (a), liquid He II flows into the beaker; in (b), it flows out of the beaker. The flow continues until the levels of liquid He inside and outside the beaker are the same but the rate of this flow is independent of the magnitude of the difference in levels. The rate of flow of liquid He through the film, per centimeter width of beaker surface normal to the flow, is shown at the right in (c)

tal level. If an open vessel with liquid He II is raised out of a bath of liquid He, the film creeps up the inside surface of the container, down the outside surface, and drips drops of liquid He from the bottom of the vessel until all the liquid He has crept out of the vessel or until the temperature has risen to T_λ.

The thickness of the creeping film (300 to 400 A) and the rate of flow through it are practically independent of the chemical nature of the surface supporting the film, provided the surface is smooth. Figure 8 (*c*) is a diagram of the rate of flow across one-centimeter width of surface. The linear speed of He atoms through the *creeping* film increases from 0 at the λ transition to about 30 cm per second at about 1.6°K. This is of the order of the maximum speed of He in superfluid flow through very fine capillaries, $\sim 0.1\mu$ in diameter (see Figure 6). The maximum speed of superfluid flow in capillaries is temperature-dependent also, starting with zero speed at T_λ and rising approximately proportional to the ordinates in Figure 8 (c). Another important similarity of the flows through capillaries and the creeping film is the apparent lack of any functional dependence of the rate of flow on the driving force; that is, the rate of flow through fine capillaries is independent of the pressure gradient through the capillary, and the rate of flow through the creeping film is independent of the difference in hydrostatic pressure at the two ends of the film. When the flow through capillaries is driven by unusually high pressures in order to exceed the maximum speed of superfluid flow, frictionless flow breaks down and resistance to flow rises enormously.

The flow of heat in liquid He II is as anomalous as the hydrodynamic flow. Liquid He II is our best *conductor* of heat, hundreds of times better than copper and millions of times better than liquid He I. The curves of Figure 9, representing some heat transfer measurements, are of special interest to us. Heat conduction in normal media is described by the equation

$$\kappa = \frac{\dot{Q}}{dT/dx}, \tag{16}$$

where the thermal conductivity κ is a property of the medium, i.e., it is independent of the magnitudes of the heat current Q and the temperature gradient dT/dx. An examination of Figure 9 shows that this ratio is not a constant for He II—the ratio is greater the smaller the temperature gradient. Furthermore, it is significant that the highest rates of heat transfer are observed at temperatures where the concentrations of normal fluids and superfluids are most sensitive to changes in temperature (compare with Figure 7).

Kapitza, working in Moscow in 1941, designed an ingenious apparatus, (Figure 10) for the investigation of the flows of heat and of liquid, either separately or together, through very narrow channels in He II. The interesting result was that when conditions were set up for the establishment of either one of these flows both flows resulted simultaneously. Hence, the previously described investigations of heat and capillary flow in liquid He II, conducted as with

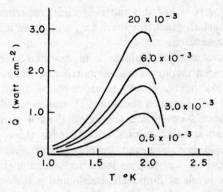

Figure 9. Density of heat current in liquid helium, for a given temperature gradient, as a function of temperature. The temperature gradients, in °K/cm, are indicated by the curves. Note that the density of heat current is not proportional to the temperature gradient as it is for ordinary heat conduction

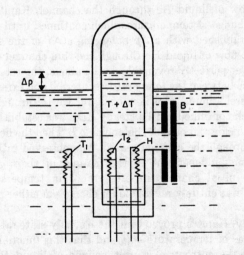

Figure 10. A schematic diagram of the apparatus used by Kapitza to demonstrate and to investigate the thermomechanical effect in He II. T_1 and T_2 represent thermometers for the measurement of the temperatures of the liquid He outside and inside a vacuum-insulated vessel in which there is an electric heater H. Superfluid He flows through a very narrow channel (10^{-5} cm) between two optically flat glass plates (B) as a result of either a temperature difference ($T_1 - T_2$) or a pressure difference Δp. A steady state is possible with Δp's balancing the $(T_1 - T_2)$'s

normal media, were either only partially under experimental control or were only partially instrumented, i.e., all factors influencing the flow were not measured.

The apparatus used by Kapitza is represented schematically in Figure 10. Its essential parts are a vacuum insulated vessel, equipped with an electrical heater H and thermometer T_2, and an external bath of liquid He II with a resistance thermometer T_1. The space inside the insulated vessel and the external bath of liquid He are connected by an annular channel only 10^{-5} cm thick, between the two thick, flat plates B. Through this very narrow channel liquid He and heat could be made to pass in either direction. From the differences in the levels of liquid He, inside and outside the insulated vessel, the differences in the internal and external pressures were determined.

Raising or lowering the vessel in the external bath creates a pressure difference and a flow of liquid He through the thin channel in B. With a flow of liquid He through the channel, Kapitza always observed a change of temperature which continued until an equilbrium was established with a Δp balancing a ΔT of the same sign, and then the flow of liquid He through the thin channel ceased.

In a manner perfectly reversible to the above, the establishment of a difference between the temperatures internal and external to the insulated vessel stimulated a flow of liquid He II through the thin channel which continued until a steady state was established with a Δp, between inside and outside, balancing ΔT. Then the flows of heat and liquid through the channel ceased. The observed ratios $\Delta p/\Delta T$ were the same, independent of the manner of their generation, whether by initial changes in pressure or in temperature. The phenomenon was entirely reversible for changes in either pressure or temperature.

Empirically, Kapitza proved that these steady-state ratios $\Delta p/\Delta T$ were functions of temperature *only* and that this function equalled ρS, which is the entropy of a unit volume of liquid He II. The equation

$$\frac{\Delta p}{\Delta T} = \rho S \tag{17}$$

can be recast as follows:

$$\frac{V\Delta p}{\rho V S T} = \frac{\Delta T}{T}. \tag{18}$$

Kapitza verified with the heater H that the heat Q required to keep a higher temperature T_0 inside the insulated vessel constant as liquid flowed into it was ρVST_0, the denominator in Equation 18, where V was the volume of the liquid He II that flowed through the channel. Hence, Kapitza proved empirically

$$\frac{\begin{pmatrix} \text{work done by liquid He flowing} \\ \text{through narrow channel} \end{pmatrix}}{\begin{pmatrix} \text{heat supplied to keep} \\ T_0 \text{ in vessel constant} \end{pmatrix}} = \frac{V\Delta p}{\rho VST_0} = \frac{\Delta T}{T_0}. \quad (19)$$

This is the equation for the efficiency of an *ideal* Carnot process in which the heat $Q = \rho VST_0$, transferred to a heat engine at temperature T_0, is partly converted into mechanical energy, which here is $V\Delta p$. The ideal or maximum possible thermodynamic efficiency of such a thermomechanical process, or of any heat engine, is $\Delta T/T_0$, where ΔT is the difference between the temperatures of the source and sink of heat. Kapitza's apparatus is, therefore, a kind of thermodynamically perfect, reversible heat engine—a kind of Carnot engine.

It is clear that maximum or thermodynamic efficiency in Kapitza's apparatus could be possible only if the flow of liquid helium through the narrow channel were nondissipative, i.e., frictionless. Kapitza proved experimentally that the heat needed to keep the temperature constant is equal to that required to increase the entropy of volume V of fluid flowing through the channel by an amount equal to (ρVST_0), which is the total entropy of liquid He II at T_0. Hence, it is said that the fluid flowing through the channel is superfluid and has zero entropy. The heat Kapitza added to keep the temperature constant was the heat of conversion to normal fluid of a fraction of the superfluid that flowed through the channel. This fraction is the same as the mole fraction of normal fluid in He II at T_0.

Kapitza demonstrated that a flow of heat in liquid He II takes place by a fundamentally different process from heat conduction in other media. In liquid He II heat transport occurs by a flow of superfluid from the cooler to the warmer region where there is an absorption of heat in the conversion of a fraction $\rho_n/(\rho_n + \rho_s)$ of the superfluid flow into normal fluid. The temperature of the warmer region falls if heat is not added to keep the temperature constant. The temperature of the cooler region rises through the increase in concentration of normal fluid in the liquid remaining after the loss of superfluid. When there is a difference of temperature and a flow of heat in liquid He II, there is also a flow of superfluid, which is counter to the flow of heat.

A flow of superfluid through a capillary, mechanically driven, changes the ρ_n/ρ_s ratios at the ends of the capillary. At the entrance to the capillary ρ_n/ρ_s and the temperature rise; at the exit they fall. Hence, a flow of superfluid through a capillary, mechanically driven, results in a change of temperature and an apparent transfer of heat that is counter to the direction of the superfluid flow.

The *complete* reversibility, in the thermodynamic sense, of the mechanical flow of superfluid and the counter transport of heat is important. It is, of course, essential for the ideal thermodynamic efficiencies observed by Kapitza; see Equation 19.

The flow of superfluid generated by a temperature difference results from a kind of osmosis, the driving force being a difference in the concentrations of normal fluid in different regions. Capillaries and narrow channels act like membranes permeable to superfluid but impermeable to normal fluid because of its hydrodynamic friction.

It is possible to use the thermomechanical effect in He II to generate fountains of liquid helium. The open, lower end of a glass tube (see Figure 11) is packed with a very fine powder to make a very great number of very narrow passages for a flow of superfluid. The

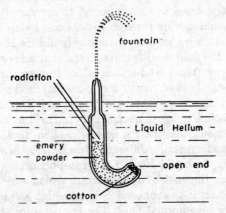

Figure 11. A sketch of a tube for generating a fountain of liquid He II—an example of the thermomechanical effect in He II. The upper end of the powder packing, inside the glass tube, is heated radiatively with a flashlight

upper end of the glass tube is constricted to develop a high pressure in the liquid He inside the tube above the powder packing. The open, lower end of the tube is immersed in liquid He II, and a temperature difference between the ends of the powder packing is generated by heating the top of the packing. This may be conveniently done by shining a low-power electric light on top of the packing.

One of the most singular characteristics of liquid He II is its *inherent* ability to *sustain* traveling trains of temperature waves practically undamped and to support the resonance of temperature waves in cavities. This phenomenon was extensively investigated by John R. Pellam at the National Bureau of Standards.

A temperature wave is an oscillation of temperature above and below an equilibrium or mean value similar to the oscillations of pressure in a sound wave. In an advancing temperature wave, temperature changes travel away from a source. A periodic temperature wave may be generated by an alternating or periodically varying current in an electric heater. Temperature waves are detected with a thermometer, for example, an electrical resistance thermometer. A thermometer with small heat capacity follows the rapid alternations of temperature with very little lag.

Temperature waves in liquid He II are named *second* sound—the adjective *second* distinguishes the temperature wave from the pressure wave of ordinary sound, called *first* sound. Ordinary or *first* sound in liquid He II, as in all fluids, consists of periodic variations of density and pressure. In *second* sound in liquid He II there are no pressure or density variations detectable with the most sensitive microphones used for ordinary or *first* sound. Moreover, second sound cannot be generated by pulsing diaphragms used to generate first sound. Temperature waves are generated and detected thermally, not microphonically. The velocity of first sound in liquid He II is about 200 m per second; the temperature-dependent velocity of second sound is graphed in Figure 12.

Temperature waves can, of course, be generated in ordinary media, in a copper rod for example, but these temperature waves are not *self-sustaining*, and resonance with them is, therefore, impossible. Hence, the significance of *sound* in second *sound* is to point up the self-sustaining and resonance characteristics of temperature waves in He II that are similar to these same characteristics in ordinary (pressure) sound. In ordinary media, the space-time vari-

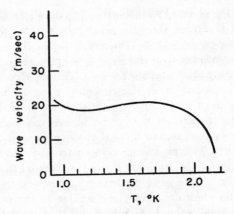

Figure 12. The velocity of second sound (undamped temperature waves) in He II plotted as a function of temperature

ations of temperature are described mathematically by the familiar heat transfer equation (for one dimension):

$$\frac{\kappa}{\rho C} \frac{\partial^2 T}{\partial x^2} = \frac{\partial T}{\partial t}, \tag{20}$$

where κ, ρ, and C are the thermal conductivity, density, and specific heat of the medium. The form of the equation for temperature variations in liquid He II, however, is that for undamped wave motion:

$$\frac{\partial^2 T}{\partial x^2} = \frac{1}{v_2{}^2} \frac{\partial^2 T}{\partial t^2}, \tag{21}$$

where v_2 is the velocity of temperature (second-sound) waves. There are fundamental differences between the kinds of physical phenomena that follow from equations like 20 and 21 because of the difference in the orders of time derivatives. Resonance is one of these differences. Other differences between the temperature waves that follow from these equations are:

1. Temperature waves in ordinary media are highly damped, that is, the amplitudes of waves with frequency ν, decrease with x like

$$e^{-x\sqrt{\pi\nu\rho C/\kappa}},$$

whereas in He II temperature waves are undamped. Actually, there is a very small damping of second sound in He II, but this is not included in Equation 21. To include it, a term with the first partial derivative with respect to time would be added to Equation 21, but its coefficient for liquid He II would be very small indeed.

2. The velocity of temperature waves in an ordinary medium depends on the frequency ν in accordance with

$$\sqrt{4\pi\nu \cdot \frac{\kappa}{\rho C}}\,.$$

In liquid He II their velocity, v_2, is independent of the frequency.

In He I, and in all media except He II, heat gets from one place to another (in the absence of convection and electromagnetic radiation) by *diffusion*. Equation 20 is of the same form as the diffusion equation

$$D\,\frac{\partial^2 c}{\partial x^2} = \frac{\partial c}{\partial t} \tag{22}$$

that describes the diffusion of a solute when the concentration c in a solution is not uniform. The symbol D is called the diffusion constant and is a property of the diffusing substance and its environment in the solution. Because of the similarity of Equations 20 and 22, the coefficient $(\kappa/\rho C)$ in Equation 20 is called the *thermal diffusivity*.

Waves described by an equation with the second derivative with respect to time, like Equation 21, are sustained by a force of restitution which acts to re-establish the equilibrium condition whenever there is a displacement from it. Because of a restoring force, waves incident on walls are reflected and returned to the medium. Only in liquid He II has a specular reflection of temperature waves by walls been observed. Since standing waves and resonance result from the interference of trains of incident and reflected waves, resonance of temperature waves has consequently been observed only in He II.

The generation of a mechanical force in liquid He II by a temperature difference was demonstrated by the thermomechanical effect investigated by Kapitza (see Figure 10). This temperature-generated force drives superfluid from a lower toward a higher temperature (see the fountain effect, Figure 11). When superfluid flow takes place through capillaries or channels offering high resistance to the flow of normal fluid, pressure differences arise. However, in bulk liquid these pressure differences cannot arise because a counterflow of normal fluid is unobstructed. Hence, in bulk liquid the counter-flows of normal fluid and superfluid take place in such a way that

$$\rho_n + \rho_s = \rho \text{ (bulk density of He II)}$$
$$= \text{constant} \tag{23}$$

$$\rho_s\mathbf{v}_s + \rho_n\mathbf{v}_n = \rho\mathbf{v} \text{ (resultant momentum density)}$$
$$= 0. \tag{24}$$

These equations express in mathematical form the inability of a vibrating diaphragm to generate temperature waves or of a microphone to detect them. Also, these equations show that in a temperature wave superfluid and normal fluid vibrate by and through each other in counter directions, since $\mathbf{v}_s$ and $\mathbf{v}_n$ must have opposite signs.

A periodic temperature wave in liquid He II above 1°K is physically a traveling periodic variation in the densities ρ_n and ρ_s of the normal fluid and superfluid. Since ρ_n and ρ_s are functions of T (see Figure 7), a change in superfluid or normal-fluid concentration means a change in T also. A force of restitution arises because a gradient in the superfluid concentration generates a flow of super-fluid to eliminate the gradient.

When normal-fluid and superfluid vibrate together in the *same* direction (i.e., $\mathbf{v}_s = \mathbf{v}_n$) there are periodic variations of the density ρ and there is a net resultant momentum ($\rho_s\mathbf{v}_s + \rho_n\mathbf{v}_n = \rho\mathbf{v} \neq 0$). This kind of vibration constitutes ordinary or first sound. Hence, first and second sound constitute two different *normal* modes of vibration of superfluid and normal fluid.

The counter vibrations of normal fluid and superfluid in second sound contain mechanical energy the density (per cubic centimeter) of which is proportional to the heat pulse in the second-sound wave. The relation of the mechanical energy to the heat in a heat pulse or temperature wave is the equation for the efficiency of a reversible thermodynamic process:

$$\frac{\text{work (mechanical energy)}}{\text{heat}} = \frac{\Delta T}{T_0}. \tag{25}$$

Compare this equation with Equation 19. A moving train of temperature waves carries a positive excess of thermal energy in the crests where ΔT is positive and a deficiency in the troughs where ΔT is negative. These excesses and deficiencies of heat travel with the temperature waves. Their motion constitutes a periodically changing heat current, $\dot{Q}$. The net heat current of a wave train is zero since the current of excesses in crests equals the current of deficiencies in troughs. The mechanical energy in the crests and troughs also moves with the waves.

$$
\begin{bmatrix} \text{Rate of transport of} \\ \text{mechanical energy} \end{bmatrix} = \frac{\Delta T}{T_0} \begin{bmatrix} \text{Rate of transport} \\ \text{of heat, } \dot{Q} \end{bmatrix}
$$

$$
= \frac{\Delta T}{T_0} \begin{bmatrix} v_2 \left(\rho C \Delta T \right) \end{bmatrix} \tag{26}
$$

$$
= \frac{\rho C v_2}{T_0} \left(\Delta T \right)^2.
$$

Because ΔT enters to the second power, the mechanical energies transported in the wave crests and troughs are equal, in sign as well as in magnitude. Standing waves are formed by countermoving trains of waves, each train carrying its current of mechanical energy. There is no *net* flow of energy in a standing wave if averaged over a full λ or a full period (λ/v_2).

An interesting feature of the standing temperature wave is the flow of heat from the lower temperature regions of the troughs into the higher temperature regions of the crests, against the direction of normal heat flow and in apparent violation of the second law of thermodynamics. But as pointed out above when averaged over greater distances and times, there is no net flow of heat, in or out of a small volume. Hence, the temperature variations and the periodic heat flow in second sound may be regarded as another case of the fluctuations of temperature and energy known to occur in all substances on a scale that is sufficiently small. In standing second-sound waves these fluctuations are periodic. In He II they are a consequence of the Bose-Einstein condensation, which creates the normal and superfluid components.

In liquid He II we have a very special kind of quantum interaction of molecules—different from the quantum effects of intermolecular forces discussed in Section 3. Intermolecular forces modify the quantum effects in liquid He II in important ways, but the phenomena of liquid He II are a result of the Bose-Einstein condensation—a consequence of one kind of quantum statistics.

5. Superconductivity: Quantized Macroscopic Currents

Another example of *macroscopic* quantum mechanics is the frictionless flow of electric current, that is, without any measurable elec-

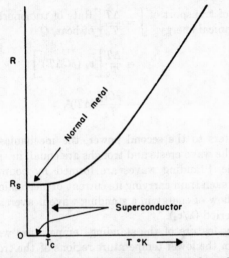

Figure 13. A plot of the electrical resistance of a normal metal (nonsuperconductor) and a superconductor, as a function of temperature. The graph shows the abruptness of the transition to the superconducting state (loss of resistance) at the transition temperature T_c for an ideal (chemically and mechanically pure) superconductor. A superconductor can be made to follow an extension of its normal-resisting curve to 0°K by the application of a large magnetic field, which destroys the superconducting state

trical resistance. The vertical line in Figure 13 indicates how sharply the resistance can completely disappear and then reappear as one lowers and raises the temperature of the specimen through the superconducting transition, T_c. The superconducting state persists only so long as the temperature is maintained below T_c.

Figure 14 and Tables 4 and 5 show how extensive the phenomenon of superconductivity is. Certain interesting features of superconductivity may be noted in the figure and tables. First, superconductivity

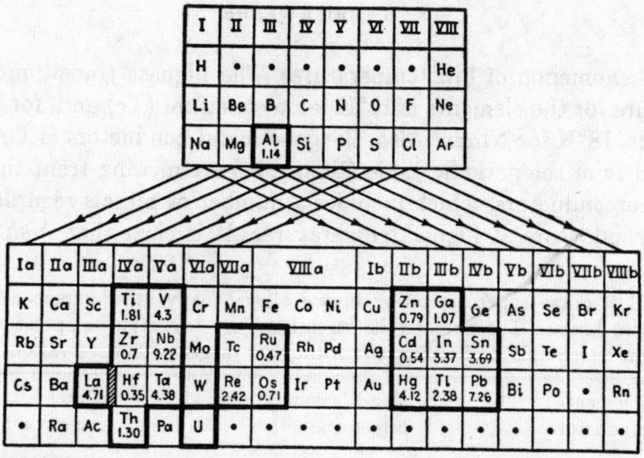

Figure 14. A diagram showing the positions of the superconducting elements in the periodic table. The rare earth elements between La and Hf are nonsuperconductors. The numbers under the chemical symbols are the superconducting transition temperatures T_c. The transition temperatures of Tc and U are 11° and 0.8°K, respectively

TABLE 4. Some superconducting compounds; many other superconducting compounds are known. The numbers in parentheses are transition temperatures T_c (at which half R_n disappeared) or they are ranges of T_c observations. Compounds marked with an asterisk (*) are intermetallic compounds

Both Elements Superconductors		One Element a Superconductor		Neither Element a Superconductor	
*Pb Tl$_2$	(3.8)	Nb B	(6)	*Ba Bi$_3$	(6)
*Tl$_2$ Hg$_5$	(3.8)	Zr B	(3)	*Au$_2$ Bi	(1.7)
Nb$_3$ Sn	(18)	Nb C	(10)	*Ca Bi$_3$	(2.0)
		Ti C	(1.1)	*K Bi$_2$	(3.6)
		Nb H	(7–13)	*Li Bi	(2.5)
		Ta H	(2–4)	*Na Bi	(2.2)
		Nb N	(15)	*Ni Bi	(4.2)
		Ti N	(1–5)	*Ni Bi$_3$	(3.6)
		VN	(1–3)	*Pd Bi$_2$	(1.7)
		Zr N	(9.5)	*Rh Bi	(2.1)
		Pb Se	(5)	*Rh Bi$_2$	(2.8)
		Ta Si	(4.4)	*Rh Bi$_4$	(2.2)
		*Pb$_5$ Na$_2$	(7.2)	*Sr Bi$_3$	(5.5)
		*Sm Sb	(3.9)	W$_2$ C	(3)
		*Sm$_3$ Sb$_2$	(4.0)	Mo N	(12)
		*Tl$_3$ Bi$_5$	(6.4)	Mo$_2$ N	(5)
		*Tl Mg	(2.7)	Cu S	(1.6)
		*Tl$_7$ Sb$_2$	(5.2)		
		*Tl Mg	(2.7)		

is a phenomenon of low temperatures. The highest transition temperature for the elements is 11°K for technetium (Tc) and, for compounds, 18°K for Nb₃Sn. Also, the good metal conductors of Groups I*a* and I*b* of the periodic table (Figure 14) are missing from the list of superconductors, which includes a number of metals regarded as poor conductors at higher temperatures. It is clear that *high* elec-

TABLE 5. Some superconducting binary alloys; many other superconductng alloys are known. The numbers in parentheses are transition temperatures T_c (at which half R_n disappeared) or they are ranges of T_c observations

Both Elements Superconductors		One Element a Superconductor		Neither Element a Superconductor	
Pb–Hg	(4–7)	Pb–Ag	(6)	W–Rh	(2–4)
Pb–In	(3–7)	Pb–As	(8.4)	Mo–Rh	(2)
Pb–Tl	(2–7)	Pb–Au	(2–7)	Mo–Ir	(<1)
Sn–Hg	(4.2)	Pb–Bi	(8)		
Sn–Tl	(2–6)	Pb–Ca	(7.0)		
Sn–Zn	(3.7)	Pb–Cd	(7.0)		
Tl–In	(2–4)	Pb–Cu	(7)		
		Pb–Li	(7.2)		
		Pb–P	(7.8)		
		Pb–Sb	(6.6)		
		Sn–Ag	(3–4)		
		Sn–As	(4.1)		
		Sn–Au	(3)		
		Sn–Bi	(3.8)		
		Sn–Cd	(3.6)		
		Sn–Cu	(3.6)		
		Tl–Ag	(2.7)		
		Tl–Au	(1.9)		
		Tl–Cd	(2.5)		
		Hg–Cd	(2–4)		

trical conductivity at ordinary temperatures is not essential, or necessarily a favorable circumstance, for the establishment of the superconducting state.

The behavior of superconductors in magnetic fields is of fundamental importance, as will be seen:

1. A strong magnetic field destroys superconductivity and restores normal resistance. The minimum field strength, H_c, that restores resistance is called the *critical* magnetic field. H_c is temperature-

dependent and is represented for many superconductors by an empirical equation

$$H_c(T) = H_{0^\circ}\left[1 - \left(\frac{T}{T_c}\right)^2\right], \qquad (27)$$

where T_c is the transition temperature for $H = 0$. Figure 15 is a graph of Equation 27. Typical values of H_0 are 280 oersteds for In,

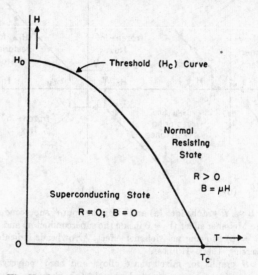

Figure 15. The H vs. T phase diagram of a superconductor. The threshold (H_c) curve is a graph of Equation 27. Along the threshold curve the normal-conducting and superconducting phases of a metal are in equilibrium

305 for Sn, 410 for Hg, 800 for Pb, and 2600 for Nb. Niobium is an example of a hard (strained) superconductor. The values of H_0 for alloys are in general of the order of thousands of oersteds, whereas they are of the order of hundreds of oersteds for soft, "pure" superconductors. The highest critical fields (in excess of 20,000 oersteds) have been observed for the Pb-Bi eutectic.

Figure 15 is also a "phase" diagram for a superconductor. Superconducting and normally resisting phases are in equilibrium along the H_c-threshold curve which separates the superconducting and normal resisting regions of the diagram.

2. When H is less than $H_c(T)$, the magnetic flux B is forced out of an *ideal* superconductor (a long cylindrical[2] single crystal, chemically pure and without mechanical imperfections), making $B = 0$ inside. This is illustrated graphically in Figure 16a. The ejection of magnetic flux from a superconductor is called the Meissner effect for its discoverer, Professor W. Meissner. A substance that does not permit

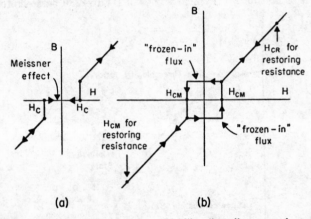

(a)   (b)

Figure 16. B vs. H graphs for: (a) an "ideal" or "pure" superconductor, showing a complete Meissner effect ($B = 0$ inside the superconductor) and (b) a superconductor ($R = 0$) showing no Meissner effect. Arrowheads indicate the directions for traversing the B–H lines.

The B vs. H graphs for mixed-phase alloys and hard (polycrystalline and strained) superconductors *approximate* Figure 16 (b). Compare (b) with an experimental curve (Fig. 17) for an alloy

penetration of any magnetic flux when there is an external magnetic field is a perfect diamagnetic. Since $B = H (1 + 4\pi\chi)$, the magnetic

---

[2] When the specimen is other than a long cylinder oriented parallel to the field **H**, the shape is nonideal and **H** is not uniform over the surface of the specimen. **H** exceeds in places on the specimen the value of the field that is uniform at a distance from the specimen. The critical value H_0 is exceeded at these places of concentration of **H** on the surface of the specimen before the field reaches the critical value at a distance from the specimen. Hence, superconductivity is destroyed and H penetrates the specimen nonuniformly. The field tangential to the surface of a superconducting sphere at its equator is 1.5 times the value of the field at a distance from the sphere.

susceptibility χ of a perfect diamagnetic, including a superconductor, is $-1/4\pi$.

Both properties, $R = 0$ (superconduction) and $B = 0$ (perfect diamagnetism), are necessary for a complete description of a superconductor. A perfect diamagnetic could conceivably be an insulator and not conduct electricity at all. A perfect conductor ($R = 0$) with no Meissner effect would *freeze* in itself and hold as long as the superconducting state was maintained whatever flux B it happened to have when it crossed the H_c-threshold curve (Figure 15) into the superconducting state. Any change in the flux through the superconductor that might have been anticipated as a result of a change in the external magnetic field would by Lenz's law induce an electromotive force and generate a current in the superconductor of just the required magnitude to restore that value of the flux existing before the change of the external field. Of course, if the critical magnetic field is exceeded, superconductivity is destroyed (see Equation 27) and magnetic flux enters the metal. Figures 16(a) and 16(b) illustrate the differences between changes of flux B in an ideal superconductor with Meissner effect (16[a]) and a metal possessing infinite conductivity without any Meissner effect (16[b]). It is clear that perfect diamagnetism is just as essential for a description of a superconductor as its infinite conductivity.

The magnetic properties of ideal superconductors seem especially simple when compared with alloys. For ideal superconductors the critical fields $H_c(T)$ for penetration of flux B (Meissner effect) and destruction of superconduction ($R = 0$) are the same. Also, an electric current whose magnetic field at the surface of a superconducting wire exceeds $H_c(T)$ destroys the superconducting state. This is the Silsbee hypothesis, named for its author, Francis B. Silsbee, of the National Bureau of Standards. Hence, for ideal superconductors there is a single function of temperature $H_c(T)$ for: (1) the field of the critical current, (2) the minimum external field that destroys superconduction, and (3) the critical field for penetration of flux in the Meissner effect. Figure 15 is a graph of this function $H_c(T)$. Transitions between the normally resisting and superconductive states are quite sharp for ideal superconductors ($\Delta T \sim 0.001°$ and $\Delta H \sim 5$ oersteds or less), as indicated in Figure 13. Metals and alloys that are chemically pure and mechanically perfect (single crystals) become ideal superconductors when formed as long cylinders and oriented parallel to the magnetic field.[3] Intermetallic compounds in Table 4 may be expected to be capable of being made into ideal superconductors if prepared very carefully for attainment of both chemical and mechanical perfection. Such perfection is very difficult to attain with intermetallic compounds. In general, therefore, the intermetallic compounds have not shown ideal behavior. Chemically impure and mechanically imperfect superconductors exhibit properties intermediate between those of ideal superconductors and alloys.

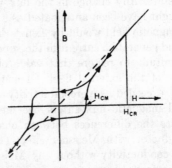

Figure 17. An experimental B vs. H curve for a two-phase alloy. H_{CR} is the critical magnetic field for an abrupt change in electrical resistance. H_{CM} is the critical field for penetration of flux B into the superconductor (Meissner effect)

It has already been pointed out that critical values (H_{CR}) of the magnetic field for destruction of superconductivity ($R = 0$) are high for alloys, that is, of the order of thousands of oersteds, instead of hundreds of oersteds for chemically pure and mechanically perfect metals. Figure 17 is a graph of the B vs. H relation for a two-phase alloy. Its most prominent feature is its similarity to Figure 16(b), showing a retention of a large amount of *frozen-in* flux B and a very imperfect Meissner effect. The value H_{CR} is the critical value of the *external* field for destruction of superconduction ($R = 0$), and H_{CM} is the so-called *penetration* field. The penetration field for alloys is of the order of a few hundred oersteds, which is comparable with the penetration fields for ideal superconductors. Figure 17 shows that

---

[3] See note 2 above.

between H_{CM} and H_{CR} the magnetic induction B is less than H, so that there is a small ejection of flux B, that is, a small residual Meissner effect. The magnetic fields of the minimum, or critical, currents for destruction of the superconducting state in two-phase alloy wires are approximately equal to or possibly a little less than the characteristic penetration fields H_{CM}. Thus the Silsbee hypothesis is applicable to alloys if critical currents are related to penetration fields rather than to H_{CR}. The transitions of alloys from the normally resisting to the superconducting state or vice versa are not sharp; instead they are generally broad, in extreme cases extending over a range of a degree or a few hundred oersteds, or more.

That the magnetic effects for two-phase alloys lack the simplicity found for ideal superconductors is obvious. It is important to realize that the magnetic effects in alloys lack thermodynamic reversibility; that is, the state of the conductor (R, B, T) depends not only on H and T but also on the particular manner, path, or way in which the values of H and T happen to be reached. This excludes the possibility of applying to two-phase alloys the thermodynamics of reversible processes.

The unusual properties of superconducting alloys are understandable on the basis that they are a mixture of a superconducting and a normally resisting phase. The superconducting regions of this mixture are supposed to show a complete Meissner effect, whereas magnetic flux B is frozen or locked in the normally resisting regions by supercurrents flowing in the superconducting regions ringing the resisting regions. To clarify this we consider a metal ring in a magnetic field oriented perpendicular to the plane of the ring so that the magnetic flux B threads the hole in the ring. We start above the superconducting transition temperature T_c with the ring normally resisting and lower the temperature. When the transition temperature T_c is reached and passed, two things happen: (1) all magnetic flux is ejected from the metal of the ring by the Meissner effect, and (2) the flux B through the hole of the ring when it became superconducting is *locked in* and may not be changed so long as the superconducting state persists. Any change in the external magnetic field that does not exceed the critical magnetic field H_c of the metal induces an electromotive force and current in the ring, which in accordance with Lenz's law is of the proper magnitude to maintain the value of flux B through the hole when the ring became superconducting. If the flux B through the ring had been zero when the ring became superconducting, B would have been maintained equal to zero in spite of any changes in the external field, so long as T_c and H_c were not exceeded. Figure 16(b) describes the $B(H)$ relation for the hole in the ring, whereas Figure 16(a) describes $B(H)$ for the metal of the ring.

In a superconducting alloy induced supercurrents surrounding the normally resisting metal prevent changes in the magnetic induction through the nonsuperconductive metal in the same manner as the superconducting ring in the paragraph above maintained unchanged the flux threading its hole. When an alloy mixture of phases is made a part of a current carrying electric circuit, the superconducting regions form a continuous path through the alloy for the flow of the superconducting current. The normally resisting parts of the mixture are short-circuited by superconducting parts.

The model of an alloy consisting of a normal and just one superconducting phase is an oversimplification. As they are generally prepared, two-phase alloys consist of crystallites with slightly variable chemical composition and variable mechanical strain. The superconducting transition temperatures and critical magnetic fields of the crystallites in the superconducting phase must therefore cover ranges of values for both T_c and H_c. As a consequence, the superconducting phenomena in alloys are not as sharply defined as might be inferred from the model used in the two preceding paragraphs.

It is natural to inquire concerning the validity of Maxwell's electromagnetic equations, relating magnetic and electric fields with currents and changing flux in superconductors. These equations of Maxwell are:

$$\operatorname{curl} \mathbf{H} = \frac{4\pi}{c}\mathbf{j} + \frac{1}{c}\frac{\partial \mathbf{E}}{\partial t} \tag{28}$$

$$\mu \operatorname{div} \mathbf{H} = 0$$

and

$$\operatorname{curl} \mathbf{E} = -\frac{1}{c}\frac{\partial \mathbf{B}}{\partial t} \tag{29}$$

$$\epsilon \operatorname{div} \mathbf{E} = 4\pi\rho.$$

In addition to these equations,[4] there are: (a) the force equation

$$\mathbf{F} = e\left[\mathbf{E} + \frac{1}{c}\,\mathbf{v} \times \mathbf{H}\right], \tag{30}$$

and (b) boundary conditions for an interface between two media: (1) the perpendicular component of the flux $(B_\perp)$ and the parallel component of the field $(H_\shortparallel)$ are continuous across an interface, or (2) $(H_\shortparallel)_2 - (H_\shortparallel)_1 = \sigma$, the surface density of a current flowing over the surface of the conductor.

Maxwell's equations are valid for superconductors. Ohm's law, $R = V/I$, which is valid for many conductors, but not all—for example, many semiconductors—is an empirical law. It has no significance for superconductors since a superconductor does not support a difference of potential V.

It is interesting to consider the Meissner effect in relation to the boundary conditions on $H_\shortparallel$. Previously, the ideal superconductor has been spoken of as a perfect diamagnetic substance, $\chi = -1/4\pi$, implying that the field H penetrates the specimen throughout. The equation $B = H(1 + 4\pi\chi) = 0$ has the solution $H = 0$ in addition to the solution $\chi = -1/4\pi$. By means of surface current $\sigma = H_\shortparallel$ over the surface of a superconductor, H and B can be made zero inside the superconductor. This surface-current model of an ideal superconductor agrees with measurements of the depth of penetration of magnetic fields in superconductors. The model of perfect diamagnetism, however, is more convenient for applications of thermodynamic theory to superconductors and is currently used.

Since electric currents are flows of discrete particles (electrons), a current sheet over the surface of a superconductor must have a finite thickness. Consequently, there is a penetration of B and H a short distance below the surface of a superconductor. On an atomic scale $H_\shortparallel$ is continuous across the surface of a superconductor and

---

[4] The curl of a vector $\mathbf{A} = \mathbf{i}A_x + \mathbf{j}A_y + \mathbf{k}A_z$ is

$$\operatorname{curl}\mathbf{A} = \begin{vmatrix} \mathbf{i} & \mathbf{j} & \mathbf{k} \\ \dfrac{\partial}{\partial x} & \dfrac{\partial}{\partial y} & \dfrac{\partial}{\partial z} \\ A_x & A_y & A_z \end{vmatrix} = \mathbf{i}\left(\frac{\partial A_z}{\partial y} - \frac{\partial A_y}{\partial z}\right) + \mathbf{j}\left(\frac{\partial A_x}{\partial z} - \frac{\partial A_z}{\partial x}\right)$$

$$+ \mathbf{k}\left(\frac{\partial A_y}{\partial x} - \frac{\partial A_x}{\partial y}\right)$$

decays exponentially ($H_z = H_s e^{-z/\lambda}$) with distance z below the surface where H equals H_s. The parameter λ is called the *penetration depth* of the magnetic field in the superconductor. For polished, single crystals, the experimental data on the penetration depth λ are consistent with the formula

$$\lambda = \lambda_{0^\circ}\left[1 - \left(\frac{T}{T_c}\right)^4 \right]^{-1/2}, \tag{31}$$

where

$$\lambda_{0^\circ} = 5.2 \times 10^{-6} \text{ cm for tin at } 0°K$$

and

$$\lambda_{0^\circ} = 4.3 \times 10^{-6} \text{ cm for mercury at } 0°K.$$

Figure 18 is a plot of Equation 31. The dependence of λ on H is small. Pippard found that $\lambda (H) = \lambda (H = 0) [1 + aH^2]$, where ($a H_c^2$) is of the order 2 to 3×10^{-2} except within 0.01° of T_c, where the effect of H on λ is much greater. If the thickness of a specimen is comparable with λ as, for example, for thin films, fine wires, and colloids, there can be only a partial Meissner effect and only a partial expulsion of magnetic flux B. This is the basis of the experimental

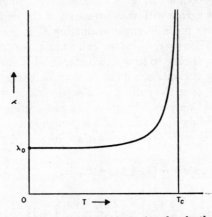

Figure 18. Diagram of Equation 31 for the depth of penetration λ of a magnetic field into a superconductor. $H_s e^{-z/\lambda}$ is the value of H at a depth z below the surface of a superconductor. The value of H at the surface of the superconductor is H_s.

determinations of λ. The penetration depth λ is sensitive to surface roughness, being larger for rougher surfaces.

It is necessary for the calculation of current distributions in superconductors to have a property equation analogous to Ohm's law for normal conductors. The late F. London proposed these two equations:

$$\text{curl} \ (\Lambda \mathbf{j}_s) = -\frac{1}{c} \mathbf{H} \tag{32}$$

and

$$\frac{\partial}{\partial t} \ (\Lambda \mathbf{j}_s) = \mathbf{E}, \tag{33}$$

where $\mathbf{j}_s$ is the intensity of the superconducting current (current per square centimeter) and Λ is a characteristic property of individual pieces of superconducting metal.

In stationary fields ($\dot{\mathbf{H}} = 0 = \dot{\mathbf{E}}$), Equation 32 is sufficient to characterize the superconductor. Whereas Maxwell's equations (28 and 29) determine the magnetic and electric fields generated by currents and changing flux B, London's equation (32) determines the supercurrent generated by a stationary magnetic field. Equation 32 for the superconductor represents a more symmetrical state of affairs than we have for a normal conductor. Stationary currents in both normal and superconductors generate stationary magnetic fields, but only in the superconductor does a stationary magnetic field generate a stationary current.

London's equation (33) is the acceleration equation: E (force) $= d(\text{momentum})/dt$, for electrons moving without resistance in a superconductor. It is not derivable from Maxwell's equations and London's other equation (32). In a rapidly changing electric field ($\nu \sim 10^9$ cycles per second or greater), superconducting (frictionless) and normal electrons are accelerated and the current in a superconductor has normal and superconducting components:

$$\mathbf{j} = \mathbf{j}_n + \mathbf{j}_s. \tag{34}$$

The normal current $\mathbf{j}_n$ in a metal whose specific conductivity is σ, is related to $\mathbf{E}$ by Ohm's law

$$\mathbf{j}_n = \sigma \mathbf{E}, \tag{35}$$

and the supercurrent $\mathbf{j}_s$ is related to $\mathbf{E}$ and $\mathbf{H}$ by London's two equations (32 and 33). The normal current, with a finite conductivity σ proportional to $1/R$, involves an absorption of energy and ohmic heating. As a consequence, superconductors show electrical resistance to high-frequency currents and normal absorption of energy in fields oscillating with optical frequencies (see Figure 19).

At 10^{11} cycles per second ($\nu \sim kT_c/h$), the skin depth of a high-frequency current and magnetic field is of the same order of magnitude as the depth of penetration λ of a stationary magnetic field in

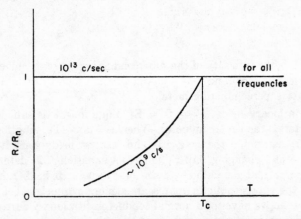

Figure 19. An illustration of the dependence on frequency and temperature of the resistance ratio R/R_n for a superconductor carrying a high-frequency current: $\mathbf{j} = \mathbf{j}_n + \mathbf{j}_s$ (Equation 34). R_n is the high-frequency resistance in the normal resisting state

a superconductor. When the depths of the high-frequency skin and penetration λ are comparable, the normal and superconducting components j_n and j_s of the high-frequency current are of comparable size. At higher frequencies ($>10^{11}$ cycles per second), the normal component j_n of the high-frequency current increases relative to the superconducting component j_s so that at optical frequencies practically the whole current is carried by normal-resisting electrons. At optical frequencies ($\geqslant 10^{14}$ cycles per second) superconducting metals show no changes in optical properties (reflection and absorption) through the superconducting transition.

Some interesting relations are derivable from Maxwell's and

London's equations. For the depth of penetration λ of the magnetic field we have

$$\lambda = c \sqrt{\frac{\Lambda}{4\pi}} \tag{36}$$

and for the density n_s of superconducting electrons

$$n_s = \frac{m^*}{e^2\Lambda} = \frac{m^*c^2}{4\pi e^2\lambda^2}, \tag{37}$$

where m^* is the *effective mass* of a superconducting electron. The term *effective mass* is used here as it is ordinarily defined in the theory of metals: $E = m^* a$, where a is the acceleration of an electron through a metal lattice under the influence of an externally applied electric field E. The effective mass m^* is different from the mass of an electron in free space because of the influence of the lattice forces on the motions of electrons. Substituting Equation 31 for λ in Equation 37 we have:

$$n_s = n_{s,0^\circ}\left[1 - \left(\frac{T}{T_c}\right)^4\right]. \tag{38}$$

Figure 20 is a graph of Equation 38. The similarity of graphs for densities of superconducting electrons (n_s) and superfluid (ρ_s) in He II (Figure 7) suggests a similarity between the superconducting and

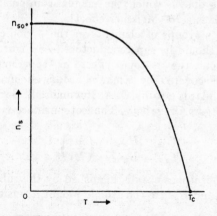

Figure 20. The number n_s of superconducting electrons as a function of T. A graph of Equation 38

normal resisting electrons in a superconductor on the one hand and superfluid and normal fluid in liquid He II on the other. A 2-fluid model, on the He II pattern, has been constructed[5] for ideal superconductors. We shall return to it presently.

Using in Equation 37 the rest mass m_0 of an electron for m^* and the empirical values for λ_0 (see Equation 31), we obtain for the ratio at 0°K of the number of superconducting electrons to the number N of atoms

$$\frac{n_{s,0°}}{N} = 0.30 \text{ for tin}$$

$$= 0.35 \text{ for mercury.}$$

Hence if $m^* = m_0$, only one electron for every three atoms is a superconducting electron at 0°K. If it is assumed all the valence electrons are superconducting electrons at 0°K, $m^* = 13.3\ m_0$ for tin and 5.7 for mercury.

Bardeen and Fröhlich, independently, proposed a theory of superconductivity which appears to contain some essentials of an explanation of superconductivity, though there are serious inadequacies in the mathematics of the theory. Three consequences of the theory may be listed:

1. It may yield the London equation (32) and show that the thermodynamically most stable state of a superconductor (lowest free energy) is one in which the magnetic intensity inside the superconductor is zero (Meissner effect).

2. It predicts groups of elements in the periodic table of the elements that should be superconductors (see Figure 14).

3. It predicts the isotope effect in superconductors, independently discovered by Emanuel Maxwell of the National Bureau of Standards and by C. A. Reynolds, B. Serin, and L. B. Nesbitt of Rutgers University. The isotope effect is expressed by the equation

$$\frac{T_{c,1}}{T_{c,2}} = \frac{H_{0°,1}}{H_{0°,2}} = \left(\frac{M_2}{M_1}\right)^{1/2}, \tag{39}$$

where the two isotopes are distinguished by the subscripts 1 and 2, and M, T_c, and $H_{0°}$ are the atomic weight, transition tempera-

---

[5] C. J. Gorter and H. B. G. Casimir, *Physik. Zeit.* 35 (1934), 963; *Zeit. f. Technische Physik*, 15 (1934), 539.

ture in zero magnetic field, and the critical magnetic field at 0°K, respectively.

Equation 39 indicates there is a connection between superconductivity and a crystal lattice that is populated with atoms of atomic weight M. The theory of Bardeen and Fröhlich is based on an interaction of the conduction electrons with the Debye lattice waves which were important for our earlier considerations (see Sections 2 and 3). Figure 21 illustrates the nature of this interaction between electrons and lattice vibrations. The normal

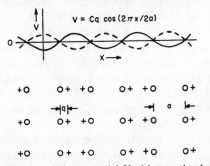

Figure 21. A diagram of the potential V of interaction between lattice ions and conduction electrons in a metal. V is a function of the amplitudes q of the displacements of the lattice ions from equilibrium positions. The lower part of the diagram represents wave displacements of lattice ions in a standing, compressional wave in a horizontal direction x. The wave length is 2a. The smallest value of a is the distance between ions

modes of vibration of a lattice are systems of standing Debye waves. In Figure 21 is shown a longitudinal lattice wave with a wave length equal to $2a$. The symbol q represents the amplitude of the displacements of ions from their equilibrium positions. A lattice wave makes a periodically varying electric potential V which an electron sees. This potential V is indicated at the top of Figure 21. Where positively charged ions are closer together, the oscillating potential V of the ions is positive and the potential energy of the electrons, $-|e|V$, is negative. Here $|e|$ is the absolute value of the electronic charge. Where ions are farther apart than their equilibrium positions, the potential V is negative and the potential energy $-|e|V$ of the electrons is positive, that is, greater than where the ions are closer together.

Lattice ions are continually in motion, even at 0°K, so that the conduction electrons of a metal are in a fluctuating potential. At ordinary temperatures, the interaction of conduction electrons and lattice vibrations scatters the conduction electrons and is the explanation of the electrical resistance of chemically pure and mechanically perfect metal crystals. At low temperatures, however, only the Debye lattice waves of low frequency are excited thermally, and very few of these will have more than one quantum of energy $h\nu$ above the energy $h\nu/2$ of the ground state. In this circumstance, the superconducting electrons are coupled to lattice waves and travel with them. There is then a higher than normal density of electrons where the potential energy $(-|e|V)$ is low (wave crests in Figure 21) and a lower density where the potential energy is high (the troughs). In this state, the energy is less than in the normal state of a uniform or random distribution of electrons throughout the lattice. The coupled electrons travel *frictionlessly* with the lattice waves which move through the lattice with the speed of sound.

The electrons coupled with lattice waves in superconductors are drawn from the top of a Fermi-Dirac distribution. In a normal resisting metal, conduction electrons are distributed over the quantum states associated with cells of volume h^3 in the six-dimensional, x, y, z, p_x, p_y, p_z, phase space. Conduction electrons are fundamental particles and are, therefore, subject to the Pauli exclusion principle and the Fermi-Dirac statistics discussed at the end of Section 3. A quantum state (cell in phase space) cannot be occupied at any time by more than two electrons; these must differ in their quantum spin states by having oppositely directed angular momentum vectors. At very low temperatures, the denominator in Equation 7 with $c = 1$ and $T \sim 0°$ equals one if $\epsilon < \epsilon_{max}$, and is ∞ if $\epsilon > \epsilon_{max}$, where

$$\epsilon_{max} = \frac{h^2}{2m}\left(\frac{3n}{8\pi}\right)^{3/2} \tag{40}$$

and n is the number of conduction electrons per unit volume of metal. This means that all energy states from $\epsilon = 0$ to ϵ_{max} are filled with conduction electrons, and no state with greater energy is occupied. Since at low temperatures systems seek states of lowest energy, the superconducting electrons are drawn from the top of the filled band of energy states.

The fraction $n_{s,0°}/n$ of conduction electrons that are super-conducting at 0°K is approximately $\Delta\epsilon/\epsilon_{max}$, where $\Delta\epsilon$ is the difference between the energies of an electron in the normal resisting and superconducting states. The dependence of the resistance of a superconductor on the frequency of a high-frequency current indicated that $\Delta\epsilon \sim kT_c$ (see the end of the paragraph with Equation 35).

The ϵ_{max} energies of conduction electrons range from about $0.5 \times 10^5 k$ to about $1 \times 10^5 k$; the coefficient of k, called the effective Kelvin temperature, ranges from 5×10^4 to 10^5 °K. At 0°K

$$\frac{n_{s,0°}}{n} \sim \frac{\Delta\epsilon}{\epsilon_{max}} \sim 10^{-4}, \tag{41}$$

showing that only a very small fraction of the conduction electrons are coupled to the lattice vibrations as superconducting electrons in the Bardeen-Fröhlich theory. We may compare this theoretical value of n_s/n with values of this ratio for tin and mercury calculated from Equation 37 (see the next paragraph after Equation 37) using the ordinary mass of the electron for its effective mass m^* in the metal lattice.

To get values of the order of 10^{-4} for $n_{s,0°}/n$ from Equation 37 it is necessary to set m^* equal to 10^{-4} to 10^{-3} times the ordinary electron mass:

$$m^*/m \sim 10^{-4} \text{ to } 10^{-3}. \tag{42}$$

According to Bardeen, the diamagnetism (Meissner effect) of a superconductor is a consequence of the very small effective mass of the superconducting electrons.

Following Equation 38 a two-fluid model of a superconductor, similar to the two-fluid model of liquid He II, was suggested. This suggestion was originally made by Gorter and Casimir at the University of Leiden in Holland. Superconducting and normal electrons correspond to superfluid and normal components of He II, and the frictionless flow of superconducting electrons to the superfluid flow of helium. The entropies at 0°K of superfluid He and superconducting electrons are zero because both are characterized by a single quantum state. In this state, superconducting electrons and superfluid He atoms are regularly ordered in momentum space, not in the geometric space in which the atoms of a crystal lattice are ordered at 0°K.

The application of thermodynamics to this two-fluid model of a superconductor is interesting. For the Gibbs function of a conductor in a magnetic field whose intensity is H, we write

$$G = U + pV - HI - TS, \qquad (43)$$

where I is the intensity of magnetization of the metal, that is, the magnetic moment per cubic centimeter. For normal resisting metal, we write

$$G_n(T, H) = U_0 - \frac{\gamma T^2}{2} V + G_{lat}(T), \qquad (44)$$

where $U_0 = G_n (0°)$ and the second and third terms are the temperature-dependent parts of the Gibbs function for electrons and lattice, respectively. The specific heat of the conduction electrons is γT. For a metal whose magnetic permeability is one, the intensity of magnetization is zero and HI is zero.

For the superconducting state, we write

$$U_s(0°) = U_0 - n_{s,0°}V\Delta\epsilon - \frac{H^2}{8\pi}, \qquad (45)$$

where $n_{s,0°}$ is the number of superconducting electrons per unit volume at $0°K$, their energies at $0°K$ being $\Delta\epsilon$ per electron lower than in the normal resisting state. The intensity of magnetization of the superconductor is $I = \chi H = -H/4\pi$, and the work done by the superconductor in a change of I from 0 to $-H/4\pi$ as the field changes from 0 to H is $\int_0^H -HdI = H^2/8\pi$. As was pointed out in the paragraph that precedes Equation 31, it is more convenient for thermodynamic treatment to regard a superconductor as a perfect diamagnetic than to treat it as a metal with superconducting surface currents. In both models, $B = 0$ inside the superconductor. For the superconductor

$$G_s(T, H) = U_0 - n_s V\Delta\epsilon + \frac{H^2}{8\pi} V$$
$$- \left(1 - \frac{n_s}{n_{s,0°}}\right)^{1/2} \frac{\gamma T^2}{2} V + G_{lat}(T). \qquad (46)$$

It is assumed here that: (1) $\Delta\epsilon$, the difference between the energies of electrons in the resisting and superconducting states, is independent of T and H, (2) that the Gibbs function for the normal electrons in a superconductor is given by the fourth term on the right side of Equation 46, and (3) that n_s is independent of H.

When the magnetic field at $0°K$ is the critical field H_0, normal and superconducting metal are in equilibrium with each other. Therefore,

$$G_n(0, H_0) - G_s(0, H_0) = 0$$

$$= n_{s,0°}V\Delta\epsilon - \frac{H_0^2}{8\pi}V. \qquad (47)$$

Whence, we obtain for $n_{s,0°}$, the number of superconduction electrons per unit volume at $0°K$,

$$n_{s,0°}(\Delta\epsilon) = \frac{H_0^2}{8\pi}. \qquad (48)$$

In a superconductor, normal and superconducting electrons are in equilibrium with each other at all values of T and H. Hence

$$\left[\frac{\partial G_s(T, H)}{\partial n_s}\right] = 0, \qquad (49)$$

and substituting Equation 46, we obtain with some rearrangement of terms for the ratio of the number of superconducting electrons at temperature T to the number at $0°K$

$$\frac{n_s}{n_{s,0°}} = 1 - \left[\frac{\gamma T^2}{4n_{s,0°}(\Delta\epsilon)}\right]^2. \qquad (50)$$

At T_c, the superconducting transition temperature, $n_s = 0$ and Equation 50 with Equation 48 yields

$$\gamma = \frac{4n_{s,0°}(\Delta\epsilon)}{T_c^2} = \frac{H_0^2}{2\pi T_c^2}. \qquad (51)$$

Equation 50 with 51 substituted, is the same as Equation 38 for $n_s/n_{s,0°}$ derived from measurements of the penetration depth λ of magnetic fields in superconductors. Values of γ calculated from values of the critical magnetic field at $0°K$, using Equation 51, are in fair agreement with the electronic specific heats γT derived from calorimetric data for the normal resisting metal when these data are fitted to the equation

$$C_n = \gamma T + 464.5\left(\frac{T}{\theta}\right)^3. \qquad (52)$$

344   F. G. BRICKWEDDE

Θ is the Debye (maximum) frequency of the lattice vibrations, and the second term on the right side of the equation is the very-low-temperature specific heat of the lattice (see the second paragraph of Section 3).

Since $C = -T (d^2 G/dT^2)_{p,H}$,

$$C_n - C_s = -T\left[\frac{d^2(G_n - G_s)}{dT^2}\right]_{p,H}. \tag{53}$$

When Equations 44 and 46 are substituted and Equation 50 is introduced we obtain

$$[C_n - C_s]_{H=0} \doteq \left[\gamma T - \frac{3\gamma T^3}{T_c^2}\right]V$$
$$= \frac{H_0^2}{2\pi T_c}\left[\frac{T}{T_c} - 3\frac{T^3}{T_c}\right]V. \tag{54}$$

This equation says that the difference between the specific heats of the normal resisting and superconducting states of a metal is the difference between the heat capacities of its conduction electrons in these two states, which is really contained in the assumptions made in setting up Equation 46 for the Gibbs function for a

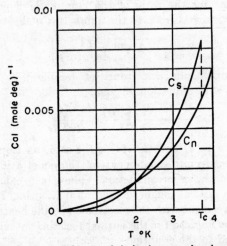

Figure 22. The molal heats of tin in the normal and superconducting states in zero magnetic field. There is no heat of transition at T_c. Compare with Figure 23

superconductor. The specific heat of the superconducting electrons is zero because these electrons are in a temperature-independent, stationary energy state. But as the temperature is changed, the fraction of superconducting electrons changes, which involves a heat of transition, $\Delta\epsilon$ per electron, making the transition. This heat of transition is a part of the heat capacity of the conduction electrons of a superconductor. There is also a difference between the specific heats of the normal resisting electrons of a superconductor and the conduction electrons of normal metal. Equation 54 has been verified experimentally, though the limits of experimental error are rather large. Figure 22 is a graph of specific heats C_n and C_s of a typical ideal superconductor, tin. Its most prominent features are: (1) a sharp, discontinuous change in the specific heat of a superconductor at its transition temperature T_c in zero magnetic field, without any heat of transition, and (2) the difference in the signs of $(C_n - C_s)$ near 0°K and near the transition temperature T_c.

The specific heat of a superconductor in a magnetic field is independent of the field if the metal is in the superconducting state, that is, so long as the transition temperature T_H and the critical field H_c (see Figure 15) are not exceeded. Above the transition temperature T_H, the metal is normal resisting and its specific heat

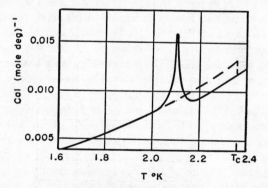

Figure 23. The molal heat of thallium in the presence of a magnetic field, showing the latent heat of transition at the superconducting transition temperature for the imposed field. The broken curve is the molal heat of superconducting thallium in zero field (compare with Figure 22). Here the transition temperature T_H, in magnetic field H, is $\sim$2.1°K ($T_c = T_{H-0} \sim$2.36°K).

follows the curve for resisting metal. See Figure 23 and compare with Figure 22. At the transition temperature T_H there is a heat of transition equal to $\int_{T_H}^{T_c} (C_n - C_s)dT$, which is zero when T_H equals the transition temperature T_c for zero field. Hence, there is a heat of transition from the superconducting to the normal resisting state, which is temperature-dependent and vanishes at the transition temperature T_c for zero field.

The relations between the thermodynamic properties of the superconducting and normal states derived from the Gibbs functions (44 and 45) for these states are in agreement with experiment. This is a check on the validity of our expression for $(G_n - G_s)$, and, in particular, for the term in G_s for the normal conduction electrons of a superconductor.

The correspondence we see between superconductivity and liquid He II is interesting and instructive, but it does not extend to the origins of these phenomena. The He³ isotope does not have a He II state. The seemingly most significant difference between the helium isotopes is the quantum statistics they follow: He⁴ follows Bose-Einstein statistics and He³, Fermi-Dirac. But conduction electrons follow Fermi-Dirac statistics, showing that quantum statistics, though important, is not the essential feature that He II and superconductivity have in common. The two-fluid models of liquid He II and superconductivity have this feature in common: the superconducting state of a metal and the He II state of liquid helium consist of intimate mixtures of two states with different energies in equilibrium with each other. The lower energy state has zero entropy and a zero, or near zero, specific heat. The higher energy state has normal thermal properties. The difference in energies of these two states is kT_λ per He atom or kT_c per electron. In liquid He⁴ the low-energy–zero-entropy state is a consequence of an autocatalytic accumulation of helium atoms in the lowest energy state, that is, the Bose-Einstein condensation. Atoms of He³ may not accumulate in any single state because of the Pauli exclusion principle, which is basic for the Fermi-Dirac statistics governing He³. In superconductors, conduction electrons accumulate in a low-energy state created through a coupling of supercurrents with lattice Debye waves or vibrations. This kind of coupling is not possible in He³, whose statistics is, nevertheless, the same as that of conduction electrons.

6. Summary

Only a few selected lines of cryogenic research have been considered in this paper. Other important lines of research, such as paramagnetism and diamagnetism, orientation of atomic nuclei, and heat conduction in solids have not even been mentioned. But the objective of this paper has been to direct attention to a very characteristic, if not unique, feature of low-temperature physics and not to review all cryogenic research. This feature is quantum mechanical effects in the interactions of whole systems of particles: electrons, atoms, and molecules. The more familiar quantum effects are properties of isolated particles, atoms, or molecules. Properties like oriented nuclei, magnetism, and heat conduction, which we have not discussed, show quantum effects of interaction also. Such effects were discussed in connection with the specific heats of solids and the differences in the vapor pressures and virial coefficients of isotopes. But superconductivity and liquid He II present us with a very different kind of phenomenon—superfluidity and frictionless flow of electric currents—that are contrary to all experience at higher temperatures. After years of research, superconductivity and He II remain a challenge for theoretical physicists and those who like to speculate. It is hoped that in trying to present a consistent picture and discussion of them here, an illusion has not been created that they have been satisfactorily explained.

Physics and the Engineer

EDWARD U. CONDON

Engraved in stone on the National Archives building in Washington is one of those mottos with which architects like to decorate public buildings. It reads: "What is past is prologue."

The story is told of a visitor to Washington who saw this while riding by in a taxi, and asked the driver, "What does it mean?"

"It means," replied the driver, "You ain't seen nothin' yet."

The preceding chapters have reviewed some of the recent progress and present problems in physics and applied mathematics. Each dealt with some particular topic. Here we shall attempt something in the way of a general summing up—perhaps even a little gazing into the future.

Many specific results of modern physics and the achievements already made in applying them to engineering have been described in previous chapters. In general these all derive from the work of physicists, especially during the past fifty years, in building up the modern theory of the atomic structure of matter.

In the nineteenth century the main facts of chemistry were coordinated in relation to the interplay of the atoms of some ninety distinct elements, to form hundreds of thousands of different compounds. The periodic table of the elements indicated a relatedness of properties of these elements which must be a consequence of common structural properties of the atoms of the elements, but the nature of these common structural properties was unknown.

At the end of the nineteenth century, the atomicity of electric charge and the close relation of fundamental atomic charged particles, as observed in electrochemistry and in gaseous electrical conduction, were recognized. It became clear that the atoms were somehow composite structures of the negatively charged electrons and the heavier positively charged protons, but the general pattern of this structure was not clear.

By 1914 the views that are held today began to emerge. Rutherford had discovered, from experiments on the scattering of alpha

349

particles by matter, that the positive electricity in the atom is concentrated in a tiny central particle whose radius is about one ten-
thousandth that of the atom as a whole. He called this the *nucleus*,
which is Latin for kernel. At the same time, 1914, Bohr gave an interpretation of the light-emitting and light-absorbing properties of
atoms by applying quantum theory to this model of the atom, in
which negative electrons traveled in orbits around a central positive
nucleus. In doing this he had to make a sharp break with the ideas
of mechanics and electromagnetism as they had been developed
earlier from study of large-scale phenomena involving the statistical
behavior of many billions of billions of atoms.

The decisive steps taken by Rutherford and Bohr have dominated
the thinking in atomic physics ever since. The period to about 1926
was occupied with a rather full working out of details concerning the
behavior of the electrons in the atom but outside the nucleus.

In 1926 and 1927 there came a revolutionary reformulation of the
underlying mathematical laws governing the behavior of atomic
particles. This is known as quantum mechanics. From the very
beginning of his work, Bohr had recognized, as has been mentioned, that in atomic processes some rather fundamental revisions
of the classical mechanics of gross matter were required. His own
work showed the need and pointed the general way. The major
change came after more than a decade of fruitful work in the direction shown by Bohr. It came in the theoretical discoveries made by
Heisenberg, Schrödinger, Dirac, and others.

These new ideas produced a general burgeoning of modern atomic
physics in several major directions at once. The stock market crashed
in 1929, and for a number of years after that our country and the
world suffered severe economic depression. But there was no depression in physics. Physics was bursting with new ideas and new experimental results in a way such as had never happened before in human
history. Quantum mechanics gave us new power and confidence in
attacking the problems of the fundamental behavior of matter.
This opened up many distinct avenues of progress which are still
being developed and extended:

First, quantum mechanics gave the basis for relating modern
atomic structure theories to the fundamental laws of chemical combination. It gave us for the first time, a basic understanding of the
covalent bond in chemistry, making possible the writing of such a

great book as *The Nature of the Chemical Bond*, by Linus Pauling. Later quantum mechanics also gave us the basis for interpretation of the facts governing the time rate of chemical reactions, a field with which the name of Henry Eyring is principally associated.

A complete rewriting of chemistry in terms of these concepts has dominated the whole fundamental research program of that science for the past quarter century in an immensely fruitful way.

Second, as a natural and related consequence of what quantum mechanics was doing for chemistry, we were given a wholly new set of principles in terms of which to advance our understanding of the properties of solid materials. The free-electron theory, for interpreting the special electrical properties of metals, was already some two decades old but had run into a dead-end street and was long blocked from making further progress by the contradictions resulting from too great a reliance on inappropriate use of classical theory.

Quantum mechanics removed those contradictions and went further. It provided the basis not only for a broad understanding of the distinction between metals and insulators but also for the proper study and investigation of that intermediate class of solids which are industrially famous today as semiconductors. In this same period, 1928–1933, were developed the principles governing the behavior of electrons in these materials. These principles are today the working tools of those who make germanium and silicon diode rectifiers and transistors.

Third, quantum mechanics completed the job of interpreting every complicated detail of the light-emitting properties of individual atoms. This period marked a certain stage of completion of the great intellectual conquest begun by many experimental spectroscopists and inspired by Niels Bohr. These developments provide the greatest available wealth of precise material for the critical testing of modern atomic theory, the basis for the present widespread use of spectroscopic methods for routine chemical analysis, and a vast extension and sharpening of spectroscopy as a tool for use in astrophysics.

Fourth, quantum mechanics provided the basis for the new science of nuclear physics, and thus provides the basis for the vast political, military, and industrial business which today we call "atomic energy." Prior to 1928 physicists paid very little attention to the central hard nut of the atom called the nucleus. This was not through any lack of curiosity about it but rather due to the facts that: (1) they were fully occupied with exploiting the other avenues of progress which have been mentioned and therefore had little time to consider nuclear problems, and (2) the energies involved in holding the nucleus together were so much greater than those governing phenomena in the outer parts that more powerful experimental tools than any then available were needed before important laboratory results could be obtained.

Thus the real birth of that science we now call nuclear physics awaited both the greater development of basic theoretical ideas and the development of new and more powerful experimental apparatus.

Neither of these was long in coming. Quantum mechanics gave the theoretical break-through when Gamow, and independently Gurney and Condon, showed in 1927 that a special and distinctive feature of the quantum modification of classical views accounts for the fundamental mechanism of the natural radioactivity of uranium and radium. Later application of these ideas to the light elements showed that these could be made to undergo artificial nuclear transformation by the use of particles having energies of only a few hundred thousands of electron volts instead of the millions hitherto believed necessary. These ideas also predicted the peculiar fluctuations with bombarding energy of the efficacy of such transmutations which were soon to be brilliantly verified in the experiments of Cockcroft and Walton and others.

About this time Van de Graaff was building his first machine at Princeton, to be followed by larger ones at the Massachusetts Institute of Technology and elsewhere. Also Ernest Lawrence was building the first of the machines which he called the magnetic resonance accelerator but which the whole world knows today as the cyclotron. So theory and experiment met in the early 1930's and started to build modern nuclear physics, some fifteen years before atomic energy was to become a subject for attention in Congress. Harold Urey at Columbia discovered deuterium, or heavy hydrogen, in 1932, and James Chadwick in England discovered the neutron that same year. With quantum mechanics and the first modern high-voltage particle accelerators now developed and available, the modern period in nuclear physics may be said to have dated from that year. With the major problems of the electronic structure of atoms already resolved, an increasing number of physicists turned energetically to the study of nuclear physics.

Progress went forward at an accelerated pace and reached another important milestone with the discovery of uranium fission in late 1938. Still another milestone was the recognition soon thereafter that this process contained within itself the possibility of a self-sustaining nuclear chain reaction which might be used explosively as a military weapon or controlled as a source of heat for turbine-driven electric power generators. The subsequent events, the long hard struggle of the physicists to interest the government, their successful development of a weapon which ended World War II in 1945, their efforts to bring about international control of this terrible weapon, and their development on governmental order of a weapon hundreds of times more powerful, which now accentuates our uneasiness and insecurity—all these form too long and involved a story to be told here.

Suffice it to say that these and other consequences of research in modern physics brought the physicists to the attention of the government. The results have not been very constructive or helpful toward further progress of science in America, for there has been an essentially complete failure on the part of the government to recognize and support fully the importance to national security of fundamental scientific progress. It is true that a National Science Foundation was established after long delay, but it was immediately hamstrung by being given appropriations for the nation as a whole that are smaller than the amount of money which many medium-sized American industrial enterprises spend on scientific work to improve their own products and manufacturing processes.

During the period in question, roughly the first half of the twentieth century, there were correspondingly great changes in technology and industrial development. In 1900 there were almost no automobiles, there was no radio telephone, there was no long-distance telephony, there was no aviation, and of course there was no television. At that time, although interchangeable parts were being used in manufacture, the continuous assembly line for production had not been introduced. Mechanical refrigeration was not widely used, and so the production and distribution of perishable foods was on a totally different basis from what it is today. Nor was there any air conditioning. There were no plastics nor any textiles produced from new fibers developed by chemical industry. There were only the first faint stirrings of a motion picture industry, and there was no color photography. Very few young people attended high school, and fewer yet went to college. In short, the conditions of life were quite different. A number of diseases like typhoid fever, which in those days took thousands of lives annually, have now been almost completely eliminated by the use of new research results of medical science.

War was a relatively simple business. American loss of life in the entire Spanish-American war was under 4000, or about one-twentieth the number of lives lost in the now outmoded type of atomic bombing of Hiroshima and Nagasaki that occurred less than half a century later. Johnny was more likely to come marching home then then he is now.

At the turn of the century the population in America was less than half what it is today. During the period from then until now, not only has our population doubled, but there has been an enormous growth in the productive establishment which makes for us all the material goods represented by the things we have now, and did not have half a century ago. These great changes have been wrought by our engineers developing an expanding technology under the stimulus provided by competitive free enterprise capitalism. Of course the engineers did not do these things alone, but it is important to note, even in the medical field, how much of the achievement in public health improvement stems from the work of the water supply and sanitary engineers.

The particular feature of the enormous changes in technology and industry to which I wish now to direct attention is this: the basic scientific principles of physics which underlie a very large part of this technological change were already known to physicists in the nineteenth century.

Thus, although automobiles were new, the internal combustion engine was not, and steam engineering was well advanced. Although there was no aviation, wind tunnels had been built and the forces of the air on airfoils was under study. There was no radio telephony, but electromagnetic waves were known and being used for telegraphy. Barring very recent developments it would seem that the only great technological principles of importance which have been developed in this century are (a) the control of the plate current in an electronic vacuum tube by varying the potential of the grid and (b) the development of the making of high-polymer substances by polymerization of unsaturated organic compounds. This may be a little extreme, and perhaps one or two others should be added, but to do so would not alter the main point that I am trying to make.

That this situation existed, together with the great technological advances made in the first half of this century, forces us to recognize the enormous fruitfulness for technology of the discoveries made in nineteenth-century physics. Let us recall that at the beginning of that century men stood in complete ignorance of the scientific principles underlying the design of efficient heat engines and that they had essentially no knowledge of the quantitative laws of electricity and magnetism. At its end, steam engineering and railroading were fully established, the electrical power industry was well on its way, and the scientific basis was at hand for most of the technological advance thus far made in this century.

Another characteristic feature of engineering in the first third of the present century, say, was the considerable time lag—of several decades—between the discovery of basic scientific results and their exploitation by an expanding technology. It is of interest to speculate on the causes of this lag. Some think it may have been occasioned by a saturation of the available capital and the available entrepreneurial initative, so that these necessary factors were unable to absorb rapidly the many new things latent in the discoveries of nineteenth-century physics.

Others think that the main cause of the lag lies in the training and outlook of the engineering profession in those days. They say that much of the teaching of engineers as it was then carried on tended to induce in them a static outlook toward the content of basis science. Physical science was taught in those days more as a finished system than as a growing thing, the way it is regarded nowadays. While the engineers are young and in college and their minds are relatively plastic, they learn most of whatever they are going to learn in a lifetime about fundamental physics and chemistry. Then they become established professionally by the time they are thirty, so runs this view, and spend the next thirty years or so in exploiting the fixed store of basic science and mathematics they acquired as undergraduates. This view, if it is correct, not only explains why there is a time lag at all but also interprets for us why this lag is about the duration of one human generation.

It is difficult to choose between either of these inherently plausible views. Probably there is some truth in each of them.

Instead, let us turn our attention to another major trend which has developed rapidly in this century as affecting the interactions of physics and the engineer. This is the enormous growth in the application of basic science to organized industrial research.

At the turn of the century and for a decade or two thereafter, there were no industrial research organizations that in any way resembled the laboratories which today are an essential part of every progressive industrial enterprise. It is true that some concerns like to trace their research programs back to this period and earlier, but when we examine closely the basis of their claim, we find that the research laboratory consisted then of one or two scientists and a few assistants working with poor equipment in a small shed or an unused corner of the factory. What a contrast between this and the picture we see today of large staffs, fully supplied with expensive equipment, all housed in splendid modern buildings surrounded by spacious gardens. Dozens of such laboratories now exist where there were none even thirty years ago, and hardly a week passes that we do not hear of the building of another one. It is not uncommon today to hear of manufacturing firms that spend an amount equal to several per cent of their gross sales on the activities of their own research and development laboratories. So well established is this practice that nowadays investment analysts view with disfavor the stocks of firms which do not support their own research programs.

What is the point and purpose of industrial research? Every firm has a certain set of manufacturing facilities to make products within a general field. The job of its engineering department is to operate these facilities and to seek constantly to introduce new product designs and improved manufacturing methods. The engineering department often finds itself limited by the lack of basic scientific data. Moreover, if the proposed new product is radically new, the problems which it presents will be very different from those which the engineering department is accustomed to handle. The function of industrial research is to remedy these deficiencies.

In order to do so, the research department must maintain a scientific staff of high competence in the broad fields of science that are relevant to the company's activities, the field of relevance embracing scientific areas likely to be of importance to the future of the company as well as to its actual current interests.

Without going into more detail, the point being stressed here is that the large-scale development of industrial research laboratories in the past thirty years has completely changed the relationship that hitherto existed between physics and the engineer. Formerly it might easily be true that a competent engineer might never personally know any physicists in his lifetime other than the professors who taught him as an undergraduate—and often even these he might avoid ever seeing again throughout his professional career. But now all this is quite different. Today the engineer is apt to make his career with a manufacturing concern which maintains a staff of physicists in its research laboratory. He is thrown into frequent contact with them, a contact which he finds stimulating and directly helpful, because they too are directly concerned with the same field of relevance he is.

All this works toward speeding up the tempo of technological change. It does this in two ways: by providing a direct channel for the prompter flow of new scientific results into the hands of the engineers and by providing a feedback channel through which the expressed needs of the engineer may more directly stimulate effort in new fields of scientific inquiry that are needed for already formulated technological needs. Because of these things, one should expect that in the near future we shall see a reduction in the time lag between scientific discovery and industrial application, say from an average of about thirty years or more to something like ten years or less.

All these changes are producing new demands on engineering education in this country—demands which are not being met satisfactorily. We shall have to face up to them before long or find that these deficiencies will act severely to limit further progress and even our ability to defend ourselves against aggressive tendencies of other national groups. Our educational system for science and technology is today inadequate in two respects: quantity and quality.

As a nation we have failed to make school teaching a sufficiently rewarding profession to enable it to attract and hold the kind of teachers who can inspire students with a zeal for science, in sufficient numbers to meet our needs. The crisis is so severe that many high schools have been forced to give up the teaching of science. In others it is taught in a perfunctory manner by poorly trained teachers whose main interests lie elsewhere, thus deadening the students' interest in the subjects. The same is true of mathematics teaching, without which engineering training is impossible.

These remarks must not be misconstrued: I am not criticizing the valiant band of those who against these odds try to operate effective schools. Rather, the community which makes the task such a hopeless one for the teachers is to be censured. Unless we do something soon, and drastically, something like more than doubling the meager investment per capita that we make in teaching school science and mathematics, then further major expansion of industry will be severely limited by the lack of students equipped to go on.

At the college level, assuming a sufficient number of qualified entrants, new problems confront us. Except in a few places, American engineering education has been short on scientific fundamentals and long on what it likes to call practical instruction. On close examination the practical courses turn out to be vocational indoctrination in how to do specific engineering jobs along the lines of already established practice. Instead of preparing the young engineer for a world of change, such instruction tends to deaden his natural curiosity and to force him into the rut of conventional thinking at an age when he should still be indulging in daring flights of fancy.

Of course it is true, and probably always will be, that many engineers will do more or less routine work in stabilized industries. But even for these it would be better, for cultural reasons if no other, to give them a stronger dose of fundamental science than they are now getting. For research laboratories there is a growing tendency to try to meet this lack by an increasing use of graduates from special engineering physics curricula, but there are not enough of these, the shortage being even more acute relative to the demand than exists for engineering graduates generally.

Therefore, at the college level there is a great need for increased emphasis on fundamental scientific and mathematical training, with decreased emphasis on a stereotyped, routine handbook formula approach.

With the great shortage of well-trained engineers that is now upon us, and which would persist for a decade even in the unlikely event that corrective steps were to be taken promptly, it becomes important to back up our trained men with laboratory technicians and assistants. In most engineering organizations today the situation is as it would be in a hospital if a meager staff of doctors also had to do all the nursing. We are hampered in our efforts to do much about this by the lack of schools organized for the training of technicians for modern physical and chemical research laboratories. More and

more the larger industrial laboratories are being driven to the un-
satisfactory expedient of trying to operate training courses of their
own, but without very satisfactory results. This kind of need is being
felt especially keenly in the armed services, where vast sums have
to be spent on general vocational training of technicians before their
special training on military devices can begin.

It would be of interest at this point to gaze a little into the future.

The safest prediction one can make about the future is that it is
in detail inpredictable. Of course, we do not know what form color
television sets will take a few years from now, nor how long it will
be before 5 million such sets are made annually. But it is safe to say
that production rate will be reached within a decade.

Likewise, a person would be foolish indeed who said just how soon
and to what extent transistors and other devices based on recently
discovered properties of semiconductors will alter the structure of the
electronic and communications industries, but it is more than safe to
say that large developments of this kind will occur within a decade.

Moreover, I do not think there is the slightest question but that
power from uranium fission will be an economic reality within a
decade. I venture to say that within two decades a large proportion
of the new central station generating plants will be using uranium
instead of coal as fuel. Things are at last moving rapidly in this field;
they would already have been much further along but for the
decision to concentrate on weapon development instead of power
development.

Within a decade we will see enormous changes in the organization
of business due to the introduction of large-scale electronic computing and data-processing machines and to the widespread introduction
of automatic electronic devices to regulate machines in factories.
These devices will produce changes in all industry, during the rest
of the twentieth century, on a scale commensurate with the changes
of a century or so ago which we call the Industrial Revolution.

All these things are of the nature of natural, easy, and safe extra-
polations of present technology based on known science. If you ask
me whether new industry will be based on cosmic rays or mesons,
or on the construction of rockets for exploring outer space, or
whether men will find the means to get very deep below the earth's
surface in a quest for new mineral supplies, you know that I am
being quite truthful when I say that I do not know. Some of these

things may be in store for us, as well as others not yet mentioned even in science fiction. But one cannot tell what they are any more than one could predict what will be of most interest in the pages of the *Physical Review* ten or twenty years from now.

But if we ask what changes in the world of greatest and most far-reaching effect are expected to occur in the second half of this century, the answer seems absolutely clear—barring the cataclysm of a World War III in which the total destructiveness of hydrogen bombs would rob the answer of all possible interest.

There is no question but that the outstanding great change that will occur in large measure before the year 2000 is the extension to all mankind of technological and industrial development which is analogous to what is now the nearly exclusive possession of a small fraction of the world's population. By that time we should expect to see electric power and manufacturing industry operating indigenously to supply the needs of peoples everywhere. In consequence, even the world's existing population will make wholly unprecedented demands on the consumable mineral resources of the earth.

Index

A

Absolute zero, 293, 294
Absorption of gases, microwave, 50, 52
Accelerator, 139, 142, 148
  as X-ray source, 166
  constant potential, 145
  electron, 146, 166
  electron linear, 172
  economic limitations on size of, 159
  electron pulsed magnet, 159
  fixed magnet, 151
  heavy particle, 149, 159
  induction, 160
  linear, 155, 169, 170, 173, 192
  magnetic, 138, 143, 150, 170, 172
  magnet of, 151
  magnetic resonance, 151, 352
  particle, 137, 140, 194, 352
  phase oscillations in, 156
  proton, 12, 151, 158
  proton linear, 170, 172
  resonance, 149, 170
  R.F., 154
  very high energy, 167
Accelerator electrode, 151, 170
Accelerator tube, 145–149, 172
  potential distribution in, 146
Acceptor, 213, 217, 227, 228, 241, 242, 244, 245
Acoustic pressure, 4
Acoustics, 2, 15
Adiabatic demagnetization, 293
Adiabatic expansion of compressed air, 293
Air conditioning, 353
Aerodynamics, 2, 6
Air, liquefaction of, 293
Aircraft, landing of, 18, 26
Aircraft stacking, 19
Airplanes, high-speed, 8

Alfer, 265
Algebra, modern, 1
Alnico-5, 278, 279
Allowed transition, 95, 96, 112
Alloys
  magnetic, 262, 280
  superconducting, 326, 330–332
Alpha decay, 93, 97
  lifetime of, 99, 100
Alpha particle, 27, 72, 73, 75, 92, 98, 111, 138
  acceleration of, 153
  emission of, 94–95
  scattering of, 349
Alternating gradient focusing, 188, 192
Alvarez, L. W., 170
Ammonia, microwave spectrum of, 52
Amplification, 251
  electronic, 232
  transistor, 235, 248
  vacuum tube, 248
Amplifier, 229–231, 235, 251
  electronic, 247
  molecular, 64–65
  semiconductor, 232, 235
Analogue computers, 26
Analysis, chemical, 59, 60
Andronikashvili, E. L., 311
Angular momentum, 39, 40, 50, 54, 55
  of atom, 29
Angular velocity, 51
  rotational, 50
Anisotropy
  crystal, 288
  magnetic, 289, 290
Anisotropy constant, 287
Annihilation, 43
  of electron pairs, 45
  pair, 122, 123
  three-quantum, 44
Antiferromagnetism, 256–259

361